Choosing The
DANCE

Recognizing Your Purpose In The Pain

TK Daniels

Choosing The Dance
Recognizing Your Purpose In The Pain

ISBN-13: 978-0-9915923-5-7 (print)
ISBN-13: 978-0-9915923-0-2 (ebook)

(website) www.tkscreations.com
(email) choosingthedance.@gmail.com

Dedication

I dedicate this story to my daughter, Micah T. Richard for inspiring creativity during tough times. Listening to the radio was unusual, but the cable was off and I needed to drown out the silence. You didn't complain nor even ask why the TV was not working. Instead, you asked that I dance with you as 'FM103.5 The Bomb' kept us entertained for the night. In those moments I realized that I could have sought my usual place of cold comfort in the back of my closet or chosen to dance with my little darling.

Dancing, laughing, and tickling my precious princess brought me enough joy to forget about my financial issues; at least for that night. That night I also recognized my power to seek light in the midst of darkness. I reluctantly danced with you to make you smile; however, that night I started on my path of choosing the dance.

To my sister, Miesha Bridges for reminding me to use my voice, encouraging my strength, and demonstrating your love.

To my mother, Linda Patterson for believing in my abilities to change the world. Thank you for being my biggest fan, for your Love, Encouragement, & Support.

For all of the bruised & broken souls, I encourage you to recognize your purpose in the pain and then choose your dance to align with your purpose. Be Brave!

I stand with you,

TK Daniels

Contents

Acknowledgments

Brenda (mom) Narcisse, thank you for always believing in, laughing & crying with, loving, supporting, and lifting me up when my vision was dim. Thank you for being a vessel for my deliverance. I love you!

Miesha Bridges, thank you for being so gorgeous and so patient while we got the perfect shot. You look Great on the cover!

Micah Richard, I truly appreciate you sharing in the dream. Great dance pose on the cover. You are God's greatest gift to me!!!

Moray Reaves, thank you for lending your creative dance moves (can you pick out yourself on the cover?)

Stephannie Mitchell, thank you for beating my face (is that what they say now?) for the photoshoot and highlighting my inner beauty.

Doug Williams, thank you so much for recognizing and delivering my vision by way of your 35 mm camera.

Jose Rios, thank you for finding my lost manuscript when my pc crashed. Thank you for recommending several back-up methods, for your support, & encouragement. You have saved the day on numerous occasions.

Judi Peterson, thank you for taking my ideas to the next level by lending your creative talents to create the book cover. You Rock!

Elton Bradman, thank you for sharing your editing expertise & tone; you never once changed my voice… you only made it better.

ProofProfessor, thank you for your efficient & thorough editing services.

Self-Publishing School Mastermind Community, thank you for the swift kick in the patootie, along with the education & encouragement.

Glenn of www.sarcopress.com, thank you for taking Choosing The Dance to the next level! Your work is Prompt & Perfect!

Life is a Dance

Life is like a dance that happens around you, unless you make it happen for you. I have participated in many dances in my life, but until I learned that I had the power and the right to take control of the situation at hand, rarely did I lead.

In this story, "the situation" is synonymous with "the dance" and I will share how I navigate through each dance, good or bad. Did you know that you can choose the dance in which you participate, say "no thank you" to an unworthy opponent, or back out of an accident about to happen? I did not know. But as I was led through life's unkind moments, I learned, eventually, that I could control my dance or guide my destiny to happier endings. Once I paid close attention, I realized that I could alter my life situations by strategically choosing to participate in the dance that would best benefit my world and me. Right in the midst of life's happenings, I began to examine things, and that's when I learned that not only could I choose my own dance, but I actually had the right to do so. Knowing that I could choose the dance was half the battle, and through God's grace, mercy, and direction, I learned how to exercise my choice!

After many years of allowing someone else, or my emotions to dictate the dance in which I partook I began to realize that I could have chosen differently. I endured many dance without much thought. Now I realize that if I had exercised my choice wisely, most of the dances would have resulted in better or at least different outcomes. My Daddy often says, "Things always look worse than they are until you are on the other side of the storm," and I used to believe him. I have to admit that he's right about a lot of things, but in my experience, that little piece of "Daddy knowledge" has not been accurate. I am now on the other side of a long string of rough dances, and when I look back, each dance was just as rough as I remember it being. If I had the option, I'd replay some of the dances just as they happened because the growing pains were worth the lessons learned and the strength gained. Conversely, many of the dances served little value besides highlighting the fact that I had been conditioned to let life happen around me as I prayed through each trial dreaming about better tomorrows.

As you thumb through the pages of my journey, you will get a glimpse of the dances I allowed. If you read my story and notice any similarities to the displeasing situations in your life, demand that the dance STOP! Then you make the choice to change partners, songs, or the type of dance altogether. Move to a more enjoyable dance, because life is too short for you not to choose the dance that is best for you and your journey.

When I review each situation as a dance, I can equate the experience to a particular dance and then decide how to proceed. It seems simple, but exercising my choice is anything but simple, and it takes a lot of practice. In his books *The Power of Now: A Guide to Spiritual Enlightenment* and *A New Earth: Awakening to Your Life's Purpose,* Eckhart Tolle talks about being present and in the moment, and I have learned that accepting and dealing with any situation as a current and present event is the first step to choosing my dance. If you find yourself unable to stay in the present, I recommend taking deep breaths through each moment until you can focus on the current situation as it is, a current event that requires current attentions. Focusing on past disappointments as a cause to your current pain, or dreaming about a future you desire without taking action toward making it happen, will not help you in effectively moving toward your preferred reality.

Throughout various counseling sessions, I have been advised to take life one day at a time, but my issues required that I take life one moment at a time. Because I am analytical, it helps when I look at each situation as a dance, an experience that is usually enjoyable. Putting a difficult situation in the same category as dancing helps me view the situation from a "this too shall pass" perspective, and from this vantage point, I can create a plan on how I will proceed. Will I slow-dance through this pain? Samba through the worry? Hip-hop my way around the argument? Crump it out after a long impossible day at work? Or sit the dance out altogether, thus not giving strength to another unnecessary dance… i.e. one of Mother's many complaints?

This thought process reminds me that I am in control of my life and how I choose to handle situations—how I choose to dance! I also gain strength when I remember that God declares the end from the beginning and knows all things; so by faith, my problem is already resolved. I just need to trust in God and live long enough to see how He performs His miracle for the current situation.

One of my favorite Bible verses is Romans 4:17 (KJV): "As it is written, I have made thee a father of many nations, before him whom he believed, even God, who quickeneth the dead, and calleth those things which *be not* as though they *were*." I rely on this verse— specifically the end, "God, who, called those things which *be not* as though they *were*"—when I see no way out of a difficult moment. The passage references God telling Abraham that even though he was nearly one-hundred years old and his wife Sarah was ninety and barren, they would have a child. As the story goes, Abraham and Sarah did have a son. In fact, not only did Abraham have a son, he became the father of many nations. This is not what amazes me about this passage, however. What impresses me most is that in a situation that seemed impossible, Abraham had faith and believed in God's word.

I minored in English in college, but it took a while before I could fully understand the last part of this verse. At first, I interpreted the phrases "God, who quickened the dead" (which reminded me of His power to raise the dead) and "calleth those things which *be not*" (the current impossible situation) "as though they *were*" in the present tense. Grammatically, this made more sense. But God did not need me rewriting His word. He gave me the revelation knowledge to see the verse as it is written: "He called those things that *be not* as though they were (past tense— already done!)," which leads me to realize that God had already fulfilled Abraham's heart's desire and more ("father of many nations?" I've never read that Abraham asked to be the father of many nations), and this fulfillment happened before Abraham was living in the reality of fatherhood. My belief is that

Abraham's faith allowed him to see, live, and have what God had already done for him and his life. And since God is the same yesterday, today, and forever, which means that He will do the same type of things today if we're faithful. I now know that he will do the same type of things for me. If I seek first the Kingdom of God, and all His righteousness, the things I worry about will be taken care of. In the midst of a painful, troublesome storm, I realize that God's Word is powerful! I am still learning more about choosing my dance, and although there will be dances I should endure so that I gain wisdom and strength, there are dances that I should avoid. God help me as I figure out which is which.

As the eldest child in my family, I've decided that it is my responsibility to journal life's painful lessons and share them with others, specifically my sister Alex. My hope is that she, as well as others, will be in a better position to choose their dances wisely. As my heart bleeds onto these pages from a place of sincerity, I pray that God's love ministers to the many lonely empty places as He embraces the hearts of everyone reading these words. I pray that each person feels God's assurance of peace and comfort during each dance that awaits them. My decision to share insight with Alex is not an easy choice, but I know that sharing my pain may allow her the option to make better choices when faced with similar dances. Besides, offering a warning through my lessons learned is the Godly thing to do, even though it means I'll have to let her see a side of me that she does not expect exists. Alex has always been selfish and self-serving, and although she played a major role in making a few of my storms the most difficult times of my life, I feel obligated to my creator to share obstacles that she may avoid, should she choose to take heed.

As you move through my story, you will see that although my life may have seemed flawless from the outside, I suffered in silence many midnights as I drifted through this dance otherwise known as the situations of life. Life is one big dance comprised of a lot of mini-dances, and whether or not we know this little fact, we do get to choose how we manage through each dance.

Because Mother raised me to appear faultless, I was too ashamed to scream for help when I was at my lowest, and although I hid imperfections as I daydreamed my way through life, most of my life was in one form or another a series of low points. Mother's expectation was that her family would display dignity through all situations; we learned to strive for perfection, and when we failed, we were not offered a soft place to land. Instead, if and when we failed, we were told to jump up, shake off the dust, and hide the scars before anyone noticed.

As I relive my experiences, I ask that you look for the bigger meaning in each situation in your life. Realize that God Himself has personally breathed inner beauty into each of us. Take in the lessons of my pain, and learn through my failures so that you don't have to sacrifice your own peace to gain growth. Be great to yourself because you're worth every effort necessary for your happiness. And finally, make decisions that make you proud of who you are; fearfully and wonderfully made! Situations are presented daily... Choose your dance wisely!

Lineage

A big part of sharing the many dances of my life necessitates that I introduce myself, as well as the major dancers of my life party. At the very least, I will identify the characters and their relationship to my world.

I have not always been thankful for my family; during the really dark moments, in fact, I hated that God allowed me to be born into such a tormented family unit. However, God is so gracious, and through His grace and mercy, I found my way to love and appreciate my lineage. Without *them*, there would be no *me*, and without darkness, the glow from the light would not be recognizable.

My name is Jonnie Johnson. I am the eldest of my parents' two children and I have two beautiful daughters. I have never spoken about some of the things I am about to share, but I open my life for the world to examine so that I may help someone through the many situations in their life. Speaking about my dance gives a deeper meaning to the pains that I've experienced, and it helps me through my own healing process. I refer to life's situations as "the dance" because this reminds me that just as if I were at a dance, I have a choice if, when, and how I participate. I may even choose to sit out the dance. Now it took me a long time to learn that sitting out the dance does not mean sitting out on life. Thank God for this eventual enlightenment.

Childhood presented the options Mother allowed, or so I thought at the time. Mother, or Mrs. Eloise as she likes to be called in public, is not a bad person, but she has made bad choices from time to time, and who hasn't? I grew to see the good in her heart, although I often had to look at her through Godly eyes to catch a glimpse of the dimly lit good shining from her aching soul.

Mother is a proud woman who insists that her family maintain a perfect appearance in all forms, at all times. We had the best of everything: the biggest house, the finest furnishings, the fanciest cars, the most hired help, the best schools, and so on. Yes, we had the best of everything, but Mother never showed her love the way I would have wanted her to. Mother is not very demonstrative with positive emotions. When we were younger, she was very strict with my sister and I, and she set very high standards for Daddy and anyone else in her circle. Mother demanded that we maintain the image she worked diligently to create; my sister and I endured various lessons in etiquette so that we'd stand apart from others in every area of our young lives. Mother insisted, "Any child of mine *will* be stronger than other children, in all fashions of life." In fact, she told anyone who'd listen that she had prayed for sons because she considered men to be the stronger sex. Her prayers were not answered, however. To her dissatisfaction, she gave birth to two healthy baby girls, and she decided to grant her daughters an advantage in corporate America by giving them (us) male names. Jon Terrence and Alex Terrell, two baby girls, born eighteen months apart, both given boy names.

I picked up the nickname Jonnie the first time my grandmother Dear held me in her arms. Jonnie wasn't the name Mother had chosen, but it was close enough and sort-of catchy, so I became Jonnie T. Johnson to family, and as I grew older I became JJ to colleagues or in business dealings. At an early age, Alex began telling people that Alex was short for Alexia, which was her way of coping with her traditionally male name. Neither of us speak of our middle names too freely because we do not like them, but don't want to rock Mother's boat. We tip-toe around thoughtless decisions Mother makes so that we avoid havoc and maintain some level of calmness in the family.

Daddy is the sweetest, most loving, caring, generous man I've ever met. I have always believed that he deserves a wife much better than Mother. They are so different, but their marriage works thanks to his take-and-give attitude. He takes whatever Mother gives. Daddy is a quiet, God-fearing man, whereas Mother is a demanding, pretentious, overbearing bully. I refer to her as a bully because of the way that she treats others, especially Dear, Daddy's mother and my favorite person in the whole wide world!

As good as Daddy is, Dear is a million times better, a true saint, so much so that I swear I've heard her having personal conversations with God on several occasions. You know, the kind of conversation where you hear two voices even though she's in the room alone. I know the voice must have been God speaking to her because the atmosphere was beautiful and the voice made the sweetest, softest sounds that ever graced my young ears. I grew so accustomed to the atmosphere of confusion and discontent in our home that I immediately notice an environment of patience, love, hope, and beauty when I see one.

I realized at an early age that Dear was different, the kind of different I craved to be near. She was the antidote to the sick world I lived in and when we were apart, I felt as though I got barely enough oxygen until I saw her again. Thankfully, my parents worked a lot, which meant that Alex and I spent most of our time at Dear's house. I hated going home, and I would cry myself to sleep most nights because I missed her so much, even though she was only about a mile down the road.

Mother, who felt my connection to Dear was unnatural, wanted to punish me, but Daddy disagreed. To make my nights away from Dear more bearable, Daddy would come into my room, unbeknownst to Mother, and hold me until I fell asleep. He wasn't Dear, of course, but his arms presented a familiar, God-like love. If Dear is like a first cup of tea, with its strong aroma and bright essence, Daddy is like a second cup that used the same tea bag; same flavor, but not as strong. Perhaps Daddy's strength pales in comparison to Dear's because Mother constantly sucks the strength from his cup.

Mother and Daddy run their own company, so Alex and I spent much of our childhoods at Dear's house, which we all preferred, except Daddy. He missed being around his girls, but he was grateful that we were being raised by Dear. Because we were little girls who liked little girly things and acted in little girly ways, Mother preferred to be around as little as possible. I was very emotional and would cry easily, and Mother would say, "I don't have time for tears, so dry up the waterfall!" Needless to say, I did not feel the love; Dear, however, loved me and taught me about God's love. She taught me to find the joy in my tears, to recognize God's love, to love others with godly and nonjudgmental pure love, and most importantly, how to receive God's love. I thank God every day for Dear!

Mother is an only child, and her parents passed away when she was a child. We are her only family. She has mentioned an aunt in passing, but she's not forthcoming with any information about her family or childhood, so we've all learned not to speak of the subject. I presume that she didn't learn to love when she was younger because she didn't have very many opportunities to practice it. This is the only way I make sense out of her not showing us the love a mother should show her children. Nevertheless, God sent us to Daddy and Dear, so our circle of love is almost complete. I even believe that Mother loves us but she's just not good at showing it.

To give an accurate view into my universe, I am going to begin my story with me on top of the world. I had persevered though many struggles and had gotten to a point in life that made sense. I did not have a good childhood, but I had always maintained my focus on the *right* things, and I knew that one day my suffering would have meaning.

My grandmother and best friend Dear taught me that if I kept the faith, the outcome would outweigh all those moments of anguish. When I turned ten years old, I made the decision not to cry anymore when life became painful. Crying did not reap any benefits, or so I was lead to believe by Mother, so I began to escape painful realities by diving into my daydreams and believing my tomorrows would be better than the painful present.

At the time, I didn't realize that in the midst of problems, I would focus primarily on future dreams without dealing with life as it happened. I used future hopes as an escape, and therefore, I learned to live a large portion of my earlier life in my mind, focused on the bright future I planned to build for myself.

As life happened around me, I wore a smile painted across the façade that masked my true face. I grew accustomed to hearing that I "was such a pleasant young lady," which made Mother happy and meant that for that moment, life was tolerable. Not that I would much notice because I was too busy inside my mind planning my future. My life's plans included a big house with more space than I could ever use, a fine sexy car, a spare vehicle for fun, and a family. I also wanted a meaningful and important career that would afford me the means to maintain the luxuries that, although present in my childhood, belonged to Mother and therefore, could only be enjoyed by her rules. I would also have a husband that worshiped every breath that flowed from my innermost soul.

What I forgot to include in my dream was a healthy, well- adjusted "me" who dealt with life's obstacles. My life's dream would be different, of course, if I had a second chance at youth, but I don't, and this is why I am sharing my story; so that others may learn from my mistakes.

My wish is that you realize that you can choose your dance. Learning to choose your dance is not easy, so be patient with yourself. In fact, I did not learn to choose my dance until later in life. Once I grew tired of life happening around me, I learned that I had a choice. Once I recognized life as a dance I slowly but deliberately learned to choose the dances that best suit me in any given moment, time, or space.

Most people come from a family with some type of dysfunction; no family tree is perfect. Learn to love your lineage and appreciate each unique individual who helps make you who you are. Even ones who have caused the most difficulty to your life have meaning. Perhaps I would not have grown to know God for myself without the blemishes, spots, and wrinkles decorating my family tree. Family members are who they are, so I am trying to accept this fact as I thank God for the impact they've had on my life… good, bad, and indifferent. God, I thank you for my lineage!

World Flare Life

"**W**orld flare" is what Dear calls our life; a life where dreams have come true. Like any life my life has taken several turns, but at this point in my story I am finally living the life that I dreamt about for so long. I am a young executive, the Vice President of Marketing in charge of the entire Western division for a Fortune

500 advertising company. I live in a private, exclusive, gated community in a 7,000-square-foot home with more space than I will ever need. I have several vehicles parked outside. I have a wonderful husband, Kevin, who is beautiful from head to toe, left to right, front to back, and everything in between. He also just so happens to adore every breath that pours from my innermost soul.

Just as I planned, I have two beautiful daughters, eight-year-old Kali and Tia who turned six three months ago. Dear, my grandmother and best friend in the whole world, lives with me and allows me the pleasure of making her life posh. I am truly blessed. I don't have as much money as Mother, nor is my real estate company as lucrative as her company, Leisurely Connections, a dating service she started her first year in college, but I live a very comfortable lifestyle, and I'm happily on my way to exceeding Mother's financial worth.

I knew early in life that my dreams were elaborate and would come at a hefty price, so in college I studied and invested in the stock market and I've benefited quite nicely. My investments turned a profit, I re-invested in stocks, bonds, and property, and when the real estate business grew larger and started to require more time than I wanted to invest, my closest friend Vanessa and I started J-Ness Realty. Vanessa manages most of the affairs of J- Ness Reality so that I can pursue my dreams in the advertising world. Vanessa's parents own a chain of five-star hotels around the world, which Vanessa helps oversee, so managing a local real estate company is a natural fit for her. Conversely, I have dreamt about being in the advertising business all my life; therefore, being the more-or-less silent partner in J-Ness Realty affords me the freedom to follow my dreams and focus on my advertising career. My ultimate goal is to own my own advertising company. Mother constantly warns me to be more involved and "watch the books," but Vanessa comes from a family with money, and because her family is generous with their wealth, her worth currently exceeds mine—she has no reason to steal from our company, not that she would ever even consider it. Besides, I have known Vanessa all of my life and I trust her explicitly.

My life is wonderful and I thank God for bringing me out of the hell that most call a childhood and into the euphoria in which I currently reside. Although I am financially comfortable, content, and want for nothing, seeing Dear's eyes light up when I spring another elaborate surprise brings me the deepest happiness. Kevin and I work long days, so Dear takes care of the girls; they love her, and we all thank God that Dear is front and center in our lives. As a small symbol of our appreciation, we insist that she join us every year on our family vacation. We recently returned from our 24- night world cruise aboard the *Queen Mary 2*, where we set sail in Dubai, picked up souvenirs in Athens, took in sights in Barcelona, visited the Maritime Museum in Southampton, while relaxing and enjoying our comfortable suites in between the on-land festivities. My assistant carefully planned the entire vacation so that everyone would thoroughly enjoy their time at sea. Kevin and I were able to enjoy evenings alone because Dear was happy to sit on the balcony of her suite with her feet elevated while the girls slept after a long day of cruise activities. Because our rooms were adjoined we checked in on Dear and the girls after our evening of dancing before we turned in to enjoy each other's private moments.

Kevin never ceases to surprise me with elaborate acts of love. One starry evening he has three members of the ship's band play romantic songs right outside our balcony while he massages me from head to toe and back again—if you know what I mean. Kevin is a very thoughtful and sensitive man who can always make me smile, which is why I eventually trusted and married him once my career was stable. He always says that there is no problem we can't solve and as I look into his eyes I know he believes this, so I believe too. Besides, I was ready to let down my emotional walls and fall into his awaiting arms.

Relationships require work and during our world flare days Kevin and I worked well, but this was not always the case. Building a relationship of love, tolerance, forgiveness, and trust takes time.

When I met Kevin he was a struggling college student and did not see himself fitting in my world. He was not born with what he calls "a silver spoon in his mouth", meaning that his family isn't rich; therefore he's had to work hard for everything he has. I was proud to tell him that Mother was not paying for my education. My focus and dedication earned me a full academic scholarship, which made me to feel a bit more independent. Kevin was busy trying to fit into my world while I was anxious to jump into his. Mother never knew, but for our last year of college, Kevin lived with me because he could not afford to pay for both school and housing. That was the year I learned to enjoy coming home. Having dinner with Kevin became the bright spot in my day. He was too good to be true, but I loved him so I made a valiant attempt of controlling my insecurities. Despite my fears I fell deeper in love every time I looked into his eyes, and for the first time in my life I was experiencing romantic love. Before Kevin, my first loves were Dear, daddy, and accomplishing my dreams. I sometimes became afraid that Kevin would hurt me, but for the most part I enjoyed loving and being loved.

Soon after receiving our diplomas the loving world of Kevin & Jonnie came to an abrupt end. I received a phone call offering me a high-paying job as part of an advertising team in Paris, and without thought, I said yes! Kevin and I barely had time to say goodbye before I was on my way to the other side of the world. Although I was anxious to start my new career, tears rolled down my cheeks the entire flight because I was leaving my two loves behind. Dear would always be my grandmother and no amount of distance would ever change that, but Kevin was gone forever—at least that was what he told me. Through my tears, I gained clarity and as soon as my plane landed I called Kevin and told him I would come home at every chance to see him. Kevin was hurt that I chose a job over our relationship and therefore did not share my optimism, but I kept telling myself that we would find our way back together. Six years and a child later, we did just that and now our time apart is but a distant memory.

All through his time in law school Kevin attempted to forget us; searching for comfort in the arms of other women. His saving grace was Dear. He would take her to lunch or dinner once a week, and this is when their relationship strengthened. I later learned that he would lay in Dear's arms and cry over the emptiness that I left in his heart. Dear prayed for him, read the Bible with him, and encouraged him to trust in God. Dear also encouraged me to tell God what I wanted and trust Him to deliver what was best; of course, I prayed for Kevin's return to my arms.

Dear never betrayed Kevin's trust. I never knew they were meeting until Vanessa saw them having dinner one evening. At that point in my life, I was living in Paris, working at a top advertising firm, and making my climb to the top of the world and toward this 'world flare' life. There was no way that I was going to let distance come between me and the man of my dreams. We had a history to continue creating, and Paris was just a minor snag. I will elaborate more on the ups and downs of Kevin and me later. At this point in life I am accomplishing all of my dreams. I have a husband who loves me, two beautiful daughters, a successful career, more material goods than I'll ever use, and my grandmother / best friend front and center in my life. I am living a world flare life, thank God! Needless to say, world flare is a temporary state of mind.

Rejected Heart

Long before our world flare life there was the paid internship in Paris...

The two years in Paris go by quickly due to the heavy workload and me keeping tabs on Kevin via Vanessa's assistance. She tells me where she see him, whether he is dating or not, who he is with, and when he is at the movies alone. She has so much information that I swear she must have been purposely spying on him; and I would expect no less. Her reports are always the same. Even when he is out with someone else, his smile appears empty and lonely. Although I am pleased that Kevin's rejected heart has not moved on I am sad that I hurt him so deeply. I truly did not mean to hurt him. Soon after I left, Kevin stopped accepting my calls and I understand why. We trade occasional emails, which is all that I have the time for as I focus on my climb up the corporate ladder.

I am happy with the internship because it is very educational and brings much recognition my way. Because of my success in Paris I am a highly sought-after marketing executive in the advertising arena. Besides, living in Paris as a young, single woman is lovely. My dreams are on track, I am a marketing executive before the age of thirty, but my heart aches for Kevin.

Prior to returning to the states I am able to demand the right conditions with a top firm in my hometown. A month before I leave Paris, Vanessa lines up a beautiful four-bedroom townhome in a gated community so that I may securely step from the plane into the comforts of my own place. Due to her failing health, Dear has moved in with Mother and Daddy; and although she never complains I can hear in Dear's voice that she is unhappy. I am anxious to see her so when the plane lands I go straight to Daddy and Mrs. Eloise's house for a long overdue reunion.

When I arrive at the front door, I can hear Mrs. Eloise yelling at Dear. I walk in to see Dear sitting in her favorite chair, quietly listening as Mother scolds her for using the decorative towels in the downstairs bathroom. I could see tears fill Dear's eyes as she tried to smile through another unnecessary lecture administered by Mother. There is no stopping the waterworks display once Dear and I embrace. She says her tears are tears of joy; however, I can feel both frustration and relief in each droplet that fall from her cheek and onto my shoulder, penetrating my skin and making its way directly to my heart. I feel so guilty for leaving Dear to suffer through Mother's devices so without a word I lead Dear to her borrowed room, we pack a few things, and I escort Dear out of these living conditions for the last time. I ask one of the housekeepers to send the rest of Dear's things to our new home.

Needless to say, Dear and I stay up almost the entire night talking, hugging, and planning the decorations for our new home. I vow that she would never have to live in that hell again. Until she peacefully trades her stay here on earth for her heavenly crown, she will live with me protected from Mother's torment. Securing a place of refuge for Dear is one of my proudest moments.

Once Dear is comfortably settled into our new home, I call Kevin to let him know that I am back. His response is startling. He lets me know that my putting a job over our love is a hurt that cannot be repaired, and that he is not interested in seeing me. I am shocked! How dare he? Well, I am not the kind of woman to chase a man. Although Dear really loves him and would love to see us together again, we agree that he needs space, and I reluctantly leave him alone to lick the wounds of his rejected heart.

Kevin's harsh words pierce my heart to the core and love slowly leaks from the wound carrying bits of my soul with it. Although I agree to leave Kevin to his wounds, it's not easy. I truly love him so I still send the occasional text message to let him know that I miss him. His reply is always the same, and always devoid of any feeling, "I'm praying for you and I wish you the best." What in the hell does this mean? Could the love we once shared really be over? I try to bury myself in work, but at night my heart aches from the emptiness.

Although I dated before, Kevin is my first and only true love. Through his love I learned to trust. Brick by brick he tore through some of the walls that were guarding my trembling heart. We held our relationship together through college which was no easy task, thanks to our busy lives and many distractions. Has my decision to jumpstart my career really finished us? His cold demeanor indicates that he has moved on, but my inner being does not want to accept his decision. If not for Dear, her prayers, my faith in God, and my busy career, I may be tempted to seek relief through synthetic means such as drugs, food, promiscuity, or perhaps even the unthinkable... death.

I grow tired of merely existing and I soon find distraction in Mitchell, who would be everything I could want if only my heart did not still belong to Kevin. Mitchell calls me a difficult nut to crack but he refuses to give up and before long we are a couple. I gradually let him into my world, we find ourselves spending every spare moment together, and slowly my wounds seem to heal. I welcome Mitchell to take the spot in my heart that Kevin once occupied.

Mitchell is eager to flaunt his wealth so he enjoys taking me on trips when we can pull ourselves away from work. I am finally burning through the many hours of unused vacation time to enjoy accompanying him on business trips at his company's expense. I refuse to lose another man by putting my career first, so I go with him whenever I can tear myself away for a day or two. I consciously focus on making him a priority, and I think he realizes my efforts even when my heart is reluctant.

Our most romantic vacation is the week we spend in Tahiti. I enjoy the company-supplied massage, mani / pedi combo, and swimming in the perfectly heated pool while he attends meetings. When the meetings are over, I allow him to attend to me! As Mitchell makes love to me I find myself wondering if Kevin ever thinks about me while he is intimate with whomever he is bedding. Mitchell can see the distance in my eyes as he kisses my midsection, and no matter how much I deny any residue of the pain left behind by Kevin, displayed like a flashing neon sign across the outside of my chest is my rejected heart.

Wonderful Life With Mitchell

Mitchell is the CEO of an engineering firm, and therefore, he calls most of the shots. Because he is an executive, he understands my long work hours and he agrees with the choice I made to leave Kevin and pursue my advertising career in Paris. Mitchell, a devout bachelor, says he has never been in love before me, which is a big turn-on. I feel honored that I am the woman who has gained his love and I'm trying to return the sentiment because I realize any woman would consider herself privileged to have his heart. He is very attentive, and although he realizes that at least a piece of my heart still belongs to Kevin, he goes above and beyond the call of duty to make me smile. Mitchell is a great guy, and I am happy to share this wonderful life with him. He is 12 years my senior and he really wants children. I've grown accustomed to his attentions and I want to make him happy, so I agree to the idea of being barefoot and pregnant… someday.

Mitchell and I spend two years of unwedded bliss in a whirlwind of passion and fiery embrace and I am sure we will share the rest of our lives together. Because of this certainty—and the love that I eventually force-feed my heart in an effort to wipeout any residue of Kevin—we happily agree to begin our family, despite our unmarried status. Although I know better, Mitchell and I secretly try to conceive for over a year and finally, I am unmarried and with child. All of the magic that accompanies pregnancy seems to signal the end of our never-ending blissful moments.

It's obvious that Mitchell is not up for the emotional rollercoaster of pregnancy. Perhaps our combination of bliss mixed with momentary feelings of love is not enough to maintain us through my mood swings and unpredictability. I'm saddened when I recall happier times. Why does the love seem to always fade? In his twenties Mitchell had been briefly married and then divorced. I vowed that I would be a better woman than she was, even though I knew only his side of their story. He said that they never really loved each other, but that they had gotten married because it was his dying mother's wish. Eight months after their 'I dos' they said, "We don't" and were divorced. Whenever he speaks of this unhappy time in his life I promise to always love and appreciate him. Mitchell's eyes water as he speaks of his ex-wife's neglect of their marriage and her not wanting to have children because she did not want to take the time away from her career for pregnancy and motherhood. I have never met his ex-wife, but it's hard to understand how she could not have given this man whatever he wanted. I can only imagine that she is somewhere in the world missing him and at some level regretting the decision that caused him to leave. I know firsthand the damaging effects of putting a career before a great love, so I try not to judge her too much. Some woman is probably laying in Kevin's arms judging me for letting him go, and rightfully so! I wonder how my life would be different if I were carrying Kevin's baby… If I had chosen love over career.

Mitchell often speaks about his terrible marriage in comparison to our loving relationship and as he speaks I gently wipe his tears, hold him tight, and promise that everything is now okay. As I say these words to him, I hope my heart is listening because my love for Kevin still resides in an unspoken spot deep within my being.

Once I am convinced that Kevin is gone forever I persuade my heart to give Mitchell the love he so desperately requests and I anxiously do whatever it takes to make him happy.

Fast forward to the other side of happiness and you now find me spending countless nights alone sitting in my rocker/glider singing to the little one growing inside my womb. I sing uplifting spirituals in an effort to encourage the developing soul inside my tummy, as well as my aching soul.

I try to figure out what happened to the passion that Mitchell and I once shared. Even though Dear must be disappointed that I allowed myself to get in such a predicament she never utters a disparaging word. Instead, she comforts me through my pregnancy and the broken heart I nurse during Mitchell's absence. I thought it my duty to accommodate Mitchell's strong desire to be a father, so despite the strain it puts on my professional career I drag this inflated, tired body through eight months of a tedious work schedule with the hopes that everything will somehow work to our benefit.

After a long, tiring day I pull into the driveway and to my surprise Mitchell's car is blocking the garage. Usually, anything standing in the way of me and my bed would make me angry but the fact that Mitchell is anywhere in the vicinity outshines this minor inconvenience. It's as if God has personally smiled on me. Inside the house, I find Mitchell sitting on the couch with tears in his eye telling Dear that he disappeared because he was afraid, but that he's now back and wants us to be a family. The look in Dear's eyes signals me not to interrupt with the many questions that circle my inner thoughts. I follow her unspoken request and focus on the big picture, which is not easy since my hormones are angrily begging for the spotlight. Standing quietly in the doorway, I thank God for Mitchell's return and his willingness to place his heart on display for us to examine. I do my best to stifle the tears waiting to fall from my eyes as Dear encourages Mitchell with Bible verses and love.

Eventually, I get my chance to hear him explain his disappearances. As I sit across the table looking through the tears in his eyes I explain to Mitchell that I once felt like a priority in his world, but his unannounced absences prove otherwise. I want to believe that he won't walk away again, but his actions were hurtful and difficult to understand. Mitchell does not acknowledge my half-spoken request to know where I am on his list of priorities, but he says my independence and occasional emotional distance confuses him. Apparently, he thought that I would move on without a second thought about him or his whereabouts. We talk most of the night and despite my best efforts to control my emotional display, tears escape my eyelids. He kisses each tear, and eventually I reciprocate by gently wiping away the raindrops that roll down his beautiful brown face. Tonight marks the start of our renewed love and for the first time in months our baby girl rests peacefully inside my tummy. She obviously knows that daddy is home because she is at rest. Mitchell returns to his role in our lives and proves his desire to be here by catering to our every whim. I am once again enjoying this wonderful life with him.

Since his return, Mitchell works diligently to get the house ready for our bundle of joy, which is soon to arrive. He paints and assembles furniture while I sanitize and continuously shop for more clothes than any one baby could ever wear. Because I am nesting, I am bothered by the way the toilet in the downstairs bathroom looks and at my insistence, Mitchell replaces it with a new low-rise, water-efficient model. Although money is no object and hiring a contractor would be the easy route, I convince Mitchell we should do the work ourselves, and that later we will be proud of our efforts in preparation for our bundle of joy. Once the commode is removed, I convince him to also replace the tile. Even in his exhausted state, Mitchell is one in a million, so we head to the local Home Supply Warehouse for new tile.

Today has been a really busy day. It seems we are making up for the time lost while I laid in bed depressed and Mitchell did whatever it was that he did while he was missing in action. I am anxious to make everything perfect before the baby's arrival so while Mitchell installs the tile I visit a highly recommended pediatrician for a quick introduction and interview, hoping they will accept my unborn sweetheart as a new patient. As another indication that God continues to smile in my direction, Dr. Walton welcomes me and promises that she or her father, Dr. Walton Sr. will be at the hospital to greet the baby on her birthday.

It was my belief that water would gush from my vagina when it is time for the baby to explode onto the scene. But when the time comes it is just the opposite. Water trickles down my legs causing me to continually get up to pee, or at least I thought it was pee. I'm irritated, it's 3 a.m. and I am tired from an exhausting week, but I get up because I don't want to pee the bed. I don't usually turn on the light in the middle of the night because I don't want to wake Mitchell, but this time I get the strange impulse to look in the toilet where to my surprise I see "pink show", which is an indicator that our baby girl is on her way. After exactly eight and a half months, Kali has decided to enter the world a month and a half early.

Following a cesarean delivery necessitated by her sideways transverse position, a puffed-up, reddish-brown, premature baby girl with a teeny-weeny curly afro is laid across my chest as her proud father films the entire event, tears streaming through his mustache, across his lips, and down his beard. Mitchell is usually the epitome of machismo, but since returning home he has released enough tears to water our garden for several months. I enjoy his essence of manliness, but I love seeing his softer side. Kali has been home for four weeks, and Mitchell has only left our sides long enough to restock the cabinets and shower. He changes diapers in the middle of the night, feeds, burps, bathes, and plays with Kali through my postpartum depression. I thank God for bringing him back to us.

On the morning of the first day of the fifth week Mitchell tells me that he received a call from work and he has to be gone for a week. He now seems anxious to get away and he begins to pack for pending travels. For the first time since his return he appears happy to leave us. He had promised to stay with us and not travel for a year, but I guess two months equals a year in Mitchell time. Whenever I remind him of his promise, he shuts down and says that I should be thankful for the time that we have had. I am very grateful for our time, but I'm also a bit nervous because of how he disappeared during my pregnancy. Dear encourages me to place my worries in God's hands, and I honestly try.

As Kali turns six months old, her Daddy's absences have become more frequent. In between the departures my depression increases and I spend most of my spare time resting next to baby Kali as she plays between naps and feedings. My ability to escape this horrible world by focusing on 'happier times to come' fade with every day of surviving Mother's negative jabs. Daydreaming had once been my escape from unbearable realities, but my ability to daydream is becoming more difficult. Staying away from Mrs. Eloise's negativity makes my current reality manageable while caring for Kali is an ever-present reminder that I have to stay in the present. I thank God for delivering me from the evil hands of Mother. I remember as a child daydreaming about a perfect adult life as my means of escaping Mother's verbal, mental, and sometimes physical abuse. I am thankful that I am no longer living daily life subjected to Mother's abuse; however, I must admit that I am embarrassed to be in public with a new baby, no man, and an empty ring finger. I am very thankful for my beautiful baby girl, but I wish that I'd brought her into a better situation. Because of my choices I have traded Mother's torment for an unhappiness that I created. Without Dear by my side I would be lost. She knows that many of my current issues are cause by my own poor decisions, but still she supports me. It's like I caused my own world of mental and emotional abuse. Nevertheless, Dear's support is unwavering as she encourages me to wear one of the many expensive rings floating around my jewelry box on my ring finger. Her suggestion helps me to feel less ashamed while in public, but the truth is that I am unwed, with child, and lonely for the man that I forced my heart to embrace.

Although Mitchell consistently spoke of us being a family, his interests in me seems to have diminished once I agreed to give in to his desires of fatherhood. This fact hurts the most because I fill tricked. Why does he no longer want to be here? Is it because I said that I did not want to get married? Was I not fun while pregnant? Does the baby cry too much? If he would only tell me what's wrong, we can fix the problem. He promised we would conquer the world together and work through all problems, but that isn't happening.

With Dear by my side I learn once again to be proud of myself and to walk with dignity. Dear embraces me and my new baby, never uttering a negative word about the unfortunate experience. I first receive child support for Kali when she is ten months old. If not for the checks and the occasional text messages, I would not know that Mitchell is still alive. Dear promises that everything will be okay and insists that I be strong as she helps me to regain my inner peace.

As a young woman, Dear also had to adjust to single parenthood when her husband quietly moved out, leaving behind a goodbye note, three young children, and a mailbox full of delinquent bills. Dear discovered independence in the midst of troubling times; in fact, she defines the difficult moments in her life as necessary and pivotal. Marrying at a very young age Dear learned to follow her husband's lead without question, so when he left she was lost until she found her own path and chose a life that worked in her favor. Dear learned to choose her own dance as she became the mother and father for her family. She says that God brought her through each difficult time triumphantly. The strength gained through difficult times is a benefit, and I acknowledge another unexpected benefit during my hard times. My desire for Kevin resurfaces, which proves that although my heart is damaged, it's still alive.

I miss Kevin. Unlike Mitchell, who always seems to be hiding something,

Kevin was always open, honest, and a man of his word. I guess my longing for the type of love Kevin and I once shared helped me ignore Mitchell's secrecy. When Mitchell does return, I do not question his absences. Instead, I convince myself that he just needs to have his private moments. He still has his condominium on the lake and opts to spend most nights there when he is in town. I have a key, and I have thought about popping up unannounced, but even thinking about this type of activity is exhausting, and honestly, I just don't have the strength. I am caring for a baby who has yet to distinguish day from night.

After another long night of diaper changes and midnight feedings, I realize that my patience has grown short and I'm tired of Mitchell's selfish disappearances. We have a new baby and I need his help. I want Kali to have her daddy and I also want my baby's daddy front and center in our world. Not because I truly love him or because he is my first choice, but because he completes the picture and I do not want to be a single mother of a fatherless child. I did not ask for this... or maybe I did, but jeez! Although I realize that Kali probably does not miss him when he is gone for days or weeks at a time, I still want him here with us. I am sure that if she could grasp the concept, she would love having her daddy around. At eight months old, she lays in her crib singing, "da, da, da, da..." I am certain this her song is her way of saying "daddy, daddy, daddy," which breaks my heart all over again.

The unanswered questions bother me most. I thought we were happy, or at least OK. Mitchell and I had two years of un-marital bliss. *We* planned and pursued pregnancy the last year of our relationship; I became pregnant, he became disinterested, the baby was born, and daddy was gone. As work apparently becomes busier than ever, he rarely answers my calls. Sometimes I wait a few days between calls hoping he will miss me/us; other times I call several times a day to demonstrate my commitment and understanding of his workload. Whatever the strategy, when I get him on the phone he is distant and in a hurry to end the conversation. No matter what I do, the results are usually the same. I am tempted to move on to the next guy, but the next guy has not come along. What would I tell him, anyway? "I am sometimes involved with my baby's missing daddy, so please be understanding if he should walk in as you fulfill the duties he should be managing?"

By the time Kali is 11 months old Mitchell is completely gone. All communications have ceased. We were both so excited to become brand-new parents… what happened? One day we are happily pursuing a life together and the next day he is packing his bags for business trips that happen so frequently it seems he's running from the FBI. Mitchell used to have so many personal items in my home that I had to compete for counter space in the bathroom, but now I can count his personal items on one hand; it's almost like he never existed.

It amazes me that it takes two separate entities to create a child but only one to raise her; or so he must think. In any case, he is a professional man with a stable career and he helps with Kali's financial needs. However, I would take his presence over his money because I make good money, but I can never be a daddy to Kali. I want so much more than a passing thought via his monthly child support check. Realizing that my desires for the perfect family unit may never be my reality causes unbearable heartache. I retreat to Dear's arms and I cry myself to sleep trying to figure out what happened to my wonderful life with Mitchell.

What's a Picture Worth?

Through times of depression and moments of restlessness I take Kali on long drives, which helps her sleep and gives me time to think. We usually end up farther from home than anticipated and spend too much money on things we don't need. I feel guilty that Kali doesn't have her father in her life and therefore; we usually go to a toy store and I allow her to go a bit overboard with her toy selection. I dislike clutter and I am trying to instill in Kali a sense of social responsibility, so a few times a year we donate toys to a local children's home. She enjoys seeing the children's faces light up as they play with her gently used, and sometimes brand-new items. Although I spend money, I stay within my budget because I still have a goal of one day exceeding Mother's net worth.

For some reason, Kali and I both feel a little down today. It's as though there is a funk in the air, and hugs, which usually dispel this feeling, aren't working; even having breakfast on the terrace with Dear doesn't do the trick. Perhaps we are both missing Mitchell. We try to fill the void by taking one of our drives, and we end up at a toy store about 60 miles away from home, in an opposite direction than our usual route.

Kali is becoming such a beautiful little personality and the drive, her nap, and clearing of my thoughts have once again proven beneficial. We are back to our usually jovial selves laughing and making silly faces as we wander through the toy store aisles. Our giggly Saturday afternoon shopping spree comes to a screeching halt; however, when the lady in front of me at the cash register opens her wallet. To my surprise, she has a picture of someone who looks like a younger version of Mitchell, posing with her woman proudly by his side. There are no kids in the picture, just the two of them, hugging and both wearing wedding rings.

The mystery woman's wallet lay open on the counter as she hands her credit card to the clerk, while I stare at the picture, trapped by my thoughts. In my business dealings I have learned to think fast on my feet and if she were a potential client I would strike up a conversation about the picture and know everything I need to know before the cashier hands her the receipt. Not this time. It's difficult to strategize when my emotions are tap dancing on my heart.

When we were children, Mother would tell Alex and I, "be quiet until I ask you to speak" so often that I find it difficult to start a conversation in social settings, especially when my heart is involved. Once the conversation is opened, however, I have taught myself to take the initiative and lead the conversation. It took me a while, but once I overcame my fear of being slapped in the mouth for "speaking out of turn," I became good at steering social conversations toward business gain—a skill that has made millions for my advertising firm, as well as my real estate company, J-Ness Reality.

But in personal situations I still struggle. If only she'd speak to me first! Ask me about Kali! Kali is such a delightful child; however, that she waits patiently for her toys, not making a sound or drawing any attention to herself. I manage to take my eyes off the picture long enough to notice the woman's stylish appearance and welcoming smile. She looks like an older version of me, I think. Wow! Is this why he left us? Did he marry another woman?

My thoughts are interrupted by the clerk's voice, "That will be

$385.91, please." Without realizing it, I had placed all the toys on the counter. Quickly, I pay and hurry out the doors just in time to see the mystery lady drive past us, smiling pleasantly. I memorize her license plate number, and once Kali is locked into her car seat, I pull out my smartphone. As I locate Mitchell's name in my contacts and hit send, I begin to wonder if I'd seen the picture wrong. My heart is racing as I wait to hear his voice on the other end.

To my surprise, Mitchell's number has been changed, which means I can't question him or tell him off, which makes me angry. He changed his number? Why? And how dare he not give me the updated information! What if there was an emergency, if something happened to the baby, and I needed to speak to him?

I dial his office number, which rings into his voicemail because his secretary is not there on the weekend. I opt not to leave a message because he usually does not pick up his own messages. I call information and he's not listed, which doesn't surprise me because he's a private person. "Wow" is the cleanest word I can say as I realize that I have no idea how to get in contact with my daughter's father.

The last time he came to see Kali, Mitchell attempted to trade pleasantries, but I dismissed him and abruptly left him in the living room with Kali and Dear. I was angry with him for leaving and for refusing to talk about why, so I had nothing to say to him. He had also stopped by my office a few times, asking me to lunch in an attempt to be "friends," but I declined. I don't want to be his friend. I want it all or nothing! Now I see that if we were "friends" I could call him right now. Boy, I really let my stubborn anger get in the way this time! I was so determined to punish him for leaving us that I'd forgotten to think about what was best for Kali and honestly, for me as well.

I never expected this curveball, and now I am wishing I had handled Mitchell and the situation differently. The only time I see him is when he stops by the house unannounced asking to see "the baby."

I sit in the parking lot for about 20 minutes as Kali rummages through the bags of new toys in the back seat. Eventually, I decide to stop feeling sorry for myself. Anger takes over and I leave the parking lot on a mission. I feel like I have been a street fight and I just lost. Before the tears can form I realize that I have been sitting on the sidelines feeling sorry for myself, licking my wounds. Well, no more! As I drive home, I decide that I have to know more about Mitchell. No longer will I naively accept him at face value. I need to know more about Mitchell so I began to think strategically. Perhaps this is one time that I should have listened to Mother.

The next time Mitchell comes by to see "the baby," I swallow my pride and invite him inside. I try to get information about his ex-wife, but that plan goes astray when we end up in the bed, making love. I get lost in his eyes, his smile, and those smooth talking lips. Honestly, I really want to be held. As he holds me and tells me how much he misses me and wants to be back in our lives, I ditch the plan to find the mystery lady, settling for the promise of happiness and a future with our family intact. I convince myself that my eyes must have deceived me, that the man in the picture was just a Mitchell lookalike. Maybe the mystery woman was Mitchell's ex-wife and she still carries an old picture.

Anyway, what does it matter? Mitchell says he is no longer afraid of full-time parenthood. He begs me to let him back into our lives. He promises that he will be here for "his girls," and over the next few weeks, he is with us every day. Although he travels a lot for work, he is with us whenever he is in town. This time, I make sure I have all his contact information, and I store it away for a rainy day, although I don't expect rain any time soon.

One day while watering the plants in his lifeless condominium, I feel guilty for not understanding his fear of parenting, so when he returns from his business trip I truly forgive him and we start our lives again. He visits more often as we grow closer, and Kali has her daddy back in her life. I keep his presence a secret from Mother because I don't want to be judged, but she does ask why Kali talks about her daddy so much more lately. I evade her questions as I usually do by changing the subject to talk about her and her life, which always works.

Two months into our rekindled love, I am in a toy store shopping for a baby shower gift when I see the mystery lady again. I don't want to rock the boat because Mitchell and I now have a good relationship, but I have to know more about the possibility of a connection. As the clerk scans my gift, I ask if he knows her. "Oh, you mean Mrs. Rogers?" he asks. My stomach sinks while he continues, "She's in here every month buying toys, clothes, and supplies for children at local shelters. She and her husband never had children, so she donates time and money at various shelters for children, who she calls her extended family."

I realize that it's no coincidence that she has the same last name as Mitchell. I try to convince myself that she's the ex-wife who kept her married name for professional reasons, but my instincts force me to learn more.

The clerk goes on and on about Mrs. Rogers and all the wonderful ways she contributes to the community. He mentions an article in the local newspaper last month praising her for getting her company to make a huge donation to three struggling shelters. As I drive home, I accept that I have to put on my "big-girl panties" and find out more or the unanswered questions will eat me alive. At this moment, my plan is back into play.

As soon as I get home and put Kali to bed I go online and find the article about the mystery lady. I began to take pictures of Mitchell with us every time he visits. I capture him on film in every situation, even in my bed after our lovemaking sessions. I love him and I know that my plan will cause certain death to the relationship, but I put my plan into action anyway, hoping our love will somehow survive.

As I carefully devise my course of action, I begin to understand the lesson of this situation… I have a right to choose my dance.

I consider what will happen if I confront Mitchell about my suspicions; however, his past behaviors indicate that he will deny my accusations, accuse me of not trusting him, and leave me again as I try to make sense of it all. I dreadfully realize that I have to exercise patience while I pretend that everything is ok. Acting like everything is ok is how I choose to stand up for myself because the alternatives are of no real consequence (we will argue, he will leave, and I will once again be alone), so I decide to move forward with the pretense.

Once I have assembled our family photo album, our family DVD with plenty of daddy-and-daughter moments, and the calendar of our family events, I borrow Vanessa's truck and take a week's vacation from work so that I can focus on my plan. I treat this morning just like any Monday morning and get out of bed early as though I am going to work. As usual, Mitchell joins me in the shower for his morning ritual, he plays with Kali as I get her dressed, and then he leaves for work while I get dressed. As soon as he pulls out of the garage, I throw on a sweat suit, put my hair in a ponytail, put on a baseball hat and sunglasses, put Kali in a car seat in Vanessa's truck—which is parked around the corner—and follow him in the opposite direction of his office or condominium.

My stomach turns as I follow him to what I think is an alternate home he shares with his wife, ex-wife, or… who knows. I am careful to not drive too close, but I also don't want to lose him. I feel like the teenage girl in a bad high school romance movie, following the jock so arrogant that he doesn't notice he's being followed by one of his brokenhearted loves. My bleeding heart flashes across the top of the truck like a police siren, and as adrenaline rushes through my heart, I grow more determined to catch Mitchell in his lies. Despite the evidence, I pray that I am wrong about him.

I am so caught up in my thoughts that I don't realize how far I have driven or that Kali has finished her bottle and fallen asleep. I am in the same neighborhood as the toy store where I saw Mrs. Rogers. I park and watch Mitchell walk into a coffee shop and greet a woman with a soft kiss to the lips. To my surprise, the lady is not Mrs. Rogers. The two of them talk, laugh, and gaze into each other's eyes, kiss, and hold hands while I take pictures of them with a high-powered zoom lens as tears stream down my left cheek.

Right in sync with my torn feelings, only one eye sheds tears. With my right eye I shoot daggers and poisonous darts toward Mitchell, but his open display of affections indicates that he can't feel the sting. An hour later, Mitchell walks the woman to her car, tongue kisses her as though he's going to war, gets in his car, and leaves the parking lot.

I follow him to what seems to be his home. The garage door goes up automatically, he drives in, and the garage door closes behind him as he pulls suitcases out of the trunk. When did he pack and put luggage in the trunk? I quickly take a picture of the house and drive away nauseously thinking about the possible diseases I've allowed into my home by way of Mitchell's joystick. This thought fuels my anger, and I know that I have to change my strategy because now there is yet another woman in the mix. I can only imagine how many more indiscretions I will discover if I look, so naturally, I begin to look.

I am much too busy to follow Mitchell around town, so I hire someone else. Steven Gaggs previously worked as an investigator for Leisurely Connections. Mother, who enthusiastically slings her wrath onto anyone within landing distance, wrongfully terminated him. I know how it feels to be on the receiving end of her usually undeserved fury so when I'm in a position to help, I go behind her and pick up pieces of the lives she's tried to destroy. Steven suffered hard times following his unexpected dismissal from Leisurely Connections, so I offered him a job at my firm. Thanks in part to my silent partnership and my financial investment he eventually opened his own company, *SG Investigations*. His company grew to be very successful and I turned a lucrative profit, but more important than the monetary gain, I gained a friend.

I call Steven and we catch up over several cups of English tea topped with homemade whipped cream. I am embarrassed to ask for his help, but I know I can trust him to exercise great discretion and he won't judge me. The last thing I need is for Mother's name to be publically tied to her only grandchild's cheating father.

Within two weeks, Steven shows me documents that shock me to my core.

Mitchell has been married for over 20 years: He is cheating on me, his wife, *and* his coffee-shop girlfriend. In addition to the three of us, there are seven other women who share private moments with Mitchell.

I feel too many emotions to describe, but the strongest is disgust. How dare that sweet-talking, slough-foot, old-ass punk betray me! I am so tired of life dropping hurt on my doorstep wrapped in a deceptive little pretty package. How has he pulled this off for so many years? Well, he has toyed with the wrong woman at the wrong time. I have taken life's pain in stride as a necessary means to live in this world… but NO MORE!

As I sit quietly staring into my empty teacup, Steven asks, "Well Ms. J., what do we do now?" We talk about my feelings, and he consoles my broken heart for about half an hour or so until my anger turns into strength. I take the lead in devising "the plan." I thank Steven, pay him for his services, and then go into project mode.

I combine the many photos of Mitchell in a portfolio and make an appointment with Mrs. Rogers under the pretense of making a donation to her organization. I am escorted into a tastefully designed office where a sophisticated woman sits behind a very expensive custom-made desk. At first, I want to abort my plan because clearly, she is the bigger victim. How can I partake in the pain that will pierce her heart and possibly destroy her faith in her husband? As I sit in the plush chair and sip Voss sparkling water from a Mikasa glass listening to Mrs. Rogers pitch her non-profit organization in hopes of a large donation, I feel guilty. I am so guilt-ridden that I promise to have my assistant send her company a substantial donation. Gathering my purse and the unopened portfolio, I head for the door.

I decide to ditch the plan because I really like her. She reminds me a lot of myself and where I want to go in life, minus the cheating husband, of course. Although I am determined to leave her world intact, my internal dialogue will not shut up! She deserves to know the truth, but my original plan, to tell her about Mitchell in a nonchalant, hurtful manner, is no longer a viable option. Before I met her, I considered Mrs. Rogers an enemy because she wore his ring and carried his name. Now I understand that we both are clearly Mitchell's victims.

As I leave her office, she pleasantly asks, "Were you going to show me your portfolio? I spent so much time talking about my organization that you hardly had a chance to get a word in edgewise. I truly apologize."

I take a deep breath, step back into her office, and take my seat. She closes her office door and sits down with a puzzled look on her face, which intensifies when she notices the tears swelling in my eyes.

She moves around her desk, sits to my right, and gently asks, "Honey, are you OK?"

All that I could choke out is, "Your husband is cheating on us!" before my left bottom row of lashes release the flood of tears down my cheek. Without looking up, I unzip the portfolio, open it to the first page and tenderly place the picture book across her desk.

I sit quietly as she flips through the pages, amazed by the story that leaps to the forefront of her life. I say very little, yet she realizes the real reason I'm in her office. Just when I'm sure she'll throw me out of her office, she pulls four tissues from a fancy box on her desk, hands me two, and quietly asks, "Is she yours?" as she points to Kali sitting on Mitchell's lap. After my sorrowful "yes," she clears her throat, picks up her phone, and asks her assistant to cancel her remaining appointments and hold all of her calls until further notice.

Tears compete to give us both our equal share of emotional rain as I explain the photographs. She shares the reason she and Mitchell never had children. It turns out that she did not willingly choose career over motherhood. Early in their marriage, after a full hysterectomy saved her life from cervical cancer, she wanted to adopt a child but Mitchell told her that he never wanted children. In fact, he told her that he considered the hysterectomy a blessing in disguise. As she looks through the many pictures, Mrs. Rogers' eyes rest the longest on baby Kali. She surprises me when she says, "She has his smile."

She spends about an hour looking at the photos before asking, "Okay… Where do we go from here?"

I hesitate before telling her what I want to do, because I'm not an evil person, I'm just tired of Mitchell's foolishness. As I outline my idea, Mrs. Rogers picks up a pen and begins to take notes. To my surprise, she complements me on a well thought-out strategy, tells me that I remind her of her younger self, and asks if she may be part of the plan.

Over the next few weeks we secretly trade phone calls and emails, and The Plan is underway. One night at dinner Mitchell tells me he will be away on business the week of his birthday, which is the day after Thanksgiving Day. Mitchell has no idea that I know the real reason he will be unavailable that week. The week of his absence will mark Mitchell's 20th year in business, he and Mrs. Rogers' 25th wedding anniversary, and a special birthday. Therefore, he and Mrs. Rogers have invited their families, many of his colleagues, and several of his college buddies to celebrate at the Marriot.

His eyes are convincing as he lies about his business trip, which makes me angry. However, I smile and promise that I will plan a romantic weekend in a surprise location and give him a private birthday gift when he returns. This is the first time I am purposely deceiving someone, and the thought of getting revenge helps me to get through dinner with a smile.

For the next few weeks I wear sanitary napkins and tell Mitchell that I am menstruating. Mitchell is a very sexual man so I throw in headaches, toothaches, stomachaches, cramping, and whatever else to keep him on his side of the bed. After the first week of abstinence, Mitchell is mysteriously called away on business. Helping him pack is bittersweet because I realize that the next time I see him may be the last. Kali and I walk him to his car and wave goodbye as he pull out of the garage.

Once he is out of sight, I call Mrs. Rogers and tell her Mitchell is probably on his way home. We talk for hours, solidifying *The Plan*. We are close to aborting the whole idea when her phone rings and Mitchell says he'll be traveling for work until the Tuesday before Thanksgiving. His deceit fuels us both, and we decide to move forward with our strategies. From that point forward, we never look back.

Mrs. Rogers, a very spiritual woman, believes God had a hand in her laying her wallet open so that I would see the picture of her and Mitchell that day in the toy store. We do realize that God probably does not support our planned deceptions; nevertheless, in the name of payback we move forward. Mrs. Rogers was aware of Mitchell's infidelities and she had thought about removing the picture from her wallet as to avoid any embarrassing scenes. On the contrary, the picture sparked what could be the closure she's wanted for years. Some say that a picture is worth a thousand words, but should she choose this dance, Mrs. Rogers may find that a picture could be worth a large divorce settlement. Should I choose this dance, a picture may be worth hundreds of unanswered questions and freedom from Mitchell's lies.

What's a picture worth to you and which dance would you choose?

A Time of Thanks

"Thankful for the child, but not how she came to be"... Mrs. Eloise

Thanksgiving... A special time of thanks, even in the midst of chaos. Thanksgiving dinner and festivities are prepared by Mother's cook and the rest of the staff but hosted by and accredited to Mother. Anyone fortunate enough to receive an invite is expected to attend. The meal is delicious but Mother, or Mrs. Eloise as she prefers to be called in the presence of others, is present so the atmosphere is strained and tense. If not for my mental preoccupation with the pending 'plan' I may be bothered by Mrs. Eloise's complaints and disapproval of my life, my fatherless child, and my missing-in-action boyfriend. She has no idea that Mitchell is back and at my house most nights, when he's not out with one of his other women or at home with wifey. I am so conditioned to smile and daydream while watching Mother's mouth move that I almost miss the discussion about my sister's Alex lifestyle choice.

I've known that Alex is a lesbian since I walked in on her kissing a girl while in high school, but Mother had no idea. Alex is very much like Mother and looks for opportunities to cause shock and awe; therefore, Alex chooses today during dinner to come out. Alex knew that her announcement would cause Mother great embarrassment and stain her perfect family picture;

however, Mother was probably the only one surprised. Alex has flaunted her many girlfriends around town for years. She and Jillian, her current girlfriend, live together in a three bedroom house and use only one of the rooms as a bedroom. Did Mother think that one of them slept on the couch? I think not! Mother is very intelligent. It's obvious she didn't want to accept the fact that Alex is a lesbian. What is equally obvious is that Alex came to dinner intending to force-feed the facts to Mother in front of an audience.

Mrs. Eloise requests that everyone in attendance offer words of appreciation. When is it Alex' turn she ends her Thanksgiving speech with, "… and I truly thank God for the love of my life, Jillian. I thank her for being a great lover, best friend, and loyal spouse". Alex then seals her statement with a passionate kiss across Jillian's lips for each of the forty-seven onlookers sitting around the beautifully decorated table to see. The room stands still while we fearfully await Mother's reaction. The evil intentions in the atmosphere were thick until Dear whispers, "Peace, in the mighty name of Jesus."

Like Donald Trump, Mother is a shrewd businessperson, capable of striking fear into hearts with a simple "You're fired!" At that moment, we all expected heads to roll, and that Alex, along with her flavor of the month Jillian, would be escorted from the property. To our surprise, Mother responds with not the least bit of emotion. "Well, it looks like I will have a daughter-in-law soon, When's the wedding?"

It's as though Mother knew Alex's announcement was meant to cause her pain and embarrassment. When that plan fails, Alex strongly denounces any plans of marriage, and we all go back to our roasted duck, smoked turkey, honey-glazed ham, potatoes, and all the other fixings. It's as though Alex's shocking declaration never even happened, but Dear and I know the evil that hung in the air was no match for God's peace and had to leave when Dear said, "Peace, in the mighty name of Jesus."

If I want to avoid another one of Mother's lectures, I'd better get out of here before the guests leave. The look in Dear's eyes tells me she's thinking the same thing. Mother would never express her true feelings in front of company, and we don't want to be present for the bomb that will inevitably explode later this evening. Alex and I look a lot alike on the outside, but we are very different individuals. As far back as I can remember, Alex has always spoken her mind, especially to Mother. She is the only person that can hold her own with Mother. I don't understand why Mother allows her to cross so many lines. When she's provoked, Alex yells obscenities at Mother, and they even had a fistfight when Alex returned home from college one weekend and Mother forbade the staff from washing Alex's dirty laundry. Alex felt entitled to the staff's services, but for some reason, Mother was in no mood to share her staff with Alex on this particular day.

The arguing began when Mother insisted that Alex "stop acting like a spoiled brat and wash your own clothes." Things became so heated that Mother slapped Alex and told her to watch her mouth. Within seconds, the yelling turned into physical scuffling. Alex put Mother's head through the sheetrock wall in the laundry room. Alex's held Mother firmly against the wall by her neck while she pounded Mother in the face. Alex seemed to be releasing years of pent-up anger in that one moment. Mother's eyes bulged as she struggled for air, tried to wrestle Alex's hand from around her neck, and attempted to block some of the blows Alex delivered to her face. I had never seen the look of fear and desperation in Mother's eye as she hung slightly in the air with her head through the wall while she grasped at what seemed to be her last attempts of air until we pried Alex off of Mother.

Mother is not very maternal and considers her two girls an obligation. She often tells us that we should feel honored to be members of her strong family line.

Although I was frightened for Mother, I wanted to celebrate in the moment that someone had finally given Mrs. Eloise back some of her own abuse. She is evil, and she deserved every minute of that thrashing. But before I could celebrate I realized that Alex had not considered the consequences of the dance she had just chosen. I became very fearful for her, because I knew she would pay quite a penalty. As Daddy and I struggled to release Alex's grip, we knew she would be fortunate to see another day on this side of the dirt. No one had ever taken this type of stance with Mother.

I took Alex to another part of the house to calm her down while Daddy talked to Mother. As I pulled Alex from the room Mother yelled, "You'll be dead by this time tomorrow you ungrateful little bitch!" We knew this was no idle threat and the look in Alex' eyes told me that for the first time she was truly afraid for her life. Days later in fact, I was the one who received the call from the police telling us that Alex Johnson had been in an "accident" and was on her way into surgery.

Even though there is a lot about Alex that I dislike, she is still my baby sister and my heart dropped to the pit of my stomach as I grabbed my keys and raced to the car. Dear grabbed her coat and immediately began to talk to God, or I should say that she began to listen. As I raced down the freeway for about an hour, Dear sat with an intent look on her face, nodding as though someone was telling her a secret. I called Daddy from the car and I could hear Mother refuse to go to the hospital until Daddy firmly told her, "Get your purse, put on your coat, and get your ass in the car!" I had never heard him be assertive, nor had I ever known Mother to comply with such a command.

Once at the hospital I learned that Alex had been attacked and brutally beaten. She suffered two broken ribs, a broken arm, and a fractured ankle. Daddy must have talked Mother out of having Alex killed because she is still alive. After three hours of surgery the internal bleeding was under control, but Alex was in a coma. Two days later, I asked Dear why she had not asked God to wake Alex from the coma. Dear has a special connection with God and I believe that He would heal Alex if Dear asked. Dear just smiled as though she knew the plan and gently said, "Let God do His work, Jonnie. Remember that all things work together for the good. Now thank Him for what He's already done." Her deliberate faith in God assured me that everything was going to be fine. Three days had passed and my baby sister still lay almost lifeless, breathing through tubes, but Dear and I knew that she would be OK.

But the situation on the other side of the room wasn't as good. The tension between Mother and Daddy was thick, and this time, Daddy was the initiator. I heard him tell Mother, "Eloise, you'd better pray to God that my daughter recovers 100 percent! These girls are my world!" At that point, Mother walked over to Alex's bedside and stood quietly. Daddy joined her and made Mother face Alex. "Look at her!" he said firmly. Her face looked like it had been through a meat grinder. As they both watched the machines force air into Alex's frail body, Mother's eyes watered. Until that moment I never knew Mother could feel anything deep enough to cause tears. Nonetheless; the love and a healthy serving of fear flowed down Mother's flawlessly made-up face as she gently kissed the palm of Alex's left hand leaving a tablespoon of tears. I believe the tears signified the beginning of their journey toward amends. For the first time since Alex's beating, Mother seemed to not care that there was an audience of hospital staff, Dear, Daddy and I as she allowed her emotions to take center stage.

As if on cue, Alex began to regain consciousness. She immediately tried to pull the tubes from her mouth while she struggled to breathe on her own. When she reached to free herself she splashed Mother's tears onto her face. Alarms rang as the nurses raced to remove the tubes and check Alex's vitals. Once she was calm the doctor changed the bandages on her face in search of the hemorrhage that caused them to be wet. He seemed a bit puzzled, but we knew her wounds were not leaking. She had baptized herself with the love that poured from Mother's heart by way of her tear ducts.

Infection and other complications kept Alex in the hospital for three weeks. Once she was home I was happy to help with her recovery and I never uttered a word about the "random" assault. She said that she didn't remember much, but it was an unspoken truth that Mother had arranged that merciless beating by supposed strangers. We both also knew that Alex would not leave this earth without getting some type of revenge. To my surprise, her eyes watered as I explained why her face was wet when she awoke from her coma. Her only response was, "I thought my eyes were deceiving me, but I saw Mother crying right before I felt the tube down my throat." Mother and Alex are cut from the same cloth, but they are the only mother and sister I have, so I love... and slightly fear both of them. I am more like Daddy and Dear. We are all gentle and passive, especially when it comes to family affairs.

Although it's been years, I remember this time in our lives as though the events took place yesterday. Eventually, Alex and Mother mended this tare and they have never raised their hands against one another since.

As I daydream about our family's past, I can hear Daddy give his Thanksgiving acknowledgments to God, his family, and his precious granddaughter. This prompts another unnecessary remark from Mother, who looks into Kali's eyes and says with a smile, "Yes, we are very thankful for our darling Kali, although we'd rather she were here under different circumstances; perhaps with a father in attendance, married to her mother." Envisioning Mother's head through the sheetrock helps me smile through yet another one of her unnecessary remarks.

Hearing Daddy's loving words about Kali causes a genuine smile to cross my lips and when he is done I began my words of thanks with Kali,

Dear, Daddy, Alex, Vanessa, and then Mother followed by a host of others who has made my year wonderful.

Although I dare not utter her name, I quietly give thanks for Mrs. Rogers. Not only for putting up with Mitchell and his selfish behaviors, but because she is just a wonderful person inside and out. Although I wish we had met under different circumstances, I am thankful for Mrs. Rogers; she is an angel.

Just as we had planned, Dear announces soon after dinner that she is tired and asks me to take her home. We spend the evening watching movies and as we turn in for the night Dear says, "Baby J", one of her many terms of endearment for me, "I know you have to do what you deem necessary, but I am praying for you and the Mrs." I don't know why I am surprised that yet again, Dear somehow knows the intricate details running through my mind before I speak a word. She and God have a special relationship and therefore, she always knows.

I am relieved that she's brought up the subject because I am ready to talk about the "Plan". I make a pot of her favorite nighttime tea, curl up on her bed under her favorite quilt and tell Dear all about Mrs. Rogers and the "Plan". She listens attentively and offers just a few words of advice, "Vengeance is mine, says the Lord. Leave it for the Lord to fix, Sweet Pea." I can feel the love in her words. Although she knows I am moving forward with the "Plan", she never judges me. She says that she wants to hear all about the ordeal when it is over. Dear listens to me babble on about the plan as she brushes my hair, sips tea, and speaks to God in her heavenly language. I am certain that she is asking God for my protection as I lay wrapped in her quilt that has been passed down through five of Dear's generations.

Being in Dear's presence is experiencing true love; a Godly love. Dear loves selflessly and encourages me to be a better version of myself. I would be lost without her. She is my first love. As far back as my memory will take me, Dear has been my reason to reach for another day. She taught me how to love by showing me how a mother's love should feel, and it is only because of her that I know how to pass a mother's love on to Kali. When Mother is cold, distant, and purposely mean, I focus on Dear and the love she gives so freely to Kali and I.

Today is Thanksgiving, and all over the world, families are expressing gratitude and appreciation for loved ones. As for me, I am most thankful to God for giving me to Dear by way of Daddy. Dear is the most precious being I have ever known. My heart is joyous that she is front and center in our lives. Through her, I feel the love of God and the strength to look forward to tomorrow. Having Dear with us makes every day a time of thanks for baby Kali and me.

The Plan

The day after Thanksgiving is usually quiet. I either work at home or spend time close to home because the streets are crowded with anxious consumers or blocked by the annual Thanksgiving parade. Today is a bit different, however, because I am on a mission. I have a destiny to create. My stomach is in knots, and breakfast; that most important meal of the day, is the last thing on my mind.

On my morning jog, I mentally go over every detail of The Plan, leaving no stone unturned. My feet pound the pavement as I try to rid myself of the tension that pervades my body. I imagine the expressions on everyone's faces as I enter the room in my sexy-but- classy dress, but the acknowledgment of beauty pales in comparison to the satisfaction I'll feel when I see the look in Mitchell's eyes once he realizes that I purposefully betray his trust. It will dawn on him in that moment that my presence is no coincidence, and I'm certain that he'll never look at me the same once he understands the depth of my dark side. There's a part of me that wants to remain an angel in his eyes, and this desire saddens me. Why does he have to be such a jerk? Hopefully he will one day understand that the pain caused by him pushed me past my previously set limits.

I argued with my heart on his behalf for almost a year before I invited him into the space that had belonged to Kevin. Kevin will always be my first love, but I was happy with the life Mitchell and I created, and I almost wish I'd ignored the picture in Mrs. Rogers' wallet that day in the toy store. But when I fast forward through the upcoming events and visualize the payback—the look of on his face, and the satisfaction I'll enjoy from seeing him get his just reward—I choose to dance! The gaze in his eyes when he holds baby Kali is the sincere look of love, and thanks to his pride (and The Plan), he's about to lose her. I'm torn. I know The Plan is necessary, a lesson Mitchell must learn, but with every other step I hesitate to inflict so much pain on him and consider aborting the whole thing and walking away.

By the time I return home, I've talked myself back into moving forward. I shower and get ready for the day's errands. By noon, I have dropped off the necessary items at the predetermined spots, and I find myself an hour early for my two o'clock meeting with the other nine ladies.

Our main agenda is to discuss our assignments, the decorations in the Grand Ballroom, and the exact placement of each hidden camera. The Mrs. and I also want to look into each lady's eyes to confirm that we can still count on their participation, and we need to know that no one has let the cat out of the bag. We are a little worried about Molly, but my heart screams that I should be just as worried about this newly discovered darkness overpowering the light in me. Nevertheless, I ignore my love for him, as well as Dear's prayers, and move forward.

Mrs. Rogers leads the meeting as though she concocted The Plan all on her own. In fact, she seems more eager than any of us, which I don't fully understand until much later. Why does she want to ruin him? She seems very sophisticated and above stooping to such a dark place, but I guess a woman scorned has thin limits. Mitchell is really in trouble because there are ten scorned women who have combined their efforts to destroy him, with the Mrs. leading the charge.

After the meeting, which lasts an hour and a half, I have exactly three hours to drive back home and spend time with Kali before getting dressed. I feel the energy leaving my limbs, so in an attempt to maintain my strength, I force down a tuna salad on wheat as I drive home to prepare for what is sure to be an eventful evening. Tonight will be a pivotal moment in my life and I have to look and feel my best all night, so although my taste buds fail, I chew and swallow.

The hour-long drive back home gives me plenty of time to think about what my decision will mean for Kali and me. Each mile, I vacillate. If I don't participate in The Plan, perhaps Mitchell will run back to my arms, knowing I am the one woman who will stand by him when it matters most. Besides, I am the only one with his child, so I have more at stake. The others will understand if I stick by his side for his daughter's sake, right? Throughout history, women have stood by men for a lot less than the sake of their child, and my daughter deserves to grow up with her father in her life. The considerations consume my every thought, so I focus on what will make my daughter proud of her mother and equally proud to be a woman. I know that one look in her eyes will tell me what to do.

When Kali was born via cesarean, with multiple complications, she wasn't expected to live through the night. I had Mitchell wheel me to her incubator, where I told Kali that I needed her to pull through so we could start our wonderful life together. As I prayed to God, I focused on my weak little darling and sang, "Yes Jesus Loves Me," just like I did when she was in my tummy. Within 30 seconds, the oxygen level in her blood began to raise and color slowly returned to her fragile body.

I felt the breath of God sweep through the room, and that's when I noticed Dear, who always knows what I need, standing in the doorway speaking to God on our behalf. The Head Nurse, who'd already told us that newborn Kali would probably not live through the next few hours, decided there was no harm in letting Kali spend her final moments in my arms, close to my heart. I struggled to hold on to my faith as giant raindrops of love flowed from my heart through my tear ducts and onto baby Kali's delicate cheeks.

Soon Kali gathered the strength to open her eyes, and for the first time I saw her old soul. From that point forward, I knew she was more than a daughter. I had just given birth to a soul mate from a past life, perhaps, a soul who had found her way back to me. Although she was just a few hours old, the magic in her eyes leaped into my heart. My every move since that day has been to benefit her life.

The taillights ahead bring me back to reality. I exit the freeway realizing that I've been on autopilot for the past hour. I pull into the garage, walk through the door, pick up Kali, and look at her beautiful face. The smile in her eyes is innocent and pure, and without warning, my eyes water. I ask her, "Can we talk, sweetie?" as I walk into my bedroom and gently close the door.

Kali climbs onto the couch in my sitting room, which is where we've had many conversations. In her best "big girl" voice, she asks, "What you talk, mommy?" I smile, sit down and speak at a level I think she can understand as I try to assess how much she will miss her daddy if he has to go away for a "long trip."

At the end of our 15-minute conversation, she climbs on my lap and asks, "Mommy gon' be with Kali?" I softly brush her big curls away from her face and tell her that mommy will always be with Kali, forever and ever! Her immediate hug puts a smile on my face and tears of joy in my soul, which lets me know that Kali and I will be fine as long as we have each other. The Plan is back on!

As I back out of the garage, I notice Dear standing in the doorway, so I pull back into the garage to say one final goodbye. Dear slowly approaches the car, and with the gentlest touch, she assures me, "And this too shall pass." She says a quick but heartfelt prayer and tells me that although she does not agree with The Plan, she understands my need to move forward. She kisses me on the forehead, and I choke back the tears that anxiously want to glide down my perfectly powdered cheeks. I mouth the words, "I love you, Dear" as I leave. I know that she is right, but this newly-found fight in me wants to move forward.

The one-hour drive to my destination gives me time to think about my life and make plans for a future without Mitchell. Although I am in the car alone, I feel Dear's prayers and the presence of angels that surround me and even carry the car down the freeway. I can't predict tonight's outcome, but I know my life will never be the same—not just because of what I've planned, but because of who am I while pursuing The Plan. On an emotional level, I've had to go to some pretty dark places, and I've taken Mrs. Rogers with me. Or, perhaps it is the Mrs. who leads the battle.

Once I arrive at the Marriott, I enter through the south side doors and go to the room where I am to meet everyone except Mrs. Rogers, who will be with Mitchell at a gala tribute in his honor. Mrs. Rogers can't miss the gala or he will be suspicious, so she'll stand by his side and entertain their family, his executive-level employees, his colleagues, and several of his college buddies who've flown in for the event. Right from the beginning of his life, Mrs. Rogers says that Mitchell has been a natural-born leader. He is admired by those close to him and respected in the community and abroad for his contributions to non-profits and those less fortunate than he. His mother would often say that he came out of the womb organizing.

Mitchell is sharing this moment with all his loved ones, of course, so he has flown in his parents, Dr. and Mrs. Rogers, and he even manages to sneak away and call baby Kali for goodnight kisses via the phone. He is shocked when Kali tells him, "Mommy gone bye-bye". He knows I only leave home for work, church, and a quick movie every now and then, so I can imagine his surprise when I'm neither home nor answering my cell.

Finally, it is time to put The Plan into place. I check myself in the mirror near the elevator one last time and head for the room we've reserved. I am the first of the "other women" to enter the room, which makes me nervous. What if I am the only one who came prepared to go forward with The Plan?

Before these thoughts take hold Melissa and Deborah enter the room giggling with drinks in their hands. Melissa, handing me a glass of Moscato, says "Here, gorgeous! Take the edge off." Melissa and Deborah are the oldest of the girlfriends in attendance tonight, both in their forties, and they seem to get along almost as well as the Mrs. and me. Soon, Susan, Tracy, Jackie, Lisa, and Allison enter the room, followed, finally, by Molly. None of us can figure out why Mitchell is attracted to Molly, and we're sure that if anyone blows the whistle on this operation, Molly will. She's sweet, but a little short on intellect. My guess is that she makes up for her lack of smarts with other skills. I guess I'll never know.

We all have a drink or two and then take the elevator down to the festivities, as planned. As we exit the elevator, we hear music playing behind a lovely voice on the microphone. As per The Plan, we split up and enter the room through different doors and at different times so as to not call attention to The Plan in motion. There are over 450 guests at the party, and as I enter the room, right on time, Mrs. Rogers is at the podium, singing Mitchell's praises. She introduces the guest of honor, asking her husband to join her onstage, and I inconspicuously move toward the front of the crowd as Mitchell charms the listeners and thanks them for celebrating yet another successful year. He also mentions key people responsible for their part in his success.

I move closer to the stage, not sure he will see me, but then he pauses and begins to choke on his words. Yes! He sees me. Smooth as ever, Mitchell ends his speech, but just as he's about to leave the stage, I speak clearly into the microphone Mrs. Rogers has left for me by the entrance.

"Mitchell?" I call his name in the sweetest voice I can muster. "Isn't there someone else you want to thank?"

Hearing my voice ring through the room makes Mitchell move expeditiously towards the stairs in the opposite direction, all but dragging the Mrs. behind him. To his surprise, the other eight women are making their way to the front of the stage, each holding a microphone and speaking in turn while the Mrs. holds him captive on stage with a firm loving grip through his arm.

First to speak is Deborah.

"Mitchell, sweetie, I won't be able to join you for the Tahoe trip again this year. You understand, I'm sure."

Next is Melissa.

"Mitchell, tell me again why you never chose to get married."

I am not sure what to expect, but Mitchell raises his microphone to his lips and calls for security.

"Security, I need these women escorted from the room. This is a private event!" He lowers his microphone and attempts to explain to Mrs. Rogers, "Honey, I didn't want you to worry and this is why I did not mention them to you."

Just as we rehearsed, Susan, Tracy, and Jackie say one of Mitchell's favorite lines in unison: "If I were to get married, you'd be the one!"

Lisa quickly asks, "Am I still the one, Mitchell?"

Allison, a professional photographer, leans into Lisa's microphone and says "Smile, Mitchell. I know how much you like your picture taken." She snaps a picture of Mitchell standing on stage with his wife, in front of his family, friends, and fans.

When it is Molly's turn to speak, she yells, "Why, Mitchell? Why? I really love you! I am the only one who stood by your side when you found out you had pancreatic cancer. Now that you're out of remission, who will be there? When your own mother is not there, I am! Because I love you unconditionally. I'm here!"

My first thought was, "This is not a part of The Plan!" I knew she'd be the one to stray, but before I could finish my thought, I realize what she'd just said.

Cancer?

Did she just say Mitchell has pancreatic cancer?

Silence fills the room except for Molly's sobbing. We are all in shock, and the look in Mrs. Rogers' eyes tells me she feels the same way I do. We are pulling a terrible prank on a dying man. Suddenly, his sins don't seem so bad, not when compared to death. Every loving feeling I have ever felt for Mitchell returns, the floodgates abruptly open.

Without thinking, I leap onto the stage and I find myself by Mitchell's side. I forget about my loyalty to the Mrs., gently take his face in my hands, and force his eyes to find mine. As tears gloss over his pupils, I ask, "When were you going to tell me? What about Kali?"

With the slightest movement, his head moves from left to right, signaling that something is wrong. I quickly realize that Mitchell has lied to Molly about having cancer. Mrs. Rogers, tears in her eyes, comes into focus.

My fury returns and not a moment too soon because I was seconds away from professing my love for this liar. Mitchell told me that his parents were deceased, but thanks to Mrs. Rogers, I learned the truth, and I recognize them from a photo in Mrs. Rogers' office, standing behind Molly. His mother with tear-stained mascara marks down her cheeks and his father standing proud and firm as if this scene could very well be his.

Mitchell looks as if he's about to run, but Mrs. Rogers stops him before he can get any closer to the stairs. "Mitchell, what's going on?" Mrs. Rogers asks. I see him putting together another lie, so I interrupt and return to The Plan by speaking into the microphone.

"Mitchell, isn't there someone else you'd like to thank for making your life bright?" The look on his face is priceless.

"How did you find me? Security, please remove this woman!"

Mitchell explains to the Mrs. and the crowd that I am a stalker who has been following him for several months. I stand quietly because I want to hear the rest of the lie he is effortlessly creating. He tells the crowd that he has a restraining order against me and assures everyone that the police will arrest me as soon as they arrive. His denial feels like a dagger through my heart.

Dizzy with disbelief, I take several steps away from him until the Mrs. tenderly grabs my hand to keep me from walking backwards off of the stage. Her gentle squeeze reminds me that we made the right decision, and she motions to security to leave me be.

We lock arms as I say again, this time more forcefully, "Mitchell, is there someone else you want to mention?"

Mitchell looks right at me and says, "Lady, I don't know what you're talking about! I'm asking you nicely to please leave, or I will have you arrested for not complying with the restraining order. Never come to my office again! And please stop following me!"

Thirty seconds ago I wasn't sure I'd be able to start the video we'd made for the occasion, but the forcefulness in his voice pisses me off so much that I hit play on the remote that's in my hand, activating the overhead projector. First is a DVD of Mitchell holding baby Kali, prompting her, "Say daddy." The home video shows Mitchell in every family setting befitting a doting father. Participating in Kali's birth, celebrating her first birthday, teaching her to walk, lounging in my house in his bathrobe, spending time with my family and friends. For her protection, Kali's face is blurred. The home movie ends with him thanking me for blessing him with Kali, professing once-in-a- lifetime love to me.

Mitchell stands shocked as though he has seen his life flash before him.

Just then begins another slide show of Mitchell's relationships with each of the women. As the scenes flash on the big screen, the women in the pictures join us on the stage. Mitchell attempts to leave, but the Mrs. blocks his path and whispers something in his ear, and he stays put. I later learn that her brothers, who are in on The Plan, were armed and ready to put a bullet in Mitchell's knees if he tried to leave.

As the crowd murmurs and the other ladies watch Mitchell, I become sick to my stomach and walk off the stage towards the door. Before I leave, I give my card to Mitchell's parents and tell them they can call if they want to know their only grandchild. His mother holds my hand for a brief moment, smiles, and then quietly says, "Thank you. We would love to know her." I leave the Grand Ballroom and all of Mitchell's mess with anger in my heart.

I get about three miles away before I have to pull over so that I can safely fall apart. After ten minutes or so, I get myself together enough to get back on the freeway. As I drive home, I emotionally drift in and out of light and then darkness. The rage rises and then subsides, allowing me to feel the anger and the pain that are deep in the pit of my belly. My tears form a continual stream that flows past my dimples until I am about a mile from home.

When I pull into the garage, Dear meets me at the door with my favorite slippers, comfy pajamas, and her favorite quilt. She has prepared a pot of tea and has a fresh box of tissue on her nightstand. I fall into her arms and wordlessly let my tears cleanse my soul. When I am able, I change into my pajamas, and curl up on Dear's bed in her favorite quilt. Sipping tea, I tell her all about the party that will be a pivotal moment in our lives forever. As she brushes my hair and offers me words of comfort, my mind drifts. At this point I'm not sure if I chose this dance or if this dance chose me. Either way my heart is broken, yet relieved. Not certain I made the right choice, I say a quiet prayer for Mrs. Rogers, and I replay the Plan in my mind until the sandman rescues me for the night..

Perfection

A lot of time has passed since that pivotal night. From what I see in the media, Mrs. Rogers will certainly make out well from the divorce. She checks on Kali about once a month, and although we don't really speak about the details of the divorce proceedings, she periodically thanks me for the courage I exercised in blowing the whistle on Mitchell. Her words of comfort usually come when I need them the most.

Mrs. Rogers says Mitchell's frequent travels and mysterious absences always gave her the feeling he was being unfaithful, but he constantly reassured her that he'd never jeopardize their marriage. He would emphatically say, "Yes, women flirt, and sometimes, I even flirt back, but I know which lines not to cross, and lying down with another woman is a line I would NEVER cross!" Well, now we all know how big of a liar he proved to be.

She admits that moving forward with the divorce was not easy, but her self-respect demanded it. She and Mitchell were together for most of her adult life, and parting ways took a lot of strength— strength she gains partly through our many conversations, which also inspire me to look forward to my future instead of searching for things that I could have done that might have kept Mitchell and I together.

At first, Mrs. Rogers says, she had difficult bouts of loneliness, but she's now dating a gentleman friend she's known for 20 years. Although he always wanted more than just friendship, he respected her enough to wait for opportunity to give them a chance. She is happy about the dance we chose, and even though I was one of the "other women," the Mrs. and I created a friendship out of this most unusual circumstance, and I feel that her well wishes are sincere. Mother tells me to watch my back with her, but the Mrs. has proven to be an upright woman of God who's looking forward to the next chapter of her life. Even weirder is how she prays for me through my moments of sadness.

The Mrs. and I never speak about my loneliness or why I have moments of depression, but we both realize that I miss her estranged husband. In fact, my semi-depressed state has sent Dear into serious fasting and praying. Because she is closer to God than anyone else I've ever known, it doesn't take long for my world to take a turn for the better. One day, as I stand in line at the grocery store, I hear someone behind me ask, "How is your day?" It has been a stressful day at work, and I am not in the mood for a one-liner from yet another slick gentleman, however; this is different. I recognize the voice but cannot place it until I turn around. To my surprise, it's Kevin!

Standing there in a tailored Armani suit, his smile is like a warm gentle embrace. I smile right back, even wider, and soon we are talking as though the negative moments between us never existed. He's different, more mature and self-assured than I ever knew him to be. His voice is deeper, and he stands tall, his head held high with confidence.

I never thought I'd see his spirit recover from the damage I did by leaving him for Paris. I never thought we'd be able to have another conversation without him reminding me of how I failed us. But here we are, standing outside the store, talking, laughing, and reminiscing for over an hour. I don't realize how much time has passed until Vanessa calls to check on me.

Over the next couple of weeks, Kevin and I trade phone calls, text messages, and emails. Soon I find myself smiling throughout the day for no apparent reason. I think of Mitchell less and less as Kevin reclaims his rightful place in my heart; a move that is solidified when he meets Kali for the first time and they fall in love with each other almost instantly. When an otherwise shy Kali reaches for Kevin as though she's known him for years, and he picks her up and hugs her as though she's his, I know that life will never be the same. The hug is the most precious moment I've ever witnessed. This moment is the beginning of the rest of our lives together.

With God's help, Kevin and I sort through things, and for the first time in a very long while, I am truly happy. Understandably, Kevin has some reservations about my priorities, but we agree to discuss all decisions as a family and to keep God at the center of our lives. I continue to receive monthly child support checks from Mitchell, but he has not come to see Kali since that pivotal night The Plan took place. To my surprise, his absence goes unnoticed.

Kevin and I never stopped loving each other and now that God has blessed us to find our way back into each other's arms, we vow to never part ways again. Kevin, who always wanted children, wants to adopt Kali, but Mitchell doesn't respond to the petition, so I don't move forward. Nevertheless, Kali knows Kevin as daddy, and a bloodline could not make the bond stronger. Once they find their way into each other's hearts there is no turning back.

A year to the day that I ran into Kevin at the grocery store, he takes Kali, Dear, and me out to dinner. He loves each of us, he says, and asks that we allow him to join our family as a husband, daddy, and grandson. Kevin, ever the romantic, leaves no stone unturned. He offers me a stunning Tiffany Legacy 4.7 carat cushion-cut, surrounded by bead-set diamonds in a platinum setting engagement ring, along with the matching Tiffany Legacy Channel-set band. For Dear, there is a solid gold chain-link bracelet, and Kali gets a half- heart gold necklace. Kevin explains to Kali that he'll wear the other half of the heart around his neck to signify his commitment as her daddy, and he'll wear a male version of the chain-link bracelet to honor his commitment to Dear as her grandson. The proposal night is another beautiful chapter in the story of our lives.

Within a year, we are married, and eight months later, after a delightfully easy pregnancy, we welcome Kali's little sister Tia into the world. I didn't realize that pregnancy could be so wonderful or that a man could so gently and lovingly deal with my emotional outbursts and postpartum tears. As though God is rewarding us for trusting Him, Kevin is made partner at his law firm, and we purchase our dream house within four years of us putting God first in our lives. Not only has my true love returned, I am married to my best friend, we are blessed with two lovely daughters, and Dear is living a marvelous life in the west wing of our dream home; a home in which we have more rooms than we'll ever need. We have a family car, an SUV, two sexy sports cars, a truck, and a bank account that continues to grow, enabling us to give back to our community while maintaining the lifestyle I always knew I would have.

In hindsight, Mother's abuse feels worth all the pain that I had to endure to get to this dance. Perhaps her abuse was God's way of making sure I'd never take any of this for granted. I always knew I'd be rewarded for enduring such a terrible childhood; in fact, dreaming about a better tomorrow was what got me through the worst moments. As my face grew numb from her slaps, I would go to a happy place deep within my mind, into my perfect world—a world I have finally realized through prayer, thanksgiving, diligent work, and focus. I always held onto the faith that God would bring me through the hell if I were a good girl, and today it's evident that my dark days are over.

While a teenaged Alex smoked, cussed, cut school, had sex in our parent's bed, snuck out to attend forbidden parties, and disrespected Mother, I wanted to prove to God that I was worthy of His eventual blessings. Mother still flings a terribly harsh tongue in my direction, but her mental, emotional, and spiritual abuse glides right over my head. I have finally made it to my perfect life, so her words no longer hurt me. I am now confident enough to leave her presence before she gets angry enough to inflict physical harm upon me. I pity her attempts to hurt me, and I secretly delight at watching her get frustrated because she can no longer elicit the old reactions—silence, a fake smile—that were symptoms of my fear. I was once an empty shell, raped of the joy that should have been nurtured when I was a child. I am now truly happy, and I genuinely smile, from a place of peace and satisfaction. Mother can no longer cause me pain, and I refuse to ever again allow her that type of power over me. I refuse to be subjected to her evil because her world is unhappy. I'm not sure if she will ever understand, but the fact is, she can no longer hurt me because I have made it to the mountaintop of my perfectly planned world.

I chose the dance of The Plan. My choice led to many lonely, tear-stained moments, but it was in these moments, as I fought to stay on this side of reality and not escape into a dream world, that I grew closer to God.

The painful years Kevin and I spent apart have made us stronger. We realize that we'd rather go through this life together, dancing to whatever rhythm life throws our way. Although I never worry about him cheating, he is sensitive to my experience with Mitchell and keeps me abreast of his whereabouts. Kevin is home every evening, even if he is in the office working. His heavy workload helps him appreciate my workaholic tendencies and my eventual decision all those years ago to accept the internship in Paris.

I love everything about my life; my husband, my two lovely daughters, my best friend Dear, our accomplishments as a family, our spirituality, and all God's blessings. My reality surpasses my childhood dreams and this, my friends, is my perfection!

Without Warning

J ust as God's faithful servant, Job was beset with misfortune, my perfect, prosperous world begins to fall apart, brick by brick.

To be clear; I dare not compare myself to Job's righteousness nor my walk with God to his, but I am blessed. As an active church board member who attends services regularly, I am very thankful to God for exceeding my expectations in the area of blessings. I want for nothing! I have accomplished more than I thought possible by this age, and I am comfortable in my wonderful world.

I smile to myself as I read my department's numbers during my monthly executive meeting. I remember a time when just barely exceeding our quotas by the end of the month meant one of my management staff's heads was about to roll, which would send a ripple of fear through the department. I've learned to relax a bit since then. Tomorrow is the last day of another month, and we strategize about ways to bring in larger financial returns next month. I smile because have a few ideas I'm quite confident about. My fellow executives look worried as they stare at their iPads, scrolling through pages of financial reports and failed marketing strategies, but I am so happy with my life that not even a conference room full of stress can rock my joy.

After our four-hour meeting, I still have reports to complete, so tonight will be another long night. I drive home on autopilot, hoping to make it in time to kiss the girls goodnight before they are asleep. Tia interrupts Dear's bedtime Bible story with a loud "Mommy!" when she notices me peeking around the door, and she shouts with excitement as she jumps into my arms from Dear's bed. Kali, much too polite to interrupt Dear's story, welcomes me home by shyly flashing me one of her billion-dollar smiles.

Dear finishes the story while I go into Kevin's office to steal a kiss from my handsome husband of seven years. The love in his eyes as he glances at his watch says, "It's late, young lady, but I understand," right before we exchange a passionate embrace. I am usually the last one in—Kevin, who often brings his work home, tries to be home no later than six every evening.

I would feel guilty if Dear were not here helping us raise the girls. She no longer drives, but she gets along quite well for a woman coming up on her 100th birthday. God has preserved her well, and we often joke that Dear is healthier than most people half her age and she will probably outlive us all. We have a cook, driver, and a moderate staff to make her life comfortable, so her only duty is to continue supplying us with her continuous stream of love and wisdom.

Although we are both exhausted, Kevin makes love to me for about an hour; he says my love gives him the strength to express his adoration. I'm just happy to be on the receiving end of his high sex drive, and I say prayers of thanks as I drift off to sleep in his arms. I love my life and I don't know what I'd do if any of the players were to change.

The next morning I drive to the office accompanied by the melodic praise sounds of J. Moss. My commute is unusually smooth, almost as if someone has called ahead and cleared traffic. First on my agenda is an encouraging email to my department, "Today is the 1st day of the month. Please be prepared to share your strategies on our 10 a.m. conference call. This team has the talent to close strong this month, so while we close strong let's focus on making next month stronger! Have fun while reaching towards excellence. I appreciate each of you, Sincerely, JJ."

As I hit 'send,' my admin notifies me of a mandatory 9 a.m. meeting with Langley Berkowitz, the president of marketing, and his four VPs. Langley is more uptight than usual, a fact I almost fail to notice until he opens his mouth. "In a late deal last night, our firm was acquired, which means that we may lose some head count."

Wow! I think as he continues, "The news is set to hit the media this morning, and I want you to get in front of this story with your teams. Although there is some duplication of staff, our jobs are secure."

How will I spin this news with my team?

Langley clears his throat and closes with, "Until further notice, the teams should continue with business as usual. That's all I know, and I'll keep you posted as I learn more."

My teams will certainly be concerned about their jobs. Hell, I'm a little concerned. The country is in a recession!

I share the news with my team and try to reassure them, but my faith is a little shaken. I have never been in an acquisition, but I do keep my ear to the ground, and I know acquisitions can be brutal. Nevertheless, I mask my concern with a smile as I tell them, "Let's stay focused, team. These things can take years." By lunchtime, I have several proposals in my inbox outlining some pretty good advertising strategies. We are going to prove that we are a solid team that can work through disturbing times.

I had planned on going home early, but I hang in there with my team, which has chosen to stay late. I glance at my phone to check the time and see if I've missed any calls or text messages. It is eight o'clock, and Kevin must be really upset. I have only one missed call, and it's from Dear. I call her, but just as Dear answers, Langley knocks on my door. "Come in, Langley. Dear, I will call you back."

Langley says he's glad I'm still here because he has news he'd rather deliver in person. Several of our executives and half of their staffs will be "riffed," victims of a "reduction in force", he says in his monotone manner. I tell him I'd just spent the day reassuring my teams. "When is this supposed to happen?" I ask, "and how do we decide who'll be riffed?" Langley doesn't have all of the details, but he does know that the severance packages will be very nice. The look in his eyes tells me there's something he doesn't want to say. "What is it, Langley? What are you not saying?" I ask. "There is some duplication at the executive level," Langley says slowly and deliberately. "So am I being riffed"? I ask. "Nothing has been finalized", he says, but it appears that he might lose some of his executive team members. This news wouldn't usually bother me because "I'm a good catch", I tell myself, but we're in a recession and it's been a while since I had a job offer. Langley says he will keep me posted.

In the car outside the office, I text Dear to tell her I'm on my way home. I don't want to call her because she'll hear the worry in my voice, and I am not ready to talk about the possibility of a RIF, which would put me back on the job market for the first time in over 15 years. I try not to think about being jobless, replacing those scary thoughts with images of me lying in Kevin's arms, where I always feel safe.

Finally, I am home. I kiss my two sleeping beauties on their cheeks, say good night to dozing Dear, and crawl across the bed, exhaling at last in my husband's arms. He's the levelheaded one, and he'll know how to reassure me that everything's going to be just fine.

To my surprise, he seems cold and distant. When I ask him if he's OK, he lets me have it with both barrels.

"I don't know why you would rather be at that job than here at home with your family at a decent hour! Your daughters are always asking, 'When is mommy coming home?' I'm tired of covering for you!"

I can tell there's something else bothering him, and I know that if I listen long enough, he'll get to the real issue. I don't read between the lines well, but I do my best to get past the words coming out of his mouth and understand the root of his irritation. Perhaps his anger, which has been simmering for a while, really is just about my workaholic tendencies.

I listen without defending myself. At this moment, I have no fight in me. I usually slip into a daydream when faced with tough moments, but Kevin's fury has caught me so off guard that I don't have time to run inward. Instead, I stand on the receiving end of his verbal blows, paying close attention to his every word.

Eventually, he runs out of steam. I try to swallow past the knot in my throat so I can choke out an apology.

This is not at all how I planned this night to end. I need him to hold me and tell me that everything will be OK. He seems to need the same thing as he paces back and forth on my sheepskin rug in his street shoes. I walk over and offer him a hug. I'm afraid I'll fall apart if I try to do anything else.

He refuses me. "You don't have anything to say?" he snaps. I stand silent, facing him, and it takes all my strength to keep from going limp.

Kevin gets back into the bed, turns over, and closes his eyes, so I quietly gather my nightclothes and retreat to our private restroom for a long overdue shower. I desperately scrub every part of my body in an attempt to wash the day's disappointments from my being, and I ask God to send Kevin to the shower. I love him so much and I probably deserve his fury, but after what happened at work, tonight is not a good night to get beat down even further.

I realize after about ten long minutes that he's probably not going to join me. My emotions finally catch up with me, and I crumble to the shower floor. I cry like a baby as the water mixes in with the tears streaming down my face.

This has been a long awful day and crying somehow makes me feel a little bit better. At this point I long for a do-over to this day that went awry without warning.

Dismissed

Three days pass and I have not heard another word about the acquisition; Langley seems to be in a good mood, so the news must be good or at least I hope so. I'm feeling confident as I make my way to a mandatory meeting with the head of our Human Resource department. I expect to find out which members of my team will receive a severance and who will remain on board.

I soon find out, however, that the meeting is about me: I am handed my dismissal paperwork, which outlines my generous severance, medical information, 401K, stock options, and everything else one needs to know when being released from a career.

One of the firm's last requests is that I finish out the week to serve as moral support for the members of my team who will also be dismissed over the next couple of days. Even though I am really angered and hurt, I agree to stay to the bitter end hoping they'll need my services past the final date listed on my paperwork. A second condition is that I not discuss this meeting with anyone within the company until after my last date, the fifth of the month. As far as anyone knows, I have avoided the axe. How dare Langley not show up to this meeting and then walk around like he is on top of the world. Perhaps that's it. I likely found out that he will not lose his job.

I am at a loss for words. How will I tell Dear? How will I tell Kevin, who's still angry because of my long hours? What he doesn't know is that I'm spending the extra time with other members of the Executive team transferring all of my accounts and resolving outstanding customer issues. Again, I hope someone recognizes my value and work ethic, especially in the worst of circumstances, and realize that the decision to release me is a mistake. Then I will be able to tell Kevin the whole story, and he will forgive me for the unusually long hours away from the family. Nevertheless, the fifth day of the month arrives and Andre the security guard stands watching *me*, an Executive Vice President of Marketing in a well-established thriving firm that *I* helped grow, as I pack my belongings preparing to exit the premises for the last time. Taking controlled breaths, I sort through 15 years of collections as I intentionally avoid making eye contact with anyone, especially Andre. Seven years earlier, my purse was stolen from my office while Andre was on duty, and although the security video clearly recorded the incident, Andre neglected to report the findings. Once the footage was reviewed, not only was the culprit identified, but it was also revealed that Andre had been asleep on the job. He was suspended, and he narrowly held onto his job in exchange for a severe demotion. Andre blames me for his reprimand and decrease in position and pay, because building management had closed the case and considered the theft a misfortunate circumstance until I insisted on (and paid for) a full investigation. Andre has spent the past seven years trying to regain his manager of security position, to no avail. Ironically, he's the security guard assigned to my area, tasked with making sure that only personal belongings leave the building.

Because of the merger, 75 percent of the staff is packing their belongings. Compared to the years of blood, sweat, and tears we gave to make this company a lucrative and sought-after firm, our severance packages are mediocre at best. On every one of the building's twenty-three floors it feels like Black Monday, but I am determined to maintain my composure and professionalism as I reassure employees and pack my belongings.

Although I've never been dismissed from a job, I consider this termination just another test along my successful career path. I am certain that somehow, I will overcome this current obstacle. As I mentally reassure myself, I can see Andre look down at my expensive shoes with scorn, glad that he has the privilege of escorting me from the building for the last time. Before his demotion Andre would tell anyone within earshot that I was the sexiest woman in the building. Even now I can feel his glaring eyes undress me, how disgusting! I am a bit uncomfortable as his eyes thoroughly scan the way my tailor-made suit compliments every curve of my fit body. I work hard to keep this body in shape and am use to the stares, but is he really being so bold? His eyes seem to say that in exchange for a brief secret encounter, he will forgive any bad blood between us. His escalated fantasies overtake his reality, which is obvious by the growing bulge of his manhood about to burst through his zipper. I can take no more of his obviously lustful stares, so I clear my throat in an attempt to interrupt his noticeably distasteful thoughts. Andre immediately adjusts himself, his disdain returns, and he checks his watch as if I am on a time limit.

Although bothered by his lustful thoughts, it is important for me to maintain my dignity. I focus on displaying few emotions. Several employees are verbally expressing their negative emotions, but I remain the strong example and offer little reaction as I tell anyone that asks, "God has a bigger plan." My strength is my signature, and I am determined to leave the building with my pride and dignity intact.

The fifth and final box is loaded on a hand truck, and I am ready to exit. As I push the boxes towards my office door, Andre says he will need to examine the boxes, and that I'll need to reopen them all. I can feel my blood pressure rise as I release the hand truck in its upright position, look directly into his eyes, and antagonistically tell him, "You open them and remember that the camera is still recording your every move, so try not to fall asleep on the job again. I will be right back."

I have to get out of there, so I push past Andre and go into the nearest restroom to collect and reassure myself. "I am well educated and have successfully climbed the corporate ladder," I tell myself. "I will get another job, even in the midst of the current recession." A few minutes later, I emerge fully confident and ready to take the final steps of this journey.

As I return to my office, I notice that my boxes are closed and have not been touched. Realizing that Andre was toying with me, I decide to retaliate. Just to spite him, I tell him to push the hand truck as he follows me to my car. He dare not refuse my request as Langley gives me a big hug and asks me to stay in touch. Once at the car, I insist that he load the boxes into my trunk, which needs rearranging. Once the boxes have been neatly loaded into the carefully rearranged trunk, I thank Andre, smile slightly, and extend my hand. Andre hesitates but decides that a final handshake will not hurt. Once our hands connect, I catch Andre off guard and pull him into my bosom.

Our lips only inches apart, I sexily whisper, "I've noticed how you look at me. Have you noticed me watching you?" Stunned, Andre stutters, "Uh… no, not really." I continue, "You've never noticed me watching you walk, talk, or just stand there being handsome?" Andre is pleasantly surprised. After standing only inches apart for about 30 seconds, he eventually places his free hand on my thigh. "I never knew. I have never seen you look at me." I lean in closer as Andre licks his lips and smiles with his eyes, preparing for the inevitable kiss. I place my free hand on his neck, pull him slightly forward, and firmly place my knee into his stiff man part with all of my might. Andre falls to the ground, gasping for air, and I quickly get into my car, lock the doors, and start the engine. Once I'm safely in the car, I roll down my window and ask, "Was my final walk all that you thought it would be?"

Andre is still out of breath, but I continue. "You've never noticed me watching you because it never happened." Andre, now up on his knees, is still attempting to regain complete control of his breath. "Thanks for the memories," I tell him with a slight chuckle as I drive away. I laugh until I realize that Andre may press charges. With that thought, my laughter subsides but does not completely disappear because I'm afraid that tears will take the place of the laughter.

After driving around for about an hour, I notice the time and realize that I've haven't seen mid-day outside of the office in several months. I dedicated a big portion of my life to that company for 15 years, and I am a bit lost. Going home now will force me to talk to Kevin, and I am not ready for this conversation. Besides, I would probably blame him for my termination, which wouldn't be fair. I think about going to my real estate office to visit Vanessa because she always knows what to say, but I am in no mood for a real conversation. I just want to be alone with my thoughts.

I decide to drive. Tonight is family night and I will have to go home eventually, but for now, I just want to drive and think about my next game plan. I steer the car, but I can't feel the steering wheel under my hands because I am numb. Five days into what was to be a month of promise and statistical gains, I am lost and I can no longer see my future. We have plenty of money in the bank, Kevin's career is thriving, and my severance is equivalent to three years' salary, so I am not really concerned about our finances. But now that I don't have a daily purpose, I'm not sure what I will do. Creating advertising packages and marketing strategies for others bring me joy and purpose. I love looking at a brand and figuring out how to make it a household name.

Now what? I'm sure I will find another job soon, but I don't want to have to look. Besides, what will Mother say? "You must have done something for them to let you go and keep others." I won't have an answer for her because I am perplexed as to why I was chosen to be riffed over Jim Patrickson, who is never in the office, or Roshanif Akhim, who is newer to the company.

I can't figure out why. Why me? I was too prideful to ask. I sat there matter-of-factly, listening to HR outline the terms of my departure without asking why or requesting another chance. Perhaps I can help Vanessa manage our real estate company, J- Ness Reality. This recession has caused a bit of a strain on the company; maybe I can lend my expertise. But Vanessa, who is good at selling anything, still manages to turn profits each month, so she won't need me there. Besides, I love being a silent partner. Real estate is not my passion—it's hers, and working together every day might put a strain on our relationship. Nevertheless, it is an option.

I am not sure how I got in this store or in this line, but I pay cash for another pair of very expensive shoes so that Kevin doesn't find out I spent this much money on the day that I was laid off. I flash the cashier one of my fake smiles as my mind replays the same message over and over: "Now what? What am I going to do in the morning?" I face the realization that I have made my career the biggest part of my life. Now that I've been dismissed, my world feels empty and I don't really feel like choosing a dance right now.

Betrayed

Today is another day of driving around, shopping, and anything else to fill my day. I still have not told Kevin about losing my job. I will eventually tell him, but not today. Instead, I have driven around for several hours, and it is now late in the afternoon. I'm no longer in the mood to shop or drive. Dear and the girls will be at their piano lessons and Kevin will still be at the office. Perhaps I should go home to and hide these boxes from my office and take a hot bath before anyone comes in to interrupt my "me time." Maybe I will even surprise the girls by showing up at their piano lessons with a treat.

When I pull into the garage, however, Kevin's car is here. My initial response is to pull out of the garage and go to Vanessa's house until much later, but she is probably still in the office, and I don't really feel like talking about my dismissal just yet. Perhaps Kevin drove the truck today. I almost go to check the other garage, but I decide that this must be the case. If not, he will be pleasantly surprised that I am home early. Perhaps we will talk and he will forgive me once he knows that I had a reason for not making it home in time for dinner night after night.

As I get closer to the door, I hear loud music and realize that Kevin must be home. He loves to play his hardcore rap at top volume when he is home alone. As his mother always says, "You can take the boy out of the hood, but you can never take the hood out of the boy." I leave my office boxes and my brand new shoes hidden in the trunk and go looking for my husband so we can make amends. I will apologize and tell him all about my ordeal. He is not in his office so he is not working. "Good, I won't be interrupting," I think quietly to myself as I smile. When Kevin is in work mode, it's difficult for him to change gears until he decides to stop working. He must be in our room… even better. Maybe he's in the shower and I can join him. He has quite an appetite, and we haven't had sex all week because he's been mad at me. Just thinking about an afternoon of passion gets my excitement flowing.

When I try to turn the doorknob to our bedroom, I discover that the door is locked. This is weird, but Kevin might be cleaning his guns; to protect the girls, he always locks the doors when he is handling the guns. I almost knock, but the music is playing so loud that I'm certain he will not hear me. I get the key from the top of the door jam, unlock the door, and gently push it open as not to startle him. I wouldn't want him to aim a gun in my direction.

To my surprise, he is not cleaning his gun. He is in the bed, and if I were not standing here in the doorway, I would swear he and I were in the bed together because he appears to be making love to someone.

Oh my God! What have I walked in on? I freeze, unable to say a word. I can see his mouth moving as though he is scolding the other woman, but I can't hear him over the music. My breath slowly leaves my body and I am trapped by the moment, forced to watch their every movement. He is pounding her from the back as though he is angry and her legs are opened wide while she is up on her tiptoes, willingly accepting his frustrations. Why are they standing in our bed performing what seems to be difficult exercise moves? Now she has extended her left leg in the air over his right shoulder while still on her tippy toes and he is straddling her right leg, grabbing her bottom as he continues to forcefully drive his manhood inside her.

I have never seen such vulgarity and would love to run, scream, hit, or do anything, but I can't move. It is as though I am being punished by the universe, held captive and made to watch this awful display. Kevin obviously forgot to put the CD player on repeat, so the music has stopped and I'm left to hear their acts of deceit loud and clear. Why does she keep hitting my wall with her fist, and why is she biting my pillow as if to help her manage the pain? If it hurts, she should just tell him. And then she does. "Oh daddy, this hurts so good!"

I am speechless. I can't think. What does "this hurts so good" mean, and who is she calling "daddy?" I pray to God to remove me from this moment, to let me run, yell, or do anything to get their attention so that they can stop, but I am trapped by a power stronger than me as I stand and watch all their actions in silence. It is obvious that they are coming to an end because his pumps become slower and more deliberate while she screams, "Yes, daddy! Oh my god, yes!"

I feel as though every organ in my body has melted and is now in my feet holding me in this spot like lead weights. I cannot move. Why is he biting her? It obviously hurts because she keeps letting out painful expressions, but she allows him to continue. Is this what he wants?

Apparently, they are wrapping up their session. He has removed himself from her and she is a ball of exhaustion in the middle of my bed. I am sure he will notice me as he gets up to get rid of the condom, but there is no condom. Not again… Why am I not a better judge of character in men?

This is all so unreal. I never would have imagined that the love of my life would betray our marriage vows. He knows how devastated I was with Mitchell and his cheating, but no matter how terrible Mitchell and his actions were, Kevin has just won the "most devastation caused to Jonnie" award. Not only is he cheating on everything that we've ever built together, he brought his dirtiness into our home and into our bed. What if Dear and the girls would have walked in on this blasphemous scene? Oh my God! Please let my eyes be deceiving me!

It is not until she looks me in my face that I realize who she is. What is he doing with her and how long has this been going on? A second later, Kevin also sees me standing there and yet, I CAN'T MOVE!

"Oh my God, baby!" he says, putting on his boxer briefs and moving swiftly towards me.

I take my first breath in what feels like ten minutes, and I feel my body betray me further as I go limp. "God, please help me." Kevin catches me before I meet the floor, but I pass out from the lack of oxygen and the painful realization that again, I've been betrayed.

Sleeping Beauty

Judging from the darkness outside of my bedroom window and the sounds of little feet running through the house, I realize that several hours have passed as I slowly regain consciousness. I struggle to gather my composure, and from the appearance of my surroundings, I just had a terrible nightmare. "Oh my God, I'm lying on this bed," I think, before jumping up still woozy from whatever happened earlier.

I look around the room still trying to figure out what happened, if anything, before I stumble out to the family room. Dear and the girls are giggling and playing beauty shop as they comb through Dear's long gray hair and apply thick layers of makeup, eye shadow, and rouge to her pronounced cheek bones. Dear notices me and says, in her naturally cheerful voice, "Well hello. Did you have a nice nap, Sleeping Beauty?" I don't know how to respond because I think that I may still be asleep. Tia gives her usual high-pitched, "Mommy!" scream as she runs to me and jumps into my arms. Holding her helps bring me back to reality, so I just hold her tightly for about 30 seconds or so. Hearing her little voice say, "I love you, Mommy" in my ear brings tears to my eyes.

I look around and ask, "Where's Kevin?" "Daddy says that he will be home late tonight. He came to our piano lessons and saw me play the piano,"

Tia says so proudly. Her response makes me realize that my nightmare was my reality, so I slowly walk back to my room to fully check out the scene.

My imprint is still on top of my down comforter, where he must have laid me after he changed the sheets and made up the bed. The soiled sheets are in the hamper and I can smell the faint scent of sex through the incense that he left burning throughout the room and even in our master bathroom. I never realized it before this moment, but this smell of sex mixed with incense is familiar. Apparently, this isn't the first time this has happened. I always wondered why he had to burn four to five incenses at a time, and now I know one of the reasons. Even though it appears that he tried to wash the wall, I can still see her fingerprints etched in my paint. Of all people, why was he with her and why in our bedroom? Why not just go to her house? Oh my God! This is disgusting!

I teeter back and forth between reality and a sort-of dream state as I ask God to let this cup pass me. I feel the tears form from a too- familiar hurtful place, as my heart slowly rips into little itty-bitty pieces.

Dear interrupts my thoughts to tell me that God told her everything would work out for my good. She can tell by the look in my eyes that there is so much I want to say, but I don't know where to start. It would be better if she would just tell me that God has told her everything, that I wasn't dreaming, and that Kevin and I will somehow get past this moment victoriously stronger. Instead, she tells me that I slept so peacefully, like Sleeping Beauty, and that my inner-soul was at peace. "God would not allow a person dammed for destruction to find such peace and joy in their sleep state," she says. "Subconsciously, even you know that you will overcome your present trials. Read your Bible, pray, and ask God to lead you." She then laughs a little, as though God has just shown her another piece of the puzzle, before continuing. "You will try to find the answers on your own, and you may even go to some pretty dark places in search of those answers, but through it all, you will learn to trust and rely on God."

She hugs me before sitting on my bed. When she sees me hesitate

– I almost warn her not to sit there because of the filth I saw – she smiles, tells me that it's going to be alright, and then says, "Let the Lord do His work" before leaving the room.

Because I could not stomach the stench of old sex in the air or the thought of being in the den of betrayal any longer, I now lay in the bed in the guest room. The night becomes morning while I listen for any signs of Kevin, who finally creeps in like a thief around 3:00a.m. I would confront him if I knew what to say. I have grown so accustomed to allowing life to happen all over me while I daydream through tough moments that I don't really know how to handle personal matters of the heart. So, as usual, I lay there motionless and in shock until he finds me and starts the conversation with, "Baby, I'm sorry." He sits on the side of the bed with the look of fear in his tearful eyes. He doesn't even drink wine, but he reeks of strong alcohol. When he touches my hand, I can no longer hold back the lonely tear that wanders down my face swollen from crying.

Kevin gets on his knees next to the bed and asks for my forgiveness. I can do nothing more than cry and choke out a stuttered, "Where were you?" For some strange reason I'm relieved when I hear that he was not with her, as though I am winning at this sick game. I have returned to sobbing as he explains his infidelity and asks that I somehow find enough love in my heart to go to counseling so that we can get our marriage back on track. I own my part of our failed marriage and I almost understand his loneliness as I put my career first. I want to put "US" before "me" so I agree to try. I allow him to lay next to me, on top of the covers, and we talk until the sun rises.

My emotions are all over the place, and as I sort through them, I am mad, angry, and hurt that I love this man so much and want him so badly, even after he has been stained by another woman. What is wrong with me? Making love to him is like a two-edged sword. I love feeling his love, even though it cuts me deeper in my soul and tears open my wounded heart with every thrust. I'm not sure when I will be able to feel safe in his arms again, but I'm willing to try. We talk until I'm nauseate by the details. It helps that he holds me through the pain and accepts my harsh words without retaliation. When I ask about his failure to wear a condom, he says he felt safe because she was a virgin. I am sick to my stomach because I willingly gave him my virginity assured that I'd be special to him for the rest of his life. I was the only virgin he had, but now that fact has changed.

Wait a hot-blooded minute. She is no virgin! I personally know about many of her freaky escapades and I am only too happy to tell Kevin. I can tell that he's not convinced, but he knows that defending her honor would cause World War III in our household. For days, between working and caring for Dear and the girls, we talk through our hurts.

I am not really going to work, of course, but I have not shared this with anyone yet. I get up early, get dressed, and check into a suite at the Marriot, where I watch movies, cry, read my Bible, cry some more, talk to God, and sleep most of the day.

It's been seven days since I was riffed and I have still not shared my secret. Talking to Dear is so easy. I have come close to telling her, but she's been under the weather lately and I don't want to burden her. The hotel clerk hands me my room key along with the receipt dated the 12th. I wonder if I will be able to share my secret with anyone before this month is over.

I'm making my way to the elevator for the penthouse suite and my best friend is standing in the lobby as though she knows how much I need her. With a giant smile and huge tears bursting through my tough exterior, I bury my face in her neck for about two minutes before heading up to the room. Dear and I order room service, talk, pray, and watch movies all day. We have not had a day alone like this since the early Mitchell days and this feels wonderful. After a spa massage in the room and a late lunch, we order another movie. Crying has made my eyes tired, so I fight to maintain focus on the movie until Dear tells me to go to sleep and allow God to speak to me. She says that God works with me in my dream state and that this is when I am able to shut out the world and hear God best. She brushes my hair while whispering prayers asking God to speak to, and take care of her Sleeping Beauty.

Distracted

With all the distractions lately, I almost allow Dear's birthday to pass without celebrating her importance to this family, community, church, and really, anyone that comes in contact with her. It's not until I find a hand-made birthday card to her from Tia that I remember. Dear is truly a blessing to every life she touches and she deserves to be celebrated. She would be happy with a quiet birthday at home, but she realized long ago that one way we express our gratitude for everything she does is by celebrating her at every opportunity. Her birthday is one such occasion.

Kevin and I struggle to get through a day of peacefulness because I can't let go of what I saw. I still want to talk about why he chose to betray me, which angers him. How dare he get angry? He should be happy I have allowed him to remain in the house and join me in the guest room, until I learned that they also had sex in that guess room. Now I sleep in my office, on the couch, while every bedroom, with the exception of Dear and the girls' room, is being painted and professionally cleaned. He is not happy with our sleeping arrangements, but he sleeps next to me on an air mattress while I sleep on the couch, unless I decide to join him on the air mattress. Some nights, just to be closer to me, he sleeps sitting upright at the other end of the couch. Our sleeping arrangement reminds me of our days in college, when I would stay at his house. His bed was an air mattress on the floor, and because I was not ready to have sex, he would sleep on the couch at my feet on the rare occasions I spent the night after falling asleep through late- night movie watching.

I realize we cannot stay this way for long, so I've ordered all new furniture and the accompanying fixtures similar to our current setup. I loved my rooms. I planned this dream house all my life and the setup was just as I envisioned, so although I am forced to get new furniture I have replaced everything as close to the way it was as possible.

Today I decide not to check into a suite. Instead, I go to breakfast with the Mrs. and then we go shopping. As we greet each other, she immediately asks for a favor.

"Will you please call me Shelia? Although I know that your reference is from a place of respect, I consider us friends, and my friends call me Shelia." I eagerly agree.

Strangely enough, talking to her about my job loss and Kevin's infidelity is easy, so we have breakfast while she helps add perspective to this whirlwind I call my life. She also shares that she is engaged to be married, and she encourages me to make the decisions that suite me best. "Be selfish," she declares. Shelia shares that she wishes she hadn't put up with Mitchell's disrespect for so long, and that she's happy she hasn't seen nor heard from him since the final divorce proceeding. I tell her that his parents call or visit Kali about once a month, but they never speak about him or his where-abouts. Shelia tells me that she knows some headhunters and would be happy to pass along my resume when I'm ready to go back to work.

I must admit that my time with Mitchell served two great purposes: Meeting the Mrs., or shall I say Shelia and, of course, my sweet baby girl, Kali. We have a wonderful time shopping. I'm a bit saddened when she takes me back to my car and we go our separate ways, because I'm forced to return to my world of despair, alone. I drive around for several hours, and late in the afternoon I decide to go home, I finally unload the belongings from my office in an inconspicuous corner of the garage and take a hot bath before picking up Kali and Tia for family night. The girls have the privilege of planning family night and usually they choose the Fun Center for a night of pizza and games, which we all enjoy. Tonight, however, I would rather crawl into bed and sleep the entire weekend. If only I had a bed.

Realizing that the family night outing is a promise that I cannot break, I put on my happy face and arrive at piano lessons just in time for two excited girls to get in the car. They can speak of nothing but the Fun Center and Dear's birthday party only three days away for the duration of the drive. Kevin meets us there and I'm surprised and annoyed by the smell of alcohol seeping through his pores. As the girls run from room to room playing their favorite games, we exchange heated words about my insecurities and his insistence that I should trust him.

Kevin, who usually joins the fun, is in no condition to keep up with the girls because he can barely stand without stumbling. I would join them but I would rather get the truth from Kevin regarding where he's been and with whom. "Since when do you drink heavily?" I ask.

When the girls return to the table for pizza, we both try to disguise the worry that hangs over us like a black cloud. I am usually able to separate my grown-up troubles from my time with the girls, but today I feel like I am grasping at the final straws of sanity. I stare blankly in Kevin's direction as I review my life and wonder how the recent downpour of misfortune hit me so accurately. Kevin, no longer able to take my looks of disdain, stumbles to his car and burns rubber out of the parking lot without even saying goodbye to the girls. When I go into my purse to pay the cashier, I see a mini package of aspirin and wonder how many pills it would take for me to painlessly drift into an endless, peaceful slumber.

We arrive home to find Dear sleeping and Kevin absent. I lay staring at the muted television waiting for him to return, but Dear comes into the den and tells me to get up and get dressed. I am not sure why I'm getting dressed, but I have learned to comply with her requests, no matter how strange. Minutes later, I receive a call saying my husband has been in a car accident.

I rush to the hospital, where I find him banged-up but conscious. To my surprise, Alex is there, kissing his wounds and telling him he should have stayed with her tonight after all they had to drink. They both notice me standing in the doorway, and Alex continues kissing my husband because she clearly doesn't care about my feelings. Kevin calls out, "Jonnie baby, I'm sorry!" To which I reply, "You certainly are!" as I leave.

This scene leaves me more confused than ever. It's not safe that I drive home so distracted by my thoughts. They're still carrying on? Why? And after the counseling sessions and all that praying together? Why not just tell me that he wants to be with my baby sister and then leave me alone? Even the thought sickens me. When did she stop being a lesbian, and when did he start cheating? This is not the Kevin I know! Various thoughts, on different levels and with varying emotions, are hitting my mind from all directions. It would be exhausting if I could focus on me for any extended amount of time, so I try to focus on nothing. I am just about cried out, so I drive down the freeway with dry eyes staring into the night trying.

Somehow, I reach my garage. Dear has a pot of tea ready, and although I see her lips moving I cannot focus on her words as I sit across the table, distracted and blankly staring through my life's unpredictable paths.

Brown Polyester-blend Suit

After many arguments, I've come to the realization that it may be time to let go. My heart hangs in my throat as I stand speechlessly watching my husband of seven years pack his clothes. Kevin's every movement plays in slow motion. I see the history of each garment across the forefront of my mind as though I am viewing an old sentimental movie on the big screen. The brown suit, the one that landed in the corner when he missed the suitcase, was once his favorite suit. He wore that brown, polyester- blend suit to every special occasion for the first year of our relationship. He proposed to me in that suit. Now, the suit that I grew to love, hate, and love again lies lifeless, discarded in the corner as if to represent our dying relationship.

My mind scrambles for words that will make him stop packing long enough to make sense of this unraveling event, in which, thanks to his bad choices, I am forced to partner. A part of me wants to drop to his feet and beg him not to destroy us any further, while another part wants to calmly discuss and fix this mess. The biggest part of me; however, wants to take the lead crystal lamp from the nightstand and bust him across his head for betraying our marriage bed. I am sure that he confuses my gaze as anger, because pride has never allowed me to grovel over a man. But this man is my husband. Shouldn't this fact change the rules a bit? A man's actions have never made me beg because a man's actions have proven once again to be predictable. Now, for the first time in my life, I struggle to control my emotions. I've always controlled my emotions by mentally escaping, but now I cannot escape because Kevin, Alex, and everything is ever present.

I never would have predicted this feeling. I never expected to find him and Alex in *my* bed. I thought that we shared a stronger bond, or at least that he was smart enough not to have sex with another woman all over our home. The pain swells my chest so much that I find it hard to take normal breaths, and watching him remove the Dizzy Gillespie picture from the wall intensifies the sting. As he places the slightly dusty picture on our newly replaced pure white down comforter, I glance around the room noticing the many expensive, now seemingly unnecessary changes I made to *my* room choice so that it would be *our* sanctuary. What am I going to do with dark brown curtains and the statues of the lions, tigers, and bears, oh my! – on the windowsill?

The sound of Kevin's suitcase being zipped up brings me back to reality.

Kevin is getting ready to walk out the door and I am letting him go, only because I don't know what else to do. I have never asked a man to stay with me and I don't think I would know how to begin. What would I say? "I will accept you cheating and lying if you promise not to leave?"

This is my second serious relationship, and I don't want to go through another separation, which reminds me of my continued failures. I am an intelligent woman and intellectually, I know I should not want a man who just crawled out of another woman's arms, but he is my husband. It may sound foolish, but I want him to stay. Maybe if I keep standing in the doorway he will be forced to speak to me and we will talk and happen upon a way to work through this mess. I purposely picked the 15th of the month for him to move out because Dear has a standing luncheon with Daddy; but I now am second-guessing my decision to have him leave privately. I wish Dear were here! She would force us to sit down and talk about our love and the family that we're destroying. She always knows exactly what to say to make any situation better. I am trying to remember some of her comforting words of advice, but nothing comes to mind. As Kevin approaches me, I stand in the doorway forcing him to take action. After about 20 seconds of silently staring at each other; during which my torn heart leads my thoughts through a world where he grabs me, kisses me, tosses me on the bed, makes love to me until my heartache is bearable and my insides are swollen from the passion we share… Kevin's voice brings me back to reality with a question.

"What are you going to tell Dear and the girls?"

For some reason his question pisses me off. How dare he stand in my face and ask if I am going to maintain his good name to his daughters, especially when I was just having a really good daydream? I know that he did not say those words, but he is concerned that I may tell the girls that their daddy cheated on mommy with Auntie Alex. The only thing that I can think to say is, "I don't lie to my girls." Kevin angrily pushes pass me with a suitcase in one hand and his Dizzy Gillespie print in the other. I feel that I am losing the chance of saving this marriage, but I cannot force myself to go after him.

From our bedroom window, I watch him throw his things in the trunk and rub his face while looking at the house as though he is looking at it for the last time. I am glad the girls are at school and don't have to watch daddy leave. Finally, he gets in the car and drives away.

All the fighting and thinking has made me so tired. Even though I have burned the sheets, redecorated the room, and replaced the furnishing, I cannot stay in this room. I pick up the infamous brown, polyester-blend suit that Kevin left lying in the corner and go lie on top of Dear's bed under her favorite quilt. I place the suit next to me as if Kevin is wearing it, and I snuggle like we used to. Pride stopped me from groveling while Kevin packed, but now no one is here. The tears roll freely down my face as I long for Dear's comfort and my husband's arms, no matter how tainted.

Interruption

Although the first 17 days of this month have been some of the worst times of my adult life, I focus on the last-minute details of Dear's 100th birthday party, which I've planned at the Country Club. She is everything to me and deserves my best efforts even though this means that I will have to deal with Kevin and Alex in a public setting, as if things are normal. Unless I get her to talking about herself, Mother, who is very observant, will probably sense the distance between Kevin and I; perhaps I can remain busy with the staff and the guests to hide the fact that I'm not speaking to my secretly estranged husband. I am so tired of thinking about or trying to figure a way out of the mess that mysterious appeared all over me. I need a pleasant interruption to my terrible realities, so as I drive to the Country Club I think about Dear and the God that she represents.

She was not born into money or luck like Mother. She always says that she was born into God's royal family and that she made a conscious decision to represent Him in a positive light, which is why her life has been wonderfully blessed. She demonstrates that she has a lot of trust in God and says, "Even through difficult times, I always know that God is carrying me." I love hearing about her childhood and the miraculous way that she came to be. In times of desperation, I think about the faith in God I inherited from my great-grandparents through Dear. Even in my most difficult times, my inner woman knows God will bring me through. When I have doubts I think about how my great-grandmother must have felt when, as a young lady she was told she would never be a mother. Dear says that it was her mother's belief in God's Word that allowed them to walk in God's Favor, through it all.

Just about one hundred years ago, a precious baby girl was born to a faithful couple that took one look at their miracle baby and named her Dear Emily Rucker. Dear's mother, my great- grandmother, was born with a single depleted ovary and doctors told her she would never be able to have children. Eighteen years later, Dear was the first of three miraculous births. Dear was very close to her parents and considered both of them saints for giving her a childhood any child would envy.

Although Dear's father was the pastor of the local church, he allowed his children to live normal lives that were free from unnecessary religious rules. Allowing children to have an opinion was unusual in Dear's times; nevertheless, my great-grandfather says that he followed God guidance in everything, which included raising his children. He considered himself a blessed man who lived a full life until he died peacefully in his sleep, three days after his 100th birthday. Dear's mother was a missionary who, with her husband's blessing, traveled the globe helping others until without notice she also peacefully expired in her sleep two days after her 100th birthday. Now three days away from reaching her centennial birthday, Dear is healthy and happy and shows little signs of slowing down any time soon. My fear is that she, like both of my great-grandparents, will peacefully go to her heavenly home in her sleep after reaching the age of 100.

As I hand my keys to the Country Club valet, my thoughts shift without notice. How can so much pain pack itself into 17 days and so abruptly disrupt my perfect life? No job, a cheating husband, having to redecorate most of my house, betrayed by my baby sister, what else can happen? I have to stay focused on pleasantries, so I make my way to my final meeting with the Country Club's event director to review the party details. I am smiling for the first time in a long while as I picture Dear's face and the joy this event will bring when I receive a call from Kevin. For obvious reasons, I almost do not answer his call. I'm glad that I did answer because he has grim news. He found Dear unconscious in her room, and she is on her way to the hospital in an ambulance.

I drop everything and rush to her side. I am perplexed as I drive to the hospital. What can be wrong with Dear? I know that she is almost 100 years old, but she is healthy and gets around better than most women half her age. When I arrive, Dear is reclined in a hospital bed looking upward as though she is waiting for her peaceful ascent. Fear of the eventually inevitable prompts me to stop at the door for a quick prayer as I survey the situation. "God, please let her be alright." She is in her room alone, lying there and thinking about the many happy moments throughout her life.

She smiles and whispers a prayer, "Lord, I thank you for blessing me with Jonnie, and I ask that you keep an especially close eye on her. She is not as strong as she pretends to be, and I know that my absence from her life will cause great strain." She continues, "Lord, I know that we are not supposed to have favorites, but you didn't leave me much to choose from. Jonnie is my favorite grandchild, so please give her strength in her difficult moments. Please also keep my family strong. Amen."

From the sounds of this prayer, Dear is ready to go to heaven right now, and this is not acceptable because I am not ready. She doesn't even know that Kevin moved out or that I'm afraid I may lose my husband to Alex, which will surely ruin me. I need Dear here with me so I interrupt her prayer and any plans to leave me here alone.

"Dear, what happened?" I ask as I go to her bedside. The look in her eyes says that it's time, and although we've had the kind of bond that requires few words, I need to hear her verbalize her thoughts this time. I refuse to listen to what I know she is trying to say to me without words. I feel as though Dear is ready to go home with the Lord, but she has to hold on for my sake, so I reject this consideration.

I need to know what happened. Did she fall? When she struggles to speak, I kiss her and tell her to save her strength as I go find her doctor, who tells me that she is of the age that her organs are tired and are moving at a slower pace than normal. "She is three days shy of 100 years old," he says, "so it may just be her time to go." I cannot believe that his words are so devoid of emotion, until I look into his eyes and he tells me, "Jonnie, I have been her doctor for the last thirty years, and we all knew that Dear's passing would be a devastating moment in our history. She is a saint, but even saints get tired and need to go home." With tears in his eyes, he tells me that she lost consciousness because the oxygen level in her blood is extremely low; had Kevin not found her when he did we would be having a different conversation. I can clearly now hear the emotional love in his voice as he tells me, "She probably has only a week more with us, unless God blesses us with her longer."

I hurriedly return to Dear's room. I am not ready to hear this! "God, not now, I'm not ready!" I say aloud as I make my way down the hallway.

Even though we are two generations apart, Dear and I are extremely close. I have always told everyone that when the time comes I will be prepared to let Dear go because she has made my life beautiful. I feel good about my efforts to make her life equally beautiful and carefree. Dear always knew that my display of strength was a pretense and that her evitable passing would be an unbearable moment.

To make her home-going less stressful, Dear had completely arranged her funeral service years ago, appointing me to oversee her estate and make any final arrangements. I spend about an hour sitting next to Dear talking about the life that God blessed us to have together. We laugh until we both can take no more as we review the many Alex and Mrs. Eloise moments, especially the lesbian announcement at Thanksgiving. Dear laughs and seems like her old self as she can barely get through her perspective without laughing out every other word. "Sweet Pea, when I heard Alex say, 'This is my girlfriend,' the look on your mother's face made me call Jesus so abruptly I probably startled him. I can almost see him sitting with the Father and dropping everything to attend to my needs when he got that call. I have never called him like that. I thought Mrs. Eloise was going to flip that beautifully decorated table over on all of us!" She laughs heartily.

Even laying in this hospital bed, Dear's strength and energy are so high that I am certain that we will go home soon. We talk for about an hour, until Daddy and Mrs. Eloise enter the room. "You don't look sick at all, Dear," says Mrs. Eloise, with the usual snarl in her voice. Dear and I look at each other, and as if on cue, we laugh uncontrollably for a minute or so more, which angers Mother. Daddy goes to speak to her doctor, since he can't get a serious word from us, and Mother looks down her pointy nose at us, which makes us laugh more.

Wow! This feels good. I have not laughed like this in about three weeks. Mrs. Eloise's only comment before stepping out to answer her phone is, "Is this what I left work for? You two are so silly!"

From as far back as I can remember, Dear and I have always shared a close bond, which has bothered Mother and Alex. Dear's philosophy is to find the humor or blessing in any situation and let God do the rest. She says that God gave us free will for a reason: "You get to choose how you handle life's situations, so choose the pleasant route... choose your dance." This was the first time that I heard this phrase and I would later find out more about choosing the dance. As soon as Mother is out of earshot, Dear comments, "Boy, the enemy sure does try to suck the life out of any situation," and we laugh some more.

But nothing lasts forever. Kevin and Alex's entrance into the room changes the atmosphere. I sit in the corner quietly watching as they spend time with Dear until their visit is cut short when Dear speaks gently to them both. In her usually loving manner, she asks that they take a look at the picture bigger than this moment. "Do you know where you're going with this connection that you've made? Do you know the purpose?"

When neither of them answer. She continues, "You see, when we are children, we take on childish ways, but as adults we should take on the characteristics of adults, which means that we think about our actions and the consequences that follow." Her sweet voice shakes slightly as she seems to struggles for the air to make it through each sentence. Even though her heart aches from the tremendous pain that they've caused me, she maintains the warmth in her words.

"Now, there's enough love in this room to make it through any trial... don't dismiss the love for the works of the flesh." She looks at Alex as she concludes, "Jonnie is your sister, and you should never take part in causing her any pain. You have spent all of your life with Jonnie, and she will be there when everyone else has left." Then, looking at me, she says, "Never take part in bringing each other pain."

I am confused. Why is she looking at me? I'm not causing her any pain. Alex's eyes glisten as she seems to fight back the unfamiliar tears that swell across her pupils. She quietly nods while calmly leaving the room, and Daddy returns with fear in his eyes. Dear tells him, "Baby, you have to let God do his work." His boyish mannerisms are beautiful as he holds her hand and thanks her for being the ideal mother.

Kevin kisses Dear and tells me that he will take care of the girls so that I can stay with Dear for as long as needed. I follow him out to the hallway to thank him for coming by the house and finding her. I let him know that he probably saved her life, so despite my current hatred for him and his actions, I am grateful. We are talking, and we seem to be making a breakthrough as we hug and I release a heart full of emotions all over his chest. I am so tired of crying, but it feels good to be back in my husband's arms, where it seems that no harm can reach me. As he holds me and whispers loving words, I let go of the strength I pretend to have. I swear I hear him apologize and tell me that he still loves me.

"Kevin, are you ready?"

It's Alex. He immediately loosens his hold, wipes his face, and tells me he'll check on me later. What is the hold that she has on him? Is the sex that good? I work out. I'm sure I can do those things with a little direction! But I don't have time to think about this right now.

Mother leaves the hospital and Daddy and I spend the night by Dear's side. Dear has always taught me to look for the blessing in everything, and the blessing in this moment is that although my best friend lies in a hospital bed my husband held me through a very difficult moment. His embrace told me that he still cares about me, at least and he may even still love me. That was wonderful, but the bigger blessing is that Daddy and I get to spend uninterrupted time with Dear.

I focus all of my energies on this moment and getting Dear out of here. Although the many hospital monitors might not agree, Dear seems to be her usual self. We all talk for hours until we each take turns falling asleep mid-conversation. I survey the room and take a mental picture of Daddy lying next to Dear in the hospital bed, holding her in his arms as they both sleep. I get plenty of uninterrupted time with Dear, so I adjust the recliner, cover up with a few hospital blankets, and thank God, in faith, for allowing me to take Dear home tomorrow. I doze with a smile in my heart, grateful to God for the blessings that came from this Dear interruption.

A Dear Goodbye

Two days pass, and I realize that it will take a miracle to get Dear to the Country Club for her 100th birthday party. Just as I prepare to pull the plug on the celebratory gala, Vanessa has a brilliant idea. I call Shelia, who volunteers to take a break from her wedding plans to assist with Dear's party. She and Vanessa take care of the details at the Country Club while I prepare the setup at the hospital. Within a day we are ready to move forward with the party, almost as planned. Tomorrow may be Dear's last birthday and the last time most of her guests will get a chance to see her in person. I want to give everyone a chance to celebrate and to say show their love… through the magic of video conferencing!

At 4:00am on the morning of her birthday I sneak out of Dear's hospital room and go home to gather a few of Dear's items. I look in on the girls, who are sleeping like angels, before heading to Dear's room. I am tempted to look in my bedroom, but I decide I do not want to take the chance of walking in on another one of Kevin and Alex's acrobatic sexcapades. I am confident he knows to never bring Alex back into my home, especially after we just spent nearly $70,000 on redecorating our bedroom and three guest rooms in an effort to remove any remnants of their filthy actions. I am sure that he is asleep in my new bed, which is slightly disturbing because I haven't even slept in there yet. I've been sleeping in Dear's room here and at the hospital.

I resist the temptation to look in on him sleeping and turn right towards Dear's room to continue my mission. I have approximately five hours before I have to be back at the hospital. Today is the 20th, which means that this is Dear's day. I refuse to think negative thoughts, so I quietly sing, "Happy birthday to Dear, happy birthday to Dear…" while moving towards her room. I love to spoil her, and making her bedroom into a mini-palace was another small way for me to express my appreciation for her strong shoulders and the never-ending love that she exemplified throughout my entire life.

Five years ago, Kevin and I had our home custom built with two master bedroom suites because Dear deserves to live like a Queen. I think that I was more excited than Dear when she finally saw her new room. We both shed tears of joy and laughed as we walked through the room with Dear saying over and over, "Jonnie baby, this is too much, it's just too much" as Kevin watched us with a smile on his lovely lips. Kevin will never fully know the depth of our love, but he feels our bond and he has never uttered a negative or jealous word against our times of closeness together, even the times that exclude him. For the past three nights he has taken the girls, which allows me quality time with Dear. He has never felt threatened by our tears, laughter, silent smiles, as well as the unspoken language that we obviously share; instead, he created his own bond with Dear.

Kevin and Dear became close when I was in Paris, so it also made him very happen to see Dear overcome with joy when she moved into her lavish bedroom suite. Kevin, who refers to Dear as his "Best Girl," often seeks Dear's advice during their late-night conversations, which is a special time between just the two of them. When he needs to talk, Kevin will mosey past Dear's room, looking in repeatedly until she awakes and calls out to him. Through the years, Kevin learned to rely on Dear's advice for the many problems that can plague a man's life, and although he was a decent man when he met Dear, he credits her for the God in him. His parents are lovely, just not very spiritual, so he relies on Dear for her spiritual guidance and connections.

Thoughts of happier times cause a genuine smile in my heart until I walk into Dear's room and notice Kevin sleeping in her bed cuddling her favorite quilt. Darn it! I was going to sleep in here. Before I can leave, he awakes and asks in his raspy but sexy sleepy-time voice, "Hey Jon, how's Dear?" I did not want to converse with him, but I tell him how she is and we talk about the setup of the monitors for the video conferencing at today's birthday celebration. Dear will be able to see everything going on in the Grand Ballroom, and since we were unable to connect monitors outside, we've hired two videographers to move throughout the crowd and onto the patio gathering birthday wishes. Kevin shakes his head and smiles slightly when he hears that we've hired videographers. He mentions that we need to slow down on spending because we've spent about $100,000 in the last 20 days ... and I haven't even told him that I lost my job.

During our conversation Kevin tells me he misses me, and somehow, we end up making love in Dear's bed. Oh my god... is this sick? I am so confused. I am sure Dear would not object to me making love to my husband in her bed. She once told me that I should feel free to do anything at any time and in anyplace *legal* with my husband, as long as we are both comfortable with the idea and there were no other parties involved. When Kevin and I were first married, Mother's continual judgment had me somewhat of a prude until Dear had "the talk" with me, which caused me to loosen up, or so I thought, until I saw him with Alex. I don't know that I can ever be that loose.

But I can't think about that right now! Not as I lay in his arms with him stroking my hair and telling me how much he loves me as our legs are entangled. I love it here... but what am I reducing myself to, and at what cost? Why am I choosing to share my husband? Why am I choosing this dance? Maybe this means that he is choosing to leave Alex alone, but he didn't say that and I didn't stop to ask because I wanted to make love to my husband. The thought of him with another woman; my baby sister no less, sickens me. However, my love for him overpowers my consciousness, and now I have made love to my husband again... unprotected. I've left my heart, as well as my loins unprotected yet again and this reality pains my soul. I can't sort through these emotions while lying in his arms up against his manhood so I set my alarm before falling asleep with Kevin kissing my forehead as tears roll down both of our faces. "What a mess," I repeat in my mind as I fall asleep.

The soft music of my alarm gently kisses my eardrums, letting me know that it is time to get up and get going. The sun shines through Dear's hand-made curtains across Kevin's beautiful face. With little notice, he joins me in the shower and makes love to me while whispering, "I miss my wife and I want to come home!" I'm too confused to respond because although I am truly in love with my husband and I want him home, I need time to sort through my feelings, and Dear's birthday is not the day.

We get dressed and are in a warm embrace when Tia bursts through the door, "Mommy! Daddy!" with Kali following, "I'm hungry!" Although perplexed by all that is going on, I am mindful to maintain my strong outer shell as I walk around Dear's room reminiscing and gently touching the cherry wood dresser, the multicolored quilt that Dear's great-grand-mother made, and Dear's favorite pillow. After sitting for several moments and caressing Dear's favorite pillow, I become aware of the time and quickly prepare to leave. Kevin will cook breakfast for the girls before joining me at the hospital to visit Dear.

As for the girls, years ago, Dear told them that although she would be going to heaven one day, she would always be in their hearts. She told them that they should be happy when she goes to heaven because she'll be with God. Since that time, they both seem to have a healthy view of death.

On my drive to the hospital, I call Shelia and tell her all about my early morning with Kevin. She listens attentively without judgment, but warns me to be careful and realistic. "He has shown that he will betray you, and those character traits don't disappear overnight without cause," she says lovingly. I listen because she's somewhat an expert in this subject. She endured Mitchell's infidelities for over twenty years. She wishes us the best while telling me that she will be here for me no matter what happens. She has become a great friend. Before hanging up the phone, Shelia assures me that she will be at the birthday party today to help in any way needed. Although Vanessa is my best friend, I have not told her about all that has failed in my life within the past 20 days because she will want to fix the problems and may start by trying to fistfight Kevin and Alex. Although her family is upper class and she is a sophisticated woman, she has a mean temper and is overly protective of me. She says that she has to stand up for me because I don't stand up for myself. I will tell her soon, but not today. Today is Dear's day.

When I arrive at the hospital, I comb Dear's hair and help her prepare for her birthday party. Since she cannot attend her party in person, Vanessa and I have set up two-way video-conferencing monitors in the hospital room, as well as in the Grand Ballroom at the Country Club so that she and all her guests can see and talk to each other. Thanks to modern technology, she gets to attend her birthday party from the comfort of her hospital room. I will stay with Dear, while Vanessa and Shelia have agreed to play hostess at the Country Club.

To my surprise, Kevin decides to stay with me at the hospital with Dear for her party. He has the girls dressed so beautifully, which reminds me what a great father he is to them both. Kali and Tia compete for Dear's attention, and as usual, Tia wins because she is more outgoing and naturally the actress of the family. I feel bad for Kali because she is often in Tia's shadow, just as I was with Alex when we were little girls. However, I can't help but laugh as Tia dances around the room, animating every word of her version of "Happy Birthday." I also pay close attention to Dear, making sure she remains comfortable and does not overexert herself.

Once the party begins, Dear almost forgets that she is not actually there. The high-definition connections are optimal, and the technicians I hired maintain the high-quality network while panning the room so that Dear continuously enjoys the many guests at her party. Additionally, the two camera technicians move throughout the room and patios asking guests to say a word to Dear. The invitation list included 300 guests, but I am certain that there are close to 500 people in attendance. The party is beautiful, and it is apparent that Dear is truly loved.

After several hours of being cooped up in this hospital room, I insist that Kevin take the girls to enjoy the festivities and show off their party dresses. After they each kiss Dear goodbye, I walk them out to hallway, say my goodbyes, and intently look Kevin in his eyes. Without saying a word, he reads my thoughts and says, "I love my wife and will do whatever it takes to get back home. I'm *your husband*. Don't worry, we'll fix us. I've told Alex that I will do whatever it takes to get back home, which means staying completely away from her." He passionately kisses my smiling lips before leaving, and I return to the party in Dear's room via videoconference. I love my husband and am happy that he has chosen me over *her*.

Kevin has the utmost respect and love for Dear, and watching them together today reminds me of this fact. I am sure that her words of wisdom the other night had a lot to do with his request to come home and choose his wife over the fling with the baby sister. I am not sure how or if I will ever be able to get over this betrayal, but before I can get to caught up in my thoughts, Dear's baby sister, Aunt Lovely, as well as other family members of Dear's enter the room to visit.

Daddy enters the room and pulls a chair next to the recliner where Dear rests. He holds her hand as though he is still a young boy and often counts the beats of her pulse to assure that she does not grow too tired of hosting so many visitors. After his father left them when he was a young boy, Daddy became the man of the family, which created a sense of responsibility and was the beginning of his protective nature over Dear. Even though Mother has not made it easy, he has maintained his closeness with Dear.

I often extend the invitation for Daddy to live with us whenever Mrs. Eloise becomes too difficult to bear. Mrs. Eloise has always been a difficult woman, and today is no exception. But Dear is an exceptional woman, and even though she grows a bit tired, she is happy to have her family around her; even Mrs. Eloise's snappy remarks do not alter the atmosphere of love that fills the room.

In an effort to keep the mood light, I counter mother's remarks by responding positively. At one point, I walk over to mother, hug her, and say, "I'm so glad you're here, Mrs. Eloise." I don't remember ever hugging Mother without reason, and I'm not excited about hugging her now, but this is my final attempt at shutting Mrs. Eloise's mouth, and it works. Mrs. Eloise stands puzzled, wondering if my display is genuine, and she almost seems receptive to my impromptu show of affection until she realizes my true intent. She strikes back by pointing out Alex on the monitor, commenting positively on her outfit.

Alex is standing on the patio in a very short dress that outlines every feature of her fit body, which disturbs every bone of my being. Alex and I are blessed with Mother's good genes and have never had to do much to maintain our tight physiques; but whereas I choose to dress and carry myself with decorum, Alex has always dressed risqué. Everything about the way in which Alex chooses to carry herself usually disturbs Mother, but now she is trying to hurt me, so she has switched sides.

I surprise myself by saying, "You can't be serious! Look at that outfit. Why didn't she just show up in a bikini?" Mrs. Eloise says, "She's showing her sex appeal, Jonnie. You could take some pointers from your sister on casual dress because she has a great sense of style. Your suits are nicer, but your casual dress is a bit stiff." Before I can catch myself, I ask her, "What? How can you say that, Mommy? She's dressed like a tramp!"

Dear gives my hand a slight pat, which is her way of trying to calm me while reminding me not to let Mrs. Eloise's words cause a reaction on my part. Mrs. Eloise becomes instantly enraged because she has always insisted that we refer to her by her professional name especially in public. In an effort to prepare us for the "real world," Mrs. Eloise raised us in a professional environment. "Mommy" was not conducive to the professional arena, so Alex and I have referred to Mother as Mrs. Eloise for as long as I can remember. But whenever I feel the need to get under her skin, I refer to her as "Ma" or "Mommy." Now all of the attention has moved to Alex as everyone comments about her dress and the girl she is hugging. This day is supposed to be about Dear!

The camera pans to another part of the party, and not a moment too soon. Like a dog with a bone, however, Mrs. Eloise continues to rave about Alex and compare us. The two-way speakers are on, so the guests hear our conversation underneath the soft music playing at the party, and the cameras are soon on Alex and her lustful displays again. Today has been a lovely day thus far and I'm not going to allow Mother to destroy my happiness, so I excuse myself and go down the hall to the restroom. While looking in the mirror I decide that maybe it's time for me to be sexier... I can show her "sexy!"

When I return to the room, the conversation has halted, and everyone is watching the monitors inquisitively and slightly in shock. The silence is deafening until Mother asks, "Why is your husband hugging Alex and her girlfriend, and why is he looking around like that?" As I look at the screen, she gives me a play-by-play. "Alex led him onto the patio by the hand to meet her girlfriend, and if I didn't know better, I'd think they were making plans for the three of them to get together." I want her to shut up, but she continues, "I own a very lucrative matchmaking company, so I know when people are being matched." I feel as though the air has been knocked right out of my body as she puts the final nail in the coffin. "It seems that your husband also likes her dress. Point, set, match... game over!" Mother concludes, realizing that she has won again, this time with the assistance of my husband.

I am devastated as I read the look of lust in his eyes. Alex seems to be pointing to her and her girlfriend's bodies, asking, "Are you sure you don't want all of this?" Daddy quickly comes to my rescue as he hurries everyone out of the room so Dear can rest. I go to a private room to call Kevin and tell him what I, along with a room full of party guests, including Mother, just witnessed. I tell him to drop my daughters off at Vanessa's house after the party and threaten that he will never see me or the girls again after today. I really want to cause him pain, so I go further.

"You have caused my life to change for the worse, and I'm about to do the same for yours! I trust that you consider her worth losing everything. I hope you enjoyed living in luxury, with a wife who stands by your side and daughters who love and respect you, because you will not get that from her! You've just lost everything! When I'm done you won't have a pot to piss in or a window to throw the piss out of, motherfucker!"

I don't even cuss or know how to say more than the occasional "hell" or "damn it," so that word sounded weird coming out of my mouth. I don't think I emphasized it correctly, but I'm angry! I don't know if I'm more hurt by his actions or that Mother witnessed someone choosing to hurt me, which seems to cause her a sick sense of satisfaction. She warned me about him while we were in college and now she gets to be right… this is terrible! The whole thing is just terrible!

The party has been over for hours and all visitors have left Dear's side except me. We both change into comfy clothes and talk about what happened today. Well, mostly I talk while Dear listens. Her only comment is that I should trust God through it all. I have a feeling that she knows more than she is saying, but because she is feeling tired I let her off the hook for further explanation, until tomorrow.

Soon, the hospital announces that visiting hours are over. We both lay in and out of sleep in her hospital bed, and I am numb and embarrassed. Dear tells me everything will be OK, but I don't see how. I drift in and out of sleep, waking only long enough to check on Dear and move so the nurses can periodically check her vital signs. I have been falling asleep on Dear's bed for as long as I can remember, and tonight is no exception. For the past three nights, I have spent most of my spare time at Dear's bedside. I comb her hair, rub her feet, and do anything else to make her comfortable, but mostly, I listen intently to Dear's words of wisdom, with the exception of tonight. Tonight I do most of the talking while she listens. Maybe I have so much to say because of the day's excitement. How can I start the day on top of the world and end the day laying face down underneath a world of heaviness? I share my morning's events with Dear while she smiles and assures me that having sex with my husband in any room in our house is OK with her. She somehow makes me laugh, and in between catnaps we talk and laugh until about 3:30 a.m. There is so much more that I want to talk over with her about Kevin, but I don't want to dampen the atmosphere. I will get up early, go get her favorite breakfast from the diner two blocks away, and we can talk more then. Besides, we are on a wonderfully humorous trip down memory lane and I don't want to ruin the moment.

I awake to the high-pitched sound coming from one of the many monitor alarms. A nurse works around me to check Dear's vitals until the doctor arrives and pronounces her time of death. I scream when I realize that Dear has peacefully gone to heaven while we slept, just one day after her 100th birthday.

Although I anticipated this moment, I thought I had at least a few more days. The tears flow continuously. I'm not ready to walk this life without Dear! I realize that my feelings are selfish because she is in heaven and must be ecstatic to finally be by God's side, but there is a hole in my heart that will never be repaired. Who will I talk to now? No one will ever take the place of Dear!

Daddy is on his way to the hospital when he receives my call informing him of Dear's passing. After the doctor records her death, I ask him and the nurses to close the door on their way out so that I may have my final moments with Dear before anyone else arrives. I lie back on the bed, hold Dear's body as tight as I can without hurting her, and sob aloud while waiting for the family to arrive.

I speak aloud hoping that she can still hear me. "I love you, Dear… more than I know how to express. I know that you will always be with me in spirit, but I now have to learn how to deal with life without your physical presence. You are my everything. How can I go through life without you?" Over my loud sobbing I hear a quiet sweet voice say, "God is your every-thing, sweetie. Let Him work". The voice, although not audible, sounds or feels like Dear, which brings relief, but also causes the tears to flow heavier.

Daddy comes into the room and holds me and Dear and whispers,

"Rest in Heaven, mama; rest well" while tears stream down his face. Today, one day after her 100th birthday, we say our final Dear goodbye. Rest in Heaven Sweet Dear. There will never be another like you.

Ditch Digger

This terrible experience that I refer to as life continues to happen all over me as I discuss my divorce plans with the same lawyer Sheila used when she divorced Mitchell. If I weren't so numb from all of the emotional scarring I would be embarrassed by my eagerness to ruin Kevin, as I advise her how badly I want to make his life a living hell. Even though I am in the midst of planning Dear's funeral, I want to get out of this marriage while I have a small amount of my dignity intact and before he sweet-talks me into another lovemaking session. I've always been a multi-tasker, today is no time to stop.

Serving Kevin with divorce papers at his office will definitely embarrass him because I am sure that he has not shared his infidelities with his partners. I want him served as soon as possible and I want him to feel as much pain as his cold heart will allow. I am tired of being walked over so I chose to fight a little dirty.

Kevin is an attorney, so my recently retained divorce attorney, Misty Clark, tries to talk me into meeting with Kevin to talk through our differences amicably. Misty knows of Kevin and says that she can't imagine him playing hardball with me because he's known as a family man who speaks favorably of his love for his wife and children. Hearing her praise him and his loyalty piss me off and compels me to move full speed ahead with the process. Even after hearing about his betrayal of the family he *loves so much*, she asks me to take a moment to cool down so that I can think about my decisions rationally.

My anger fuels my desire to hurt him to his core, and serving him with divorce papers at the funeral may be just the type of relief my broken heart needs. He dug this ditch so I insist that she assist me with making him lie in it or I will seek alternative legal representation. Against her better judgment, Misty agrees to file the paperwork as quickly as possible and she leaves the details of how, when, and where I want to serve him in my hands.

Five days after Dear's death I sit front and center at her funeral... alone. Although I am surrounded by family members and the many friends who have come to bid their farewells to Dear, I feel very alone. For the first time in my life I am unable to reach out in some manner and hear from Dear. I always appreciated her presence in my life, but for the first time I realize that **she** was truly my "EVERYTHING", and I don't know where I will go from here. I pull myself together enough to speak eloquently about her bigness in my life. I acknowledge my selfishness because I'm not ready to let God have her. Even though I know that she is enjoying her newly issued Glorified Body and her time at Jesus's feet hearing about His life as she worships with the angels. I visually scan the room and cannot find a dry eye, with the exception of Tia. Even Mother pats the water trapped in her eyes before it runs down her flawlessly decorated face. Conversely, Tia sits on the front row smiling and looking slightly upward, as though she is having a private moment with Dear. Her actions continue throughout the day and even at the gravesite Tia is playing in the grass as though she is oblivious to today's event while enjoying a special day at the park.

Just before the casket is closed I move closer to say my final words and look upon the face that has represented the purest expression of love I've ever known. Out of my peripheral vision I notice that Alex has her arm locked into Kevin's, as though to mock me in the worst moment of my life. So far, she has been present for two of the most horrific days I've ever known. She and Mother are truly two of a kind. Anyway, this is the last time that I will get to feel the touch of my best friend, so I bend over and kiss Dear softly on her cheek. To my surprise, my emotions overtake the moment and I quietly lay my head on her bosom and tell her how much

I love and will always miss her. I don't care who sees me or if Mother is embarrassed, I need to have one last conversation with my Dear.

I apologize to Dear for being selfish because I want her to somehow miraculously come back and then I ask, "What am I supposed to do now? Who will I talk to?" The tears are endless and I don't know if I can ever leave this spot until I feel someone gently move me from Dear's bosom and into a firm embrace. Again, Daddy has come to my rescue and we both quietly say our goodbyes as the casket is closed and Dear's body is lowered into the ground.

I cannot bear to watch this grim reminder of the finality of this moment so I bury my face into Daddy's chest and scream into his white shirt. I feel a hand on my back as I am helped to my seat. I don't have the strength to fight him off, so I accept Kevin's help as he watches me fall apart in Daddy's arms.

After the gathering at the house Vanessa oversees the catering staff to ensure that everything is left spotless, and Sheila tends to the guests until the last well-wisher has left. To my surprise, Kevin did not come by the house after the burial and I'm sure Alex knows that she is not welcome in my home any longer, so she also did not show. Vanessa offers to stay with me so that I'm not alone; however, I want to be alone so I allow the girls to spend the night at her house for a family night of movie-watching and popcorn- eating. Kali reluctantly leaves my side after I've assured her that I'm ok and just need a long hot bath.

The house is quiet until the silence is disturbed by the ringing of the phone. Kevin on the other end swearing and refusing my many demands outlined in the divorce papers. I have never heard him so upset. He is obviously crying as he accuses me of ruining his final memories with Dear by having him served with divorce papers at her grave. I guess the serving service that I hired did not have the heart to serve Kevin until everyone, but he and Alex, had left the cemetery. This is not exactly the service that I paid for, but the mission of hurting him was still accomplished. Kevin and I exchange insults for a few minutes until I call him a ditch digger; "You ditch digger… Ditch digger… ditch digger!" I yell at the top of my lungs because I'm emotionally exhausted and this is the only thing that I know to do in this moment to get his attention.

Over the past three weeks I have called him everything else, "cheater, liar, sneak, family destroyer, fraud, motherfucker" (although not very convincingly), etc. so all that is left to say is "ditch digger!" in response to his attacks.

I am referring to him digging this terrible ditch that we all have to wallow in, but he doesn't' know this. His confusion not only is satisfying but causes him to pause. He finally asks, "What are you talking about?" my only response is, "Oh... you'll find out, buddy! You'll regret the day you played me for a fool" I love that he is so confused and thrown off by my awkward response.

I take great comfort that this is one of those moments that Dear and I will laugh about later, until I remember that Dear is no longer here. I instantly become angry and I almost get caught up in his moments until I feel a smooth breeze throughout the room that gives me unspoken permission to hang up the phone while he continues to rant. I silence my phone and spend the night walking from room to room talking in the air to Dear and God.

Because I am home alone I feel free to express my feelings without boundaries so I sob aloud, and then I laugh, cry, and laugh again at Kevin's response to me calling him a ditch digger. My eyes have been open all night, I guess waiting for Dear to show herself as we bring in the 27th day of this most terrible month together. Tonight she is in spirit, but nevertheless, she is with me as I discuss my life and how I will make Kevin lay in this ditch that he dug while I avoid any thought of the painful consequences ahead.

I fall asleep with laughter in my thoughts and sun shining through the window as I recall my words, "Ditch digger, ditch digger, ditch digger!" and the confused look that must have been on Kevin's face while he tried to figure out what the heck I meant.

Frozen Assets

I spend all day lounging in my pajamas, reading the Bible and watching movies that remind me of Dear. Vanessa has called to check on me throughout the day and says that she will bring the girls home after dinner. I ignore the calls from Kevin pleading to discuss our future because I know that he is now afraid of my next move. He leaves a message begging me not to move out of the country with his girls and several other messages apologizing for his behavior. His pleas fuel my stubbornness and make me more determined to stick to the path I'm currently taking. What's funny is that I don't have any moves planned, but I want him to lose sleep wondering what's next so I don't answer his calls.

As promised, Vanessa brings the girls home after dinner and once they are in bed we talk. I finally tell her about my job situation and that Kevin is cheating with my baby sister. Vanessa is horrified at all that's been going on without her involvement. She can't believe that I've handled all of this on my own and asks my permission to physically fight Alex and then Kevin. We both laugh at her request, but I know that if I give my blessing, Vanessa would find a way to assault them both. The fact that Vanessa grew up in a rich, classy, family environment has never stopped her from physically striking out when she feels justified, and right now she feels justified.

Although Vanessa and I are the same age, she is emotionally stronger and therefore took me under her wing long ago as my protector. I am reminded why I love her like I do as she devises a plan to get me out of this slump. "You have been through Hell and have lost so much in less than a month," she says as she is writing down what she considers the plan of action for each problem. She is the sister I wish I always had and like any good sister or best friend, although our real estate company is suffering financially through this recession, she offers her personal financial support. I assure her that I am ok financially due to the severance and our savings; I am just a mess emotionally, mentally, and spiritually.

She leaves me with the instructions that she jotted down on a notepad and advises me to move quickly on tying up loose ends. I know that she is right and I must take action so I will start tomorrow.

I wake up feeling refreshed with Kali and Tia lying next to me in Dear's bed. "Good morning, Mommy, where's Daddy?" Tia asks. I think it time I tell them that Daddy moved out, so we get dressed and go to our favorite breakfast café. As we wait for our breakfast I tell the girls that Daddy and Mommy have decided to take a little break to see if we want to stay married. I pride myself on telling my girls as much of the truth as I think they can handle and this moment is no different. Tia asks if she will get to see Daddy and is satisfied that she will still get to see him, no matter where he lives. Kali is a bit more observant and wants to know if this is why he has been with Auntie Alex more lately.

I am nervous for a split second. "Could she know that he and Alex have been carrying on?" I think until she continues her question, "Is Auntie Alex letting Daddy stay in one of her guest rooms until you guys work through your problems?" Her sincerity is a bit humorous. "What do you know about working through problems?" I ask her. She shyly smiles, "I know that he was mad at you for choosing work over your family." Ouch! Hearing this accusation from my child hurts my feelings deeply. I assure her that she and Tia are my first priority, and promise that I will be more available for them moving forward. We finish our breakfast and I give my credit card to the waitress, who returns in minutes to advise that my card has been denied. I am confused, but hand her another, and another, and finally I pay the $47.28 in cash. I rarely carry cash. I ask loud enough for the waitress to hear, "What is going on?" but I have a suspicion in my gut that Kevin is behind this embarrassing moment.

On the way home we stop by the bank and I'm advised that all assets in all three accounts have been frozen. Are you serious? He didn't! Once home, I am on the phone for hours calling the different credit card providers and banks in an attempt to gain more information. I leave a message for my attorney seeking direction, and when she is not available I get into Dear's bed and wish that she were here while I wait for Misty's return call.

Kali puts in a Madea movie because she knows that Tyler Perry's Madea movies always make me laugh. Kali sits in the bed next to me as I gaze at the screen. She brushes my hair and tells me that God told her that everything will be ok. It appears that she is channeling Dear, which brings a smile through the tears that I am fighting to hold back. Kali asks if I want her to call Daddy and ask him for some money.

Wow! My child is now worrying about our financial status. I refuse to give Kevin the satisfaction of knowing that he has caused any further disruption in my life. 'Never let them see you sweat', is what I always told my employees, so I maintain this strength for my girls. I assure Kali that we will be ok and I fall asleep to the gentle touch of the brush as she guides it through my hair, while Tia dances around the room as though she has a song privately playing in her atmosphere. Within an hour I receive a call from Misty advising of Kevin's actions as I listen with Kali watching my every movement. Misty tells me that Kevin has filed a counter suit and his includes an ATRO, which is an Automatic Temporary Restraining Order to protect our assets. The ATRO is why my accounts are frozen. He also filed an emergency ex parte stopping me from taking the girls out of the state until the judge rules on his request for full custody. I am unable to respond how I would like because Kali is hanging onto every word that comes out of my mouth, so I stay calm. Once I'm off the phone Kali asks if we will be ok and I assure her that we are great as I search my mind for answers on how I shall proceed.

What will I do now? I refuse to ask Vanessa for money and Mother will only delight at the fact that she was right about Kevin, as she tells me to find my own way out of the bed that I made for myself. Mother always tells me that I am too trusting and says, "You should never let a man know everything about you and your finances." She told me to keep a separate and private account so that I would have "just in case" money. I did not listen to her and asking her for money will only give her the satisfaction of being right, and she still will not give me money. I could ask Daddy, but Mother watches his spending like he's a child.

I can't believe that after almost seven years of marriage and a lifetime of love, Kevin left me with two children, in the worst time of my life, to fend for myself with frozen assets! I never knew that frozen assets could be the result of my empty threats.

Mother in Me

The first 28 days of this month have been Hell. I wonder if I can make it through the final 2½ days without further incident. It's dinner time and, although I don't feel like cooking, I can't afford to spend money on eating at a restaurant because my finances are frozen. I wish I had some frozen, prepared meals to throw in the microwave, but I've always insisted that we eat fresh, healthy food so here I am chopping, stirring, and blending until I have a home- cooked, nutritious meal.

I am usually a pretty good cook, but I guess because I am so distracted I forgot the seasoning, so this meal is pretty bland, which means that the ever-opinionated Tia is refusing to eat. Kali sees the disappointment in my face when Tia tells me that the food is nasty, so she eats quietly while Tia stares at her plate waiting for someone to come to her rescue. That someone is usually me, but this time I have a whole world of other stuff on my mind and can't afford to waste food, so I insist that she eat her food. I hand her the salt and tell her to season it a bit more to her taste. In the process of attempting to add salt she struggles due to the holes being clogged so she opens the salt shaker, tilts it slowly over her plate in an attempt to shake just a bit of salt over her vegetables. At this point, the salt jumps out of the shaker and onto her plate as though an avalanche has been released. During the whole ordeal I just sit there and watch, which is not at all like me. I am usually a very hands-on mother, but now I just sit and watch until the salt jumps out of the opened shaker, ruining her meal.

I can feel my blood reach its boiling point and when she give me a look of relief and says, "I can't be expected to eat this food now, Mommy," I lose control. I snatch her up from the table, spank her bottom with three good whacks, and send her to bed without dinner. I can't believe that I just hit my child. I have never hit my children and, because of how Mother raised us, I vowed that I would never hit a child. I think it is unfair when an adult hits a child because the fight is unbalanced. The adult becomes a bully, while the child is the helpless, defenseless one. This moment is worsened when I glance at Kali who is obviously fearful. She is looking at me in awe until she misinterprets my glance in her direction and says in a scared shaky voice, "I'm eating. Mommy, I'm eating".

I am disgusted by my actions. This is the first time that I see any part of my mother's actions being relayed through me and my actions. I slowly leave the dining room hating what I just did to my uniquely happy child, who is now in her bedroom crying and I'm sure confused by what just happened. I return to tell Kali that she doesn't have to eat that food. However, when she sees me coming back she becomes terrified, which is evident by her response to my return as she asks, "Mommy? Am I going to get a spanking too?" I can't believe that I've created the atmosphere that I grew up in right here in my own home. I want to hug her, but I don't want to scare her any further so I quietly tell her that she does not have to eat "that food" before I go to Dear's room and lock myself behind closed doors for a few hours.

How can I face my girls again? I've broken my own rule! I have never allowed them to hit each other because hitting is not allowed, at least this is what I've told them all of their lives. I don't even know what prompted me to jump up and swat her. God please help me not to become my mother.

I resurface a few hours later to find Kali holding Tia in her arms with a plate of half-eaten peanut butter and celery sticks on the nightstand. It's obvious that Kali made Tia her favorite snack before climbing into bed with her to provide comfort. This is serious because Kali hates going into Tia's messy room. Kali is very orderly, while Tia is my wild child who marches to her own beat and they usually stay in their neutral corners. I guess I created an exception to Kali's rule, because she is sleeping in her baby sister's room in an attempt to rebuild a secure atmosphere, I'm sure.

Alex and I never comforted each other through Mother's abuse when we were children, so the picture of Kali holding Tia while they sleep is a beautiful sight. It's apparent that they brushed their teeth because there is toothpaste splatters on Tia's counter. After I clean up and get ready for bed, I take a picture of my two sleeping beauties before climbing into Tia's bed with the two of them. It's a tight squeeze with the three of us in this queen-sized bed, but I need Tia to wake up with me by her side, and I just want to hold her.

Because my thoughts are heavy I didn't sleep well last night, but I obviously fell into a deep sleep at some point because I didn't feel the girls get out of the bed this morning. I am usually a light sleeper so I become a little anxious when I remember that I am in Tia's bed and she is not here with me. What if she never forgives me?

I find them sitting in the family room watching a movie with another plate of peanut butter celery and apple slices. I don't really know how to approach the situation. I don't want to interrupt their movie, but I don't want to ignore the elephant in the room. Mommy broke a rule and she needs to make amends.

I get a cup of tea and sit quietly in the corner portion of our comfy sectional. Usually Tia will join me, but she is apparently more comfortable sitting on her beanbag chair because she does not budge. Once the movie ends I gain the nerve to talk to my daughters. I quietly say a prayer for strength, humility, and direction as I start the conversation with an apology for my behavior. I tell them both how much I love them and we talk about how we are going to proceed with our newly created family unit. Dear is gone on to Heaven and Daddy has moved out and may never come back, so we discuss the importance of relying on each other. We discuss being patient with each other, exercising humility and forgiveness, and keeping our love strong.

Midway through the conversation Tia is sitting on my lap plastering my face with her usual set of 'Mommy kisses' and Kali is sitting next to me holding my hand. We have always had a strong bond and I will not allow anything to separate us. I always quote the Bible verse, "What therefore God has joined together, let not man put asunder (Mark 10:9)", in regards to me and my girls. God blessed me with Kali and Tia and I truly believe that no one or no thing has the ability to tear us apart, unless we allow separation. I refuse to allow bad situations or evil spirits to cause separation, so I will focus my prayers on strengthening our bond, because God is able.

Our talk leads us down many different paths and in the end I believe that they have both forgiven me. Now I have to find a way to forgive myself for allowing the Mother Eloise in me to show her ugly head. I always believed that Mother and I were worlds apart with regard to our actions and how we view the world or other people. However, last night I realized that I actually do have traces of Mother in me and this not only makes me sad, but also frightens me that I have the ability to be like my mother.

Realizing that the mother in me actually exists sheds a different light on my harsh judgment of her all of these years. Maybe she was just like me when she was my age with two young children, or perhaps she was born evil. This thought makes me realize that my harsh judgment is yet another trace of Mother in me. God help me to be more like you as I work to refuse the Mother in Me.

Diagnosis of the Damned

Today the girls and I have the best pajama party ever! I allow them to eat whatever they want from the kitchen, which is ok because I don't keep a lot of junk food in the house. They even prepare a plate of veggies and peanut butter with cinnamon toast on the side for my breakfast… yummy. We watch movies, cuddle under our blankets on the sectional, play board games, and tell funny stories until our bellies hurt from laughing. Truthfully, my laughter stems mostly from watching how tickled they become at the silliest of stories. I love their innocence… Their freedom. Under the circumstances, this day is perfect and I really need to feel any resemblance of what I used to know as perfection.

Although Dear is not here in body, we can feel her spirit, and Tia acts as though Dear never left, which can seem a bit weird but I will deal with her unusual activities later, if necessary. Right now I just want to focus on the good and be grateful for this wonderful day; thank you, God!

As the sun sets on this 29th day of the month reality taps me on the shoulder and reminds me that I have to get back into life, and soon. I need to find another job, call my attorney, pack the rest of Kevin's things, and get the girls back into their daily routine. They have not been to school for the past three days and seem to be getting a little restless. We are supposed to be mourning, and we are in our own way, but to an outsider or their teachers, our actions may not appear as mourning. I am sure that Mother would criticize my decision to keep the girls home if she knew we were watching movies and having fun.

Prior to the recent events that caused our lives to change so drastically, I was too busy and would have never taken a day to just hang out with my girls, but I love our time together and cherish every moment. It is difficult to believe that I let so much time pass without incorporating days like these in our normal routine. I am enjoying this time so much that I choose to be selfish with our time and haven't answered Mother's calls and I told Daddy that the girls and I were taking a few days alone to grieve.

My parents have no idea that we are over here laughing, playing, and enjoying each other, which is probably the best way that we could ever honor Dear. I'm sure that her seeing our activities brings joy to her soul. I can almost feel her smiling down on us and besides, I like who I am in these moments. She told me that I would be okay after her passing and although my world will never be the same, I'm starting to see possibilities. At this point it is too soon to know for certain, but for right now I feel like I just may make it through another day.

After getting the girls into bed I walk the house thanking God for being the head of my life and taking care of Dear. I'm sure that if He were anyone other than God the combination of my laughter and tears would be confusing. My mixed emotions remind me of sunshine in the middle of a rainstorm, but because He is God and knows me intimately I do not have to explain the complexity of my emotions. Besides, explaining my feelings would be difficult because I often don't understand what I'm feeling and how my emotions change so fast.

I look in on the girls again before settling into Dear's bed to watch the late-night news. I thank God for the many blessings of this day and as I doze off into a peaceful slumber I can feel my life heading in the right direction again.

At exactly 3:18am my ringtone wakes me and the voice on the other end says, "Jonnie, baby, come open the door." I am up on my feet and headed towards the front door before I am completely awake. I don't even realize who's on the other side of the door that I freely open. This is a scary afterthought. To my surprise it's Daddy and he appears furious, which is most unusual. He pushes past me speaking in at a whisper level as not to disturb the girls, "I don't believe that woman! I'm sorry to wake you, but I can't be in the same house with **her** for another minute." I try to make sense of his ramblings, but he's too angry so I ask no questions. I just listen. I make some tea, sip lemon ginger goodness, and listen.

After about an hour of him talking he settles into my newly remodeled master suite, turns on the television, and stares into space. Mother messed up this time! I'm not sure what she did, but it has something to do with him "eating all the meat". From what I can piece together, he must have eaten her portion of dinner. She often goes to bed without eating dinner and will get up in the middle of the night to have leftovers. She must have gotten up and found that he had eaten all of the roast or something. I am too tired to figure out this puzzle so I kiss him on his forehead and tell him that we can talk more after we've both had a few hours of sleep.

As far as I'm concerned, his being here is added goodness to the day that we had yesterday, because this house feels empty with Dear and Kevin gone. He can stay for as long as he wants. Hell, he can move in permanently because Mother doesn't deserve a man like him! I tell him that I love him as I leave my master suite realizing that this is the first time the new bed has been used since the seventy-thousand dollar remodel, which I cannot afford to pay until this divorce is settled or at least some of my funds are released.

I am not even close to being emotionally stable enough to have a rational conversation with Kevin about money, so for now I try to ignore the invoice on the desk in my office. Ignoring bills is unusual for me, but I don't have the capacity to deal with anything else right now. Besides, I don't want to disturb my current happiness with money woes or any other troubles. My heart hasn't smiled in a long while and I want to bask in this joy. I will get back into life and resume worrying about my problems in a day or two, once my strength has increased. For now I lie here in Dear's bed holding her pillow and thank God for the peace.

Not long after drifting into dreamland, delightful aromas of my favorite breakfast foods pull me out of a deep sleep and into the kitchen where Daddy has sautéed a mixture of fresh vegetables for me and turkey bacon, eggs, and pancakes for he and the girls. My heart smiles as I pour a glass of Açaí juice and am greeted by the abundance of groceries bulging from the refrigerator and pantry. Daddy must have spent a thousand dollars. He even filled the stand-alone freezer with many expensive cuts of meat and the second refrigerator with juice, water, apple sauce, Jell-O, and other healthy snacks for the girls. He says that he can tell that I haven't shopped in a while because he's never seen the cabinets this bare. "I couldn't sleep so I went to the grocery store early this morning and, before I realized my actions, I had gone to several stores and filled the truck several times with everything I thought you may need. I don't know what came over me, but I was cooking breakfast before I came to myself and realized the abundance of groceries," he says, glowing proudly. I hug him and thank him, but I know that Dear had a hand in his actions.

Daddy says that shopping was therapeutic, but I recognize his therapy session as a gift from God and I am so grateful because our pantry had gotten pretty empty. He even bought paper products, toothpaste, sanitary napkins… the right kind! So I know that God led him to the various stores and down the right aisles. This moment brings me to my favorite Bible verse, "Now unto Him who is able to do exceedingly, abundantly above all that I can ask or think, according to the power that works in me" (Ephesians 3:20). Dear God, thank you for blessing me exceedingly and abundantly above what I would have asked Daddy to do.

The joy in my heart produces happy tears. Daddy has no idea what this means to me, because I did not know how I was going to get money for food, toiletries, and the other necessary things that have been replenished. This is also a reminder that I need to trust God more. Wow, God is so amazing and I thank God for another beautiful day!!

This month has been the month from Hell. I lost almost everything that means anything to me; my job, my husband, my grandmother and best friend, my financial security, a complete family picture, my happiness, my perfect world, my dignity, an resemblance of relationship I had with my sister, my peace, my emotional stability, my emotional security, and the list could go on for several more pages, I'm sure. But on this 30th and final day of this month, my world is brighter.

Daddy has spent all day with the girls and me, which makes my heart sing. He made delicious smoked chicken sandwiches for lunch, we read books with the girls, and went to dinner and the movies before more retail therapy for Daddy, in which we all benefitted. He must be really mad at Mother, but I don't press the issue because I don't want to upset him. He seems to be in a happy place, despite eating all of Mother's meat (chuckle,

chuckle), whatever this means. She will be livid once she finds out how much money he has spent in less than 24 hours. Without batting an eyelid, he paid $1500 for a handbag because he saw how I admired it. He said, "It's only money and we only live once," as he placed his credit card in the cashier's hand. He is usually very frugal, so his gift means a whole lot and I will always cherish this purse, and even more I cherish this time of bonding. We don't get much time with Daddy without Mother scrutinizing our every word, so this time alone with him is truly a blessing. Besides my time with Dear earlier in the month and the pajama party with the girls, this day has been the best day of this month of turmoil.

Once the girls are settled into bed, Daddy and I sit down to talk. I thought that he wanted to tell me about the fight between him and mother, but all he wants to talk about is Kevin and me. He wants to know what went wrong. I reluctantly answer his questions because I don't want to be rude or disrespectful, but I would rather talk about what's going on in his world. Besides, I don't actually know where or when Kevin and I went so wrong, wrong enough for him to sleep with my sister. Daddy is very private and tries to protect Mother and her reputation, so I don't pry. I figure that he will talk about the ordeal when he is ready.

It is 9:30pm on the 30th day of the month that began with the tragic announcement that I would lose my dream job. Horrendous tragedies followed and made their way through my life as if their main purpose was to break me. Now I sit back in my recliner staring at my full belly thanking God for a perfect ending to this terrible month. I am but a few hours from putting the worse month of my adult life behind me and I can face tomorrow, next month, and the months to follow realizing that God always comes to my rescue. I don't know what tomorrow will bring, but for tonight I thank God for my Daddy and his presence in our lives. Daddy showing up unannounced reminds me that God is never far away and knows exactly what I need, even when my circumstances seem to say that He is not paying attention to me and my problems. I decide to stay in the family room with Daddy as he watches one of his old western movies because I need to be in a happy place as I witness this month exit and my new beginning enter with the first day of next month.

As if the Devil heard my thoughts, at exactly 11:39pm he sent one of his loyal soldiers to my door. Daddy and I nearly jump out of our skin as the doorbell rings continuously with determination, followed by repeated pounding. My heart becomes a little happy at the possibility that Kevin may be the culprit on the other side of the door, but then I realize that he would not thoughtlessly cause this type of disruption to the girls' sleep at this late hour. I open the door and Mother walks past me without even a hello and asks Daddy, "How long are you going to be over here?" They exchange a few unpleasant words and I'm still in the dark as to the root of their disagreement.

My parents have always argued in code and they are usually quiet, but this time they are louder than I ever remember. I run down the hall and pull the girls' doors close in an attempt to shield the girls' ears from the angry slurs, mostly coming from Mother. My first thought is to hide in Dear's room in search of solace like I did when Mother was on one of her rages in my younger years; however, I remember that she is in *my* house. Although I won't disrespect Mother, I resist the temptation to hide from her in my own home. As soon as I am in her view again, her voice elevates in my direction, "Tell her why I'm so upset! I am always accused of being evil, but I have reason this time… tell her!" Daddy speaks in a tone that I have never heard from him, "Eloise, shut your mouth!" and he has water in his eyes. Mother ignores his repeated requests and blurts out, "Your daddy has pancreatic cancer and will be dead within six months!" Before I can deal with my emotions and check my ears to ensure that I am hearing her correctly, Tia runs past me screaming, "Granddaddy, I don't want you to die… don't die, pleeeaaassseee Granddaddy don't die!" While Kali has fallen to her knees with her face buried in her hands asking God why He is allowing these bad things to happen to her. As the clock strikes midnight I realize that, although we had a couple of good days, this month never really escaped from Hell's grasps. The month just took another wrong turn and is now headed deeper into the pits of destruction. Not only has the month ended terribly, but, because of Mother's impeccable timing, the first day of the next month is forced to come with me down Damnation Avenue. I somehow thought that if I could make it out of the month on a positive note I would find the strength to change the direction of the out-of-control locomotive that I've been riding for the past 30 days, and I almost made it. Nevertheless, Mother showed up to put an end to yet another of my dreams.

The scene is surreal as I stand watching my loved ones struggle through their own separate pains as we deal with the news that God may be taking another one of his angels from our world soon. My glance around the room ends at the scowl on Mother's face. It's as though she is proud of the scene that she has masterminded. Mother looks at Daddy and says, "I hope you're proud of yourself." What did she say!?! She blames Daddy for this? She then looks to me for support of her cause. "How many times have you heard me tell your daddy to stop eating all of that red meat?" So this is what daddy meant by the 'red meat' comment.

Is she seriously looking to gain my support? Daddy could be sitting in the middle of a pile of raw red meat lined with arsenic eating it right from the animal's butt and I would not agree with her. I am torn between the familiar emotions of my childlike retreat and the newly discovered fight in me. The fight wins, but I can't disrespect her because she is still my mother. I can think of no other action so I open the front door and scream, "Get out!" My outburst shocks and seems to even frighten her a bit, but she doesn't move so I scream again and again until my demands are consumed by the return of the familiar despair that rested in the pit of my chest for most of last month. "You try to destroy everything in your path! Look at the mess that your thoughtless announcement just caused... How am I going to fix this now, Mother? I need you to leave... get out!"

As she screeches out of my driveway she takes my breath with her. I have never had a panic attack, but I can't breathe, so choking out tears is a struggle. God no! You can't have him! You have Dear... You can't have Daddy, too! My chest is tight and if I don't get myself together, the girls may also lose their mother, so I steady my breaths as I demand answers from God, "Why are you punishing me? What did I do?"

We all somehow make it to the couch. The girls cry themselves to sleep in Daddy's arms as I sit in a state of confusion trying to digest this diagnosis of the damned delivered by what seems to be one of Satan's favorite employees.

Stop!

I am normally a pillar of strength or at least I wear a mask of strength while fluttering through my world, but after being reduced to a *former* Executive VP of Marketing, an ex-granddaughter, the daughter of a man dying of pancreatic cancer, the estranged wife of a cheating liar, and the mother of two confused little girls, it's difficult to keep my mask in place. I have always been the optimistic, pleasant one and I can't stop the pretense now. What will everyone think?

Kevin and Dear are the only two people who know the real me and now they are both gone... both in the same month. Even though it is expected, I don't know how long I can go on displaying false optimism, which is why I have not jumped back into life yet. The girls have returned to school and Daddy is back home with Mother so I have a lot of time to cry and try to get it all out, but I don't think it's working because I anticipated feeling better by now, but I don't.

My life has become very complicated and my search for answers and a possible positive aspect in the midst of all of this turmoil is coming back void. I went from being on top of the world to being buried under it in about 30 days. I'm struggling desperately to hold onto my sanity, along with any remnants of inner peace that ever existed. The husband that I still love, even in the midst of all of this anger, and the sister who lived life as a lesbian since she was a young teenager have somehow found a burning love for each other. My usual distraction through painful moments is some sort of retail therapy, but shopping is not an option right now. And despite my reluctance to admit this fact; I realize that I developed Mother's expensive taste for the finer material things in life in the absence of what's really important – love and companionship. I miss the days of shopping the blues away with little to no concern about the price, but those days are over; at least for now.

Even though Mother showered our home with luxuries, I grew up unspoiled because she controlled every good thing that came our way. In other words, she shared her wealth on her terms and I guess she has every right to divvy out her money how she wants, since she worked to make it. Although I hate to admit this fact, I learned the importance of a woman's strength by watching my sophisticated, self-made Mother manage through her business dealings. I remember admiring her strength as she firmly demanded her employees and business partners to comply with her wishes and/or deadlines.

In college, Mrs. Eloise as she prefers, was a successful matchmaker to her lonely, shy college peers. She charged a small matchmaking fee, which supplemented her partial scholarship enabling her to pay her tuition and successfully achieve a PhD. What began as a part-time hobby, turned into one of the biggest most lucrative dating services of this era, making Mrs. Eloise rich beyond her wildest imagination. By her late-twenties her company, Leisurely Connections, quickly produced dating supplies such as flowers, boxed candy, jewelry, intimate body essentials, and eventually a television show.

Mrs. Eloise realized and capitalized on her knack for matchmaking at an early age, and not only chose her husband of thirty-nine years, but also vocally disapproved of Mitchell, as well as Kevin. She now joyfully reminds anyone who will listen, "I told Jonnie that neither of them was good for her, but she chose not to listen and now she is suffering the consequences." So… to add to my current misery, I have to hear the "I Told You So's" from my flawless mother.

It is difficult for me to find the strength to get out of bed most mornings, but I have to get the girls ready for school. My thoughts weigh heavily across my shoulders as I struggle to keep my tears from falling into the lightly sweetened oatmeal that I prepare for their breakfast. Although I am very tired of crying, I am also tired of wearing my 'Good Morning Cheery Face' and can hardly wait to be alone with my thoughts. I have always considered suicide as one of the biggest signs of weakness, but recently I realize that suicidal thoughts can periodically enter the mind without warning. Therefore, I am reconsidering my negative judgments of others who struggle to make sense of their problematic lives. Although I am certain that I can never bring harm to myself, my confidence in this fact has significantly decreased as my life has grown increasingly more disappointing. I often find myself with a bottle of Dear's pain pills in my hands and I don't realize when or why I have them. The realization causes me to judge myself for being weak enough to consider taking a few of her pills in the attempt to numb this overwhelming emotional pain, if just for a bit.

I find myself daydreaming so much that the girls have to call me several times to pull me back into their world. Tia asked me the other day, "Why do I have to keep calling you?" and I just smiled because these are my words coming from her little mouth; additionally, this is a valid question so I apologize for not answering her sooner. When they are around I sincerely try to give them my attention, but this is difficult with all that's going on in our world; of course, they are oblivious to most of our problems.

So far I have managed to maintain our family date night tradition every Friday, which is usually pizza or burgers at the local family fun center and can easily cost $100 after all of the food and tokens are calculated. I really should not spend money frivolously because I'm not sure when I will have access to my money again. I am tempted to tell Kevin that I lost my job and have no income at the moment in the hope that he will give me money or at least release our accounts, but this feels too much like begging so I'm left to manage through the financial difficulties on my own while he is somewhere performing obscenities with my lesbian sister.

Mother always warned me to keep a rainy day account just in case the relationship did not work as planned, but I was certain that Kevin and I would be together forever besides, we never kept secrets... or so I thought. I hate that Mother was right. Thank goodness for my habit of leaving money in jackets, old purses, and other miscellaneous places, which financed our last Friday night outing with enough change left to fill up my gas tank.

I am hopeful that my attorney will somehow gain enough access to the account so that I can pay some of these bills. I no longer answer the house phone because I don't have an answer as to when I will be able to pay the mounting bills and this is embarrassing.

Never in my wildest dreams would I have imagined myself in a position worrying about finances. I am educated, skilled, and planned for a better life than this. I guess that I forgot to plan for the unthinkable. How would I have known to plan for this? When I am not consumed with the thoughts of how my life has drastically declined, I am mentally juggling the budget and trying to shield the girls from a world that they should not know at their young age. At this point life is difficult at best and a bright destination is nowhere in sight. However, I decide that a victorious outcome is worth the fight, so I try to occupy my alone time cleaning house, sending out my resume, networking in hopes of landing a job, and avoiding the bill collectors' phone calls and/or visits.

Bedtime is the worst time of my day because the girls are asleep, the night is usually quiet, the house is spotless, and I have ample time to be alone with my thoughts. In an effort to drown out the quiet, I turn on the news and lie in Dear's bed with tears draining sadness from my eyes as though someone turned on a water faucet and walked away. I search for my strength but the pain is overwhelming. It is in these moments that I really miss Dear. I try to make her proud of me by focusing on positive outcomes because I know that she is watching, but I can't stop the pain from acknowledging its presence, especially now that I may lose Daddy.

My heart feels like it is crumbled and lying like a pile of dust in the hollow of my chest. Unable to withstand further pain and without thought I go to the medicine cabinet and pour all of the sleeping pills from the bottle into my hand. For what feels like forever but is probably closer to two minutes, I stand looking at the pills through my tear-blurred vision, trying to gather up the nerve to indulge. Without warning, the reflection of my broken spirit catches my eye in the mirror and I immediately fall to the floor with a handful of sleeping pills while I have a purifying cry. I mean the type of cry that rinses the dust from my heart cavity and pulls the negativity from the pit of my stomach. As I'm crying I notice Tia's hair ribbon on the floor, which brings me to the best part of my reality, giving me the strength to get up out of my pity and put all but two of the pills back in the bottle. As I climb back into bed I swallow two sleeping pills, place the bottle of pills within reach on the nightstand and slowly drift into a deep sleep, praying for a better tomorrow.

I remember Dear telling me that God gave us power over our enemies and right now this turmoil is my enemy. She used to talk out loud to unseen negative energy, telling the Devil to get behind her and binding evil spirits in the name of Jesus Christ. I can't remember all that she used to say or if there was a special format, so I rock myself to sleep focused on my God-given power, telling the evilness in my world to STOP! When I become too exhausted to continue to speak the word aloud, I whisper repeatedly, "Stop! Stop! Stop..." until the sleeping pills kick. I rest peacefully throughout the night thankful that at least in this moment the negative thoughts have obeyed my command to Stop!!

A Dear Connection

Daddy has been dealing with the news of his cancer announcement for about three weeks and although he often does not feel well spending the time with him is my blessing, so I choose to thank God for the silver lining in the middle of this storm. I still have not told my parents about losing my job, but I think Daddy knows something because he always leaves money on the table or brings a bag of something when he comes to visit.

I don't think that my cabinets have ever been so full. Daddy drops in about twice a week and I am always home, but he never asks why. I don't want to weigh him down any further by discussing the problems of my world, so I say nothing. I invite him in, serve him tea, and anything else to ensure his comfort. I love taking care of him. It's as though Dear's presence is stronger when he is around; and besides, he is a most gracious patient. Between his naps we talk as I sit with him while he watches his old western movies reclined in the family room. I have never been a big fan of the old black and white movies, but being in his presence away from Mother is worth dealing with a movie that lacks color or Science Fiction mystery. Besides, I read or am on my laptop during most of the movie. I often pray for him during our quiet moments, which is a welcomed change of focus. When I am praying for him I am not worrying about my crumbling world.

Last week I gave him a key to the house and told him, "Mi casa es su casa." I also told him that I love when he is here, which I think he knows, but it felt good to say.

I've decided to be more expressive and less judgmental. Perhaps too late to save my marriage, but not too late to let Daddy know how important he is to me and the girls. Loving Daddy without judgment is easy; the real test will be applying my new behavior to someone less deserving. Even though I was more expressive with Kevin than Mitchell, I now see that I could have opened up more and shared my insecurities. Kevin still does not know that I lost my job and I am probably wrong for keeping this news a secret, but doing so allows me a bigger opportunity to blame him for most of the problems going on in my world right now. I've heard that trials and tribulations can bring a family closer. Perhaps he would have understood why I was working the unusually long hours had he known that I was working to wrap up loose ends for my clients. Anyway, I don't want to think about this right now.

Two days ago I received a call from Sheila's friend, the recruiter, who states that she would like to send me out on a few interviews for temporary work as a consultant in the marketing field. I am a bit nervous, until I pull into the parking lot of the firm. The building is a single–story, small marketing company where the address is almost larger than their marquee. I can tell that they lack originality and vision by the simple décor throughout the office and the dusty plastic plants. The reality that this is a huge step backwards causes my heart to ache and I almost want to retreat; conversely, I smile and thank the administrative assistant for the generically labeled bottle of water that I refuse to drink but politely accept.

As I am interviewing with the owner of the firm, Mr. Santos, I learn that he started this firm right after college with money that he inherited after his grandmother departed this earth. I can now feel Dear's presence and am ashamed of my initial judgments. All of a sudden I want to help him in any way that I can, and without warning my feelings change and I really want this job. For some strange reason I feel that this is where I belong. I suddenly gain a sense of purpose again so I sit up, take a few sips of the unbranded water, and mentally get in the game.

Our conversation shifts in an informal direction as we both share stories about the positive effect our grandmothers had on our lives. He even refers to his grandmother as Dear Heart. Wow! We laugh as we conclude that our grandmothers were a lot alike and are probably in Heaven looking down on our meeting with smiles on their faces. Of course I'm hired on the spot and although I will be paid a meager salary compared to my wages as a vice-president, I anxiously accept his offer because I can tell that he is paying me at the top of his budget and for some special reason, I really want to help him to succeed. Besides, as a consultant I can make my own hours, with the exception of Monday and Wednesday because this is when he holds his morning meetings and expects everyone to attend.

I am joyful and feel like skipping as I leave the office after being there for over two hours. He took me on a tour and introduced me as the newest addition to the team. As we move through the office he repeatedly tells his staff to make sure that I am comfortable and have whatever I need. He expressed that, based on my resume alone, he realizes that he is getting the better deal because his business is sure to prosper based on my experience, expertise, and contacts in the marketing field. Conversely, I feel that I am the lucky one because I once again have purpose outside of home, am working in the marketing field, and have found another connection to Dear.

As I leave the parking lot I call Sheila and thank her for introducing me to her recruiter friend. However, my greatest gratitude is to God for allowing Dear to continue to watch over me because her presence is evident. That meeting was truly another God-inspired Dear connection.

How Did I Get Here?

I have worked for the small marketing firm for a couple of months and have closed three lucrative deals. Mr. Santos states that he is very satisfied with the outcome of my efforts and has even insisted that I call him Urijah. He states that he is learning a lot and considers me more of a partner than a subordinate. I agree, so we are now on first-name basis. He anxiously takes note as he watches me work with each client and has given me a bonus as his appreciation for helping to increase revenue. Although what he considers a bonus does not go very far, I am thankful for the job because working serves as a much-needed distraction from all of the problems going on in my personal life.

I usually experience more success in the business world than in my personal affairs, and this fact is beginning to weigh on me spiritually. I find myself becoming more of an introvert as I keep the doors to my emotions tightly sealed so that no one can get in to cause additional harm. Dear used to always tell me that a closed heart means that no one can get in to hurt me, but this also stops anyone from getting in to love me. I can hear her words as though she is still here speaking her wisdom, but I don't have time to focus on my heart.

The calls from my mortgage company have become more frequent and, although my attorney was able to get some of my assets released, I still need money to live. I was able to make a big enough payment to the interior design company who remodeled most of the house. This is important because they were threatening to take me to court, which would air my dirty laundry and possibly invite Mother into more of my distressed life. One of the biggest problems of being born into a famous family is the lack of privacy. I don't want the world to know that I remodeled to get rid of the filth caused by Kevin and my baby sister. Additionally, I am often referred to as a role model in the community and don't want anyone to know that I am suffering financially, emotionally, matrimonially, spiritually, or in any other fashion; especially Mother.

The money that I receive as a consultant barely covers my car note and the girls' tuition, so I have not been able to pay the mortgage as Kevin continues to live his carefree life with Alex in her home. How could I have been so wrong about him and how dare he live like a king in Alex's four-thousand square foot home equipped with a full staff, while his children may be tossed out on the street? I guess I would have to take some of the blame because Kevin is not aware of our financial situation. Perhaps he would know and could help the situation had I not told him to stay away from *my* house and out of *my* life. Despite his shortcomings, Kevin is a decent man who has a good spirit.

Daddy is still fighting the cancer and has his good and bad days. He still comes to the house a couple of times a week to escape Mother. She is convinced that his cancer is due to eating red meat, even after the doctor gave a list of other possible causes. She is relentless in her attacks and this fact will probably never change, which is why she knows very little about my life.

As I lay in bed reflecting, I realize that I must get up soon so that I can make it to the mandatory Monday morning meeting on time. My days are starting to run together. I remember the days by my business dealings, not as any particular day of the week, and today is no different. Just another day – no particular day, no clients to see today, nothing special about today… Just another day that seems to repeat several times a week. Most days I lay in bed an hour past my scheduled time to rise and realize that this is due to the onset of depression. I have never really counted, but I am certain that I hit the snooze button at least six times before I gain the strength to let go of the covers.

I feel so safe while resting in Dear's bed, my body under the 'way too expensive' sheets and my head resting on the down pillows that I bought Dear on one of the many shopping sprees in an attempt to 'pay away' the funk that only a new item would temporarily cure. I don't quite understand how and why my mood will shift like a breeze following the wind. For no apparent reason I wake up in a good mood some days and other days I am depressed, but I can't remember when or why I became depressed. From the moment I open my eyes most mornings I can tell how my day will progress.

Again, I hit snooze and pull the covers over my head and tell myself, "Okay, this is the last time." Today is another day that I lack the energy and motivation to mingle in the world, but time waits for no one so I am forced to get up with 20 minutes to spare before I should be pulling out of my driveway. I have to shower, comb my hair, and put on my 'happy' mask. My mind races as I use my last minutes to plan the time wisely.

Because I took the extra hour under my sheets, my morning is now rushed, which leaves little time for me to focus on my feelings of life in its present state. Because the girls spent the weekend with Kevin and Auntie Alex, I have an extra seven minutes of drive- time at my disposal. Running behind schedule serves as a desired distraction, which may be my pay-off. Do I choose to run late so that I don't have to deal with my life? As I zigzag through traffic, I pray that I make it to the office safely without delay or accident. If I am late, my day will worsen because I will feel judged by my co- workers as I rush into the meeting already in progress. Conversely, if I am on time I will be able to wear my mask proudly, issuing smiles to everyone, as I secretly look down my nose, clicking through the office in shoes that cost more than they make in a month, while hiding my depression.

I indulge in work or church-related projects, helping others, or doing anything that will otherwise occupy my mind, but the truth is I am emotionally lost. I feel depressed whenever I allow myself a moment to examine my feelings, and I don't know what I did to deserve this trip or how I got here. Of course, I want to blame my current disasters on Kevin, Alex, or my previous employer, but I know that my sadness is deeper than I can credit any of them for causing.

My walk into the office leaves me nine minutes to spare as I grab a cup of the free, non-Starbucks coffee and head into the meeting. During our meetings Urijah often acknowledges my successes while looking to me for approval or direction. I appreciate his confidence in my abilities; however, today I just want to be left alone in my thoughts so that I can figure out how to stay in the home that I have made my own and grown to love, despite Kevin and Alex's attempts to ruin my paradise. At noon I tell Urijah that I have to leave for meetings with prospective clients, but will return tomorrow. He has no idea of how much of a mess I am and I truly don't want to let him down in any way, but I need some time to strategize so I leave the office in an effort to manage my personal affairs. I drive down the highway deep in thought, trying to figure out how to get enough money to catch up on the mortgage, and before I realize my actions I am exiting and headed towards the office of J-Ness Reality.

Vanessa is happy to see me, and as we are having lunch I catch her up on the details of my life. She cries as I tell her about Daddy and becomes fighting mad when she learns that Kevin is living with Alex. She offers to loan me enough money to tide me over until I'm back on my feet. I am grateful but too proud to accept her offer because I know that the real estate business is slow right now, and she is probably on a budget herself. She even offers to go to her parents for money, but I refuse by telling her that I expect to gain access to my money soon. As much as I want this to be true, I have no idea when I will be able to access my funds again. My severance alone would allow the finances to live for years without working, but it's tied up in the divorce proceedings. I wish that I had not threatened Kevin and thought far enough in advance to move my money. Perhaps I should have hidden it under the mattress like Dear used to do when we were little.

Thoughts of Dear always make me smile and as I leave J-Ness Reality I am once again lost in my thoughts, while slightly angry at myself for not accepting Vanessa's monetary offer. Vanessa said that I should contact my mortgage company and work something out financially, but I am foreign to these types of dealings. I've never experienced money problems and therefore wouldn't even know where to begin the conversation, especially since I've not returned any of their calls for the past few months. Well, I have to figure out something because it's only a matter of time before Kevin finds out, and this would be terrible because he will certainly tell Alex and, just to spite me, she will tell Mother. I'm pulled to the surface of my thoughts because the traffic slows due to a terrible accident. I can see the bloodied driver of the car in the middle of the three-car collision being pulled from the wreckage as I inch by, so I begin to pray aloud, asking God to help everyone involved to reach a full recovery.

My prayer reminds me that I have access to the One who holds all finances in His hands, so once I'm done praying for the accident victims I shift to asking God to help me with my own needs. I ask God not only to help with my finances but also for humility, and it is now that I realize one of the blessings in the midst of this storm. My many blessings throughout life have enabled me to look down in judgment on those less fortunate. With this realization I am embarrassed and remorseful by my actions as I reflect on recent activities. How dare I judge the generic water, coffee, or people's decision to shop sensibly? I ask God for forgiveness and ask him to help me be more gracious in my dealing with others. I pray that my girls have not inherited my feeling of superiority. I'm grateful for my recent realization and am singing aloud with the praises blaring from the gospel station as I pull into the garage. I have a few hours before the girls are home and I am determined to use this time wisely. Perhaps I will even gain the nerve to make the call to discuss options for keeping my house.

Kevin startles me as he walks into the garage before I can lower the door and get into the house. He has a bouquet of flowers in his hand and tells me that he took them to my office in an effort to call some sort of truce. My first concern is that someone there told him that I am no longer employed. My pride gets in the way so I tell him that I am just getting home from my work as a consultant with another large firm. My instincts prepare me for a fight so I carry on about my new job for a few minutes before I realize that his spirit is humble, and as he speaks I am reminded why I have repeatedly fallen in love with this man. To my surprise he still offers his financial support, despite the lies I tell him about my current success. I eventually invite him in, we talk, and he agrees to pay the mortgage once I humble my words a bit and he learns that I was released from my job months ago and just recently started working as a consultant where I am not getting paid as much as I was receiving as VP. He is a little irritated that I did not share the news of losing my job, but understands why as he moves forward with his part of the conversation.

Kevin is a beautiful man who has me almost figured out, but just when he gets close to shedding light onto my darkness I find a way to retreat within myself and today is no different. Instead of being completely honest about the consulting job and the fact that J-Ness is not currently flourishing like it once did, I sit quietly as he speaks, leaving him to believe that his paying the mortgage will solve my financial problems. Relieving me of the house payment will certainly help, but does not get me out of the red, and still I say nothing. He used to ask if I would ever allow his love to tear down my walls. He just about had those walls down, until he betrayed me and now the walls are as high as ever. Daddy says that marriage is honorable and with trials comes strength. Well, I should be as strong as Hercules after these trials. I often feel like running away and the emotions currently overwhelming my every sense are reminding me of the old, familiar feeling of retreat.

Hanging onto Daddy's words allow me to sit next to Kevin as I watch his luscious lips move. I daydream of us getting past our problems and finding a way back to each other's arms. Nevertheless, our meeting comes to an end without incident… good or bad. As he leaves, my inner being aches and I can't identify exactly why. My hope is that I find the answer and cure to my unpredictable depression as I lay across Dear's bed. I lay reviewing the many avenues of my life before I have to deal with the girls' homework and dinner. I like to think that my depression began when I was named Jonnie, as opposed to Jacqueline, Josephine or another name that identifies me as a female.

Mother's decision to name me Jon Terrence was the first indication of her dissatisfaction with me and, although I don't like to admit this fact, I've been trying to gain her approval all of my life. Ever since I can remember, I have been referred to as being a beautiful little girl, woman, or something along those lines. However, Mother must not have thought that I deserved a pretty, precious, feminine name and this bothers me.

Equally, my feelings of doubt are linked to the comment Mother would make whenever someone gave me a compliment. For as far back as I can remember, whenever someone said, "What beautiful little girls you have," Mother would look at us and say, "But if you're ugly on the inside, you're ugly." As a child I did not understand the meaning of her words, but based on the other person's response and the glare coming through her eyes, the compliment somehow quickly became criticism. I remember trying to recall if I had been a bad girl who reflected an ugly disposition. I could always come up with something that made me an ugly little girl, even if the something was days or weeks prior.

I came to regret the look of cheer in someone's eyes when they were about to offer a compliment. Instead of feeling happy about being told that I was beautiful, I learned to withdraw into my dark place so that I could block out Mother's words about being ugly on the inside. These days I often find myself feeling alone and sad on the inside and, although I am quite fit and shapely I feel most comfortable in sweatpants, my hair in a bun / scarf, or anything else that hides my outer beauty. Of course, in an effort to maintain Mother's approval and conform to others' expectations I put on my 'way too expensive' head-to-toe attire every day before I face the world because she insists that we strive for perfection. God has given me looks and personality that most would consider a blessing, but I have often found my appearance and public disposition to be a curse. I often wish that I could just disappear, but my veneer won't allow me to fade away.

In addition to being what society considers beautiful, I work to maintain a pleasant disposition so I attract people. I strive to maintain a nice disposition so that I am not a reflection of Mother's nasty attitude towards the world. Perhaps I will one day realize that I have little control over Mother and am not the cause of her unhappiness with me, and maybe I will then choose my paths with little consideration of how she feels about my choices in life. Living life free of her judgments would be wonderful and I will work towards this utopia when I have the luxury of focusing on happiness over survival.

Reflections of life are tiring, but lying in Dear's bed for a nap before the girls are home brings a moment of comfort. I set the alarm on my phone as I mentally drift through the complexities of life, trying to figure out where I went wrong. Perhaps the roads that led me to this unhappy place will offer some clues as to how I can find my way out of this hell and into a consistent level of contentment.

I turn on the television in an attempt to drown out the repeated chatter rumbling through my thoughts in search of a cure for this funk that I've allowed myself to enter. I find myself thinking about the blessings that would come from my death more often these days. My mental torment would end, the harassing calls from the bill collectors would disappear, and

I would get to see Dear... or would I? I've heard that suicide is an unforgivable sin.

Intellectually I realize that someday the sun will shine again; however, I'm emotionally tired and it feels like a lifetime has passed since true joy visited my world. I really desire Dear's words of wisdom and my husband's arms of safety. I often told him that nothing could get me while wrapped in his strong arms. Not even Mother's negativity could pierce his embrace. I miss the perfect world that I worked so hard to create. Without warning, tears gently kiss the pillow as I repeatedly ask the atmosphere, "How did I get here?"

A Terrible Movie

Sunday morning I find myself in church in an attempt to find happiness or at least an interim husband. Today church is on fire and it seems that everyone around me is happy and praising God. God's anointing overwhelms the congregation through the angelic sounds that resonate from the choir. Although I should be praising God and counting my many blessings, I instead stare at my perfectly manicured nails, painted in *Always a Lady Lilac* nail polish, and contemplate suicide. I nod my head to the beat of the music and from time to time I even raise my hands as though I am participating in God's praises. I guess that I have learned to go through the motions, because my actions of praise are not a true reflection of my inner feelings.

Onlookers would think that I have a lot to smile about and yet I live in a world consumed by pain. I don't remember the last time I really truly smiled. Of course, my face presents a smile most of the time, but the space in my chest that once contained a healthy heart now holds a diseased organ struggling to hang onto life. Mother never allows us to display weakness so I learned to carry the weight of my world alone, while presenting the appearance of perfection. My life was a façade, until I found my perfect world and true happiness, but now that's gone. It is now more difficult to pretend that I am happy because I've experience complete happiness. I don't want to go back to pretending.

Waking up each morning has become more difficult than I ever imagined. I often lay still and refuse to open my eyes, hoping that the day will just pass me by – except for Sundays. I come to church every Sunday so that I can maintain expectations. I have belonged to this elaborate church since I was a child and everyone knows me, or so they believe. If they only knew how I wish my life would just end, but then I think about my girls. Who would raise them? I never want Mother to have any part in raising them for obvious reasons and Alex is much too tainted. Equally, their fathers are not worthy so I should stay on this side of the dirt until my girls are safe. At least this is how I feel right now. I am so ashamed of myself, but I often forget about their wellbeing in my selfish thoughts about suicide. I know several people who have endured tough times and seem really strong throughout, but for some reason my tough times feel worse when compared to theirs. I was already deeply pained from the wounds inflicted on me by Mother through my warped childhood, so it seems natural that any further pain would toss me over the edge.

The hand-clapping and toe-tapping play from a distant background as I am focused on the intense look Kevin displayed across his face as he screwed Alex in our bed. I wish I hadn't seen or caught them in the act. Her screams of ecstasy continually haunt my thoughts, as do Kevin's acts of a crazed wild man, pulling her hair and jamming himself inside her from behind. Their every movement is stuck in my mind. Her hands... the left clenching the sheets and the right clenching the headboard, while her teeth digs into my favorite down pillow. Kevin had his left arm around her waist as though he were afraid she may try to escape if he let go, and his right hand was tangled in the back of her hair. He was pulling her hair like he was trying to remove it from the roots and she seemed to enjoy his every intent. They were so involved that I not only walked in on them, but I stood there and watched in amazement for a good while. It wasn't until they both climaxed and were about to cuddle that they noticed, and then acknowledged my presence.

Kevin and I had a wonderful sex life, but it was nothing compared to what I witnessed in that moment. Why was she yelling obscenities and referring to my husband as several variations of 'Daddy'. I'm still perplexed as to why he climbed on her back as though he were preparing to ride a horse and began to bite her on her cheek. What in hell was that all about?

I always imagined that I would know what to do if I were ever faced with this type of situation, but I was frozen in my space. I was confused and horrified at the same time. Kevin was downright vulgar and she seemed to like it. That man was not my husband, or maybe it is and I just don't know him. I always thought Mitchell would be the one to put me in this type of situation; but no, it was the love of my life who performed the ultimate betrayal.

A million things flashed through my mind while I was trapped in my spot and forced to watch the vulgarity. Who is this man? Am I dreaming? Is that my lesbian sister? I'm suffocating and I can't breathe. Could that possibly feel good to her? Why is she biting my pillow? Why are they in our bed? Does Kevin hate me? What am I not doing for Kevin? What have I done wrong? Why is he not wearing a condom? How long has this been going on? Etcetera, etcetera, etcetera. I was overwhelmed with the many thoughts that consumed my mind, but the thought that seemed to play over and over were, "Why?!?

I thought that this was the worst that things could get, but I soon found out that I was wrong. My life took a turn down the wrong street and I just went along for the ride. Not once did I consider getting off of the ride.

My trance is interrupted by my daughters, Kali and Tia, as they tap me and tell me it's time to leave church. The services are over and the congregation has been dismissed as I sit trapped by the awfully detailed memory of my husband's infidelity with my baby sister.

Sunday is the day that we visit Mother and Daddy for dinner. Mother is a difficult person to be around, but the girls love her. When Mother is mean to one of the girls they stay away from her for a short while and then return to her side as though they quickly forget that she pinches them or squeezes their hand when they reach for something that she thinks they should not touch. I understand their quick forgiveness because I remember having that same type of unconditional love and forgiveness for Mother a few minutes after she slapped me across the mouth for using improper English. She is a tough one to love; nevertheless, we all somehow do. Even though they are rich and have a full staff of maids, cooks, and gardeners, Mother insists that I bring a homemade dish for Sunday's dinner. Daddy knows that I am on a strict budget so he has one of the maids cook something and he brings the dish over the night before. I then walk into the big house with the dish as though it were my creation. I no longer go to Sunday dinner to see Mother; I go to see Daddy and to watch that Mother's meanness towards the girls is limited.

Daddy is the sweetest man I know. He often lacks backbone when it comes to Mother, but I love him nevertheless. He has chosen his dance and seems content to dance with Ms. Eloise, even through her meanness. If I didn't love him so much, I would find judging him easy.

At dinner, I choke down half of the food on my plate so that Mother doesn't criticize me for not eating. By design, she doesn't know what is going on in my life and this is perfect because Mother is quite cynical. She seems to make hurting people her purpose and has always been cruel with her words. We make it through dinner and I am now on my way home.

The girls had a long day and will soon be asleep, which is perfect. I don't want to create a reason for not watching TV when we get home because the cable was turned off a week ago. Daddy took my car to the store after dinner so it is no surprise that I have a full tank of gas and cash in my ashtray. I know that he would have left more money, but Mother keeps a watchful eye on his spending.

Mother often goes through Daddy's wallet and takes money out so that he doesn't have what she refers to as excess money. She also asks for his receipts when he returns from the store. She says that she is maintaining the budget, but I think that this is just another attempt at her controlling Daddy. Ms. Eloise doesn't believe in giving handouts, especially to her daughters. She says we should earn what we get so that we have a better appreciation for life and Daddy just goes along to get along.

As I drive home I try to focus on the road, but as night quickly approaches my focus is on the sleeping pills in the bottom of my lingerie drawer next to my other unmentionables. As I pull into the garage, I am tingling with the thought of a restful night's sleep aided by supplements. I sometimes have to take four pills before they work. I am sure that the sleeping pills will not affect me adversely, or so I hope. Anyway, if I go to sleep and don't awake I will be in a better place and finally be able to rest. I trust that God will take care of the girls. I realize that this is a selfish thought; nevertheless, this is my reality. I would do almost anything to stop the terrible movie that repeatedly plays across the forefront of my mind.

Watching Over Me

For several hours now, I have tossed and turned atop my new, very expensive mattress, unable to drift into the deep sleep that was supposed to follow the numerous sleeping pills I swallowed. I thought that buying the mattress that guaranteed a restful night would be the answer; nevertheless, I lay here with a nauseated stomach full of sleeping pills followed by a NyQuil chaser.

This is the first time that I've slept in my room since Kevin's infidelity, but everything is brand new so I thought it was time that I returned to the room so that I may enjoy my investment. Besides, something about the presence in Dear's room would not allow me the strength needed to cause harm to myself. While attempting to force my eyelids to remain shut, I am oblivious to the outside world as my head swells with the thoughts, dreams, and failures that torment my quiet moments. Relaxation is a distant stranger because my mind rotates in knots around my failing marriage, decreased income, missing career, family tragedy, and the numerous bill collectors calling and visiting. I am tired of crying, tired of holding on for a brighter day, and sometimes even tired of living. Although I still have moments of disbelief, I try to accept my realities.

The question now is, "Do I search for the strength to make it through this Hell, or do I let go?" In an effort to hold down the mixture of poison that boils in the pit of my gut, I take slow, controlled breaths and allow my mind to drift. Silent moments like these torture my thoughts and it is now that I can hear Mother's voice from my yesterdays. "Jonnie, get in your room and smooth those wrinkles out of your bed." I would reluctantly go into my room and run my hands across the top of my comforter to smooth away my butt print. Mother insisted that I sit on one of the many chairs that adorned my room and leave the bed for sleeping. Then I would have to hear the long speech about how much money she spent to make her home beautiful and how anyone would jump at the chance to live in the extraordinary room that she created especially for me. Mother refers to everything as hers, "her furniture, her house", and she constantly reminds us that she is the one with all of the money. She roams the house like a dictator looking for our imperfections, and seems excited to discover and point out our shortcomings. Mother has always been hard on Alex and me, but Daddy is treated the worst. Whenever the thoughts of Mother's viciousness invade my calmness – like now – I try to think about Daddy.

My daddy is my hero. He is the most gentle and kind person I know, besides Dear, of course. Daddy rarely talks back to Mother. When asked why he does not stand up for himself, he says he loves and understands her like no one else could. Daddy says that Mother's hard exterior is a cover-up for her lovable interior. He excuses her abruptness because he understands the demands of her being a corporate CEO. He says that he knew her before the world corrupted her and he has agreed to stand by her. They have been married for almost forty years. I give Daddy the credit for holding their marriage together because he tolerates Mother and adores our family unit. Daddy is the quiet strength in our family. He often intercedes on Alex and my behalf and would take us out of the house as much as possible, when mother was being evil towards children too little to defend themselves.

Daddy is President of the Outside Sales Division of Leisurely Connections. Mother often reminds everyone that she is Daddy's boss, but he never complains. He just smiles and says that he understands her need for validation. My dad is a Saint in every sense of the word.

I can feel myself finally drifting into sleep-land, possibly for the last time, when the pain from the concoction wrestling in my belly interrupts my nice thoughts of Daddy and sends me running to the toilet. I break a nail when I fall to the cold bathroom floor just in time for the forced thrust to make it inside the bowl. As the cold toilet water splashes up against my face, I realize that I should have eaten before taking the sleeping pills and NyQuil chaser. I throw up everything, including the bile that lines my stomach, but I am afraid to move because I cannot stop gagging even after my stomach is emptied completely. There is nothing like chilled, Clorox-lined toilet water against your face at 3:37am to bring you back to reality.

As I sit on the cold floor I realize that I could have left Tia and Kali in a position to find their mother dead in the morning, perhaps with a pillow covered with vomit. This has got to be one of the stupidest decisions that I've ever made. What was I thinking? No matter my issues, they do not deserve to know that they have a weak mother who is willing to give up on life and leave them alone to fend for themselves against the demons that roam our world. Although I'm tired of crying, the guilt of my actions allows tears to flow. With every tear that causes the puddle to expand under my cheeks as my face rests atop the toilet seat, I can only imagine the scene had I not been saved from the destruction attempted by my own hands.

Once my stomach is stable and I am able to stop heaving, maybe a shower and a cup of hot chamomile tea will help me find sleep. If not, I have another restless night ahead of me and I've added the guilt of attempted suicide to my thoughts. I really need an escape because I'm not strong enough to face the problems that don't seem to be going away, but I don't feel well enough to take any more medicine, at least not tonight. My body rejecting the mixture that I ingested is an obvious sign that Dear is still partnering with God and they are both still watching over me.

Road to Death

As of late, I concentrate so intensely on my emotional pain that reality is usually distant and vague. I walk around in a daze, often forgetting where I am or what it is that I'm doing from moment to moment, and this moment is no exception.

As a passenger in a fairly expensive but unfamiliar car I struggle to remember how I got here, or even more importantly, the man's name who is driving. I don't remember being forced into this car so I must know him, but I'm too embarrassed to admit, that due to emotional instability my brain cells have failed me again. What would I say? "Uh, excuse me; although I look like I have it all together and am possibly an ideal catch, I am preoccupied trying to figure out a way to kill myself and I don't remember getting in the car… Oops, my bad…. Anyway, I know that you are not shallow enough to forget that my name is Jonnie, but I apparently am. Will you tell me your name again, please?" This is terrible, I don't just forget people; I am not my mother. I mentally rewind my steps as best I can recall trying to place the pieces of this puzzle in the right order. It's evening so I must be on another one of Vanessa's blind date set-ups, which is her attempt to help me realize that there is life after Kevin. I'm not complaining about her set-ups because, judging by his smooth complexion and luxury vehicle, this man at least has promise.

As I become more aware of my surroundings I realize that the car is moving extremely fast down the freeway and the handsome man is resting his head back on his headrest. I'm noticing how his perfectly shaped, dark hair frames his beautiful profile when I realize that his only movement is caused by the bumps in the road. With each dance of the tires, the car glides from left then to right and so does his neck as it allows his head to rest solidly at a 45-degree angle between the rolls of left then right movement. Initially, this is a bit humorous. How embarrassed will he be when I tease him for falling asleep on our date? Of course I will let him know that I'm teasing before too long and I may even let him in on my indiscretion of forgetting his name. Then the da da da sounds caused from the tires crossing the lines meant to keep us in our lane bring about sudden reality…. Oh my God! What am I thinking? This man has lost consciousness while driving and I'm in the car with him… thinking about jokes! My heart immediately drops to the bottom of my stomach as I instinctively blurt out an uncontrolled projectile yell for him to "wake up" as I try to remove his foot off the accelerator. I quickly review the situation again and realize that the gorgeous man's head is fully reclined in a backward position, with a bounce at each movement because is he DEEPLY SLEEPING!

My laughter ceases at my further realization of danger, because this is no longer funny. It's scary. It's obvious that my yells are not penetrating his comatose state so, out of fear, I slap him across the face and he still does not respond. My heart has returned to its rightful place and is beating hard and fast, and feels as though it may explode through my breastplate! I have to get his foot off the gas so I attempt to lift his leg with my left hand while clutching the steering wheel with my right. One would think that the da da da coming from the tires and all of my screaming for help, "Sir, wake up please… Oh God, please help us," would wake the dead, but he does not budge.

As quick as a blink of the eye my emotions have shifted through several stages. I have been toying with thoughts of suicide for quite some time, but now all hopes of my premature death vanish as I desperately want out of this situation… ALIVE! I do want to die, but on my own terms and at my own time. I want to go peacefully in the night with a head heavy from too many sleeping pills and thoughts of nicer times as I land safely in Dear's bosom. Not slammed up against the side of the freeway or twisted around the metal of this car requiring the coroner to identify me through my dental records. I just want to get back to my girls, which causes me to jump into protect mode and save us both from this untimely death.

As I try to figure out a way to stop this locomotive, I notice movement in the back seat and realize that there is a precious little baby boy securely fastened in a car seat. I know he's a boy because his beautiful blankets are in varied shades of blue and someone even took the time to embroider Stephen along the hem of the outer blankets. Why would he bring such a young baby on our date? The beautiful little boy must have realized the present danger, or perhaps he is frightened by my screaming because he and I are now in a yelling contest. The car swerves several times across three and then four lanes, nearly missing the middle divider, as I try to guide the car, wake the driver, and reach the brake pedal with my left foot as I straddle the center console and his lap.

Without much warning, my maternal instincts kick in and I begin to reassure the baby between my screams and prayers to the "Almighty God"! While fighting to gain control of the car, I must have slapped Sleeping Beauty twenty-seven times, but he does not respond. He doesn't even move when I elbow him in the sternum. I gave him my best shots! "Why isn't he responding? Is he dead? What is his name? What am I doing in this car, anyway?" I think as I hope that my recent behavior hasn't caused God to turn a deaf ear to my pleas. When all else is seemingly failing, I pray as loud as I can. "God please help us!" I even remind Him that there is a baby in the back, in hopes that I may benefit from any mercy that God shows this beautiful baby. What if this is God's way of granting my prior wish to die?

As if all is not already bad, I see a sharp curve ahead and the car is moving too fast to manage safely through the turn. As the sidewalk turns, I scream all of the air out of my lungs the whole way as the car continues to move forward through the metal railing, over the cliff, bouncing vigorously down the side of the mountain, crashing into a huge tree, forcing me face first into the air bag, which renders me unconscious, but not for long.

The engine bursts into flames, while the metal folds around the elements like an accordion. I am awakened by the intense fire that dance around my feet, causing an urgency to run, but I am trapped between the man and the steering wheel. My motherly instincts, coupled with my determination to LIVE give me the strength to free myself and get on my knees in the passenger seat, as I reach back to unhook the screaming baby from his car seat. The car seat buckle is jammed and I'm unable to get to the seat belt buckle because of how the seat is folded after the impact. I would use Vanessa's knife if she were here... damn! I've got to get this baby out of this burning car!I try to look through the flames that now surround the car like barbwire around a prison yard, hoping to see someone coming to rescue us, but we traveled so far down the embankment before crashing that we may never be noticed unless someone saw us fly off the highway. Although the man is dazed, he is now conscious and climbs partially across the mangled console in an attempt to help me unbuckle the baby's car seat. I know that he can't help himself, but his lack of consciousness is really starting to irritate me. He has been asleep this whole date, or whatever this is. He should be rested enough to wake up and help me get us out of this burning entrapment... Damn, weak ass!

The flames outside slowly climb through the metal, fully engulfing the front of the car and spreading. I have to get out of here! Do you hear me, Lord?!? I AM NOT DYING TODAY!!! DO YOU HEAR ME!?! My pleas are now demands and strong statements as I lodge my back against the man who is spread between the front and back seats in an attempt to get to who must be his son. I am exhausted and in so much pain from the fire, open wounds all over my body, and being jerked about while we were propelled off the freeway. However, my adrenaline won't allow me to concede to death, so I kick the folded car door in an attempt to create an escape. The impact of the crash crumbled the metal as though it were aluminum foil, making an escape seem impossible. Nevertheless, as the man continues to fight to free his son I become more determined to find a way out of this inferno. My legs are numb from kicking and the sides of my fists burn from hitting the hot glass, but I refuse to stop because I refuse to die this horrible death. I have previously favored cremation over being buried six feet under the earth, but after death! I do not want to be cremated while I'm still alive.

The intense heat hinders the man's movements and he stops trying to get the baby out of the certain death situation. Conversely, he pulls his body over the car seat in an attempt to protect the baby from the extremely hot temperature. It is as though he accepts our fate, but I refuse! The flames continue to spread, blocking the view of the outside world. Even though my life is depressing and disappointing, I pray to God for another chance. I can vividly see Kali and Tia's beautiful faces in my mind's eye as I long for one more of their hugs. I would even welcome a hug from my perfect mother. Hell, at this point, I would even welcome one of her insulting judgments. It feels as though the heat is in a tug-of-war with my lungs for the little bit of oxygen hanging in the air. My body tells me over and over that I have no more to give and tries to convince me that it's time to let go. Conversely, the fight in my spirit is strong so I hold onto hope refusing to submit to death, while I kick the partially cracked window until I no longer have the activity of my limbs.

With my legs kicking persistently through the pain, I use my last bit of energy to yell for Dear's help. "Dear, please, I'm not ready to die!" Suddenly I am pulled backwards through the driver's side door onto the safety of the outside ground. I scramble to catch my breath so that I can tell my rescuer about the man and his child who are still trapped in the car, but no one is around to tell. I rub my eyes several times before I am convinced of this fact, but whoever pulled me from the inferno did not stay around to help the man and child. What kind of sick madness is this? I can't let them die, but as hard as I try I don't see a way to the door through the blazing wall of fire. The flames are blinding and impossible to breathe through, but I must help that man and the child. I somehow made it out, so there must be a way to get to them. I look for my path of escape to no avail, so I pick up a big rock, reach through the flames, and pound on the glass, while I try to ignore my physical pain. The heat is so extreme that I can feel my bones burning through my flesh, but the defenseless baby motivates my continued efforts of rescue. It is not until the car explodes knocking me backwards, fighting to extinguish the fire that now covers my entire body, that I am forced to forgo my rescue attempts. I roll back and forth on the ground, coughing up smoke and gasping for air, trying to escape the flames that completely cover the lower half of my body. I want to pass out, but I am too close to surviving, so I can't. My arms and legs are in excruciating pain so I scoot further away from the wreckage on my side like a worm, using only my stomach muscles dragging my limbs behind. I move sideways until I hit a wall and slowly come to realize that I am no longer on fire.

Not only are the flames gone but I am rolling around through the darkness in what feels like a familiar space. Although the darkness is thick, the stench of Kevin and Alex's infidelity is ever–present, but the overpowering burnt flesh smells are tattooed on my senses. Have I died and gone to Hell? Where else would the torturous sex-scents of my husband screwing my baby sister be so real again? Instead of the usual tears that accompany these moments of recall I become angry and swing at anything within reach. My fists flailing through the air connect with the unseen, which causes an explosion all around me. Someone or something just got knocked through the night. I attempt to stand on my feet, but my legs are bound. As I claw my way around on the ground I realize that I am crawling over whatever exploded and is now cutting into my left arm. However, I am more concerned about who is holding my feet. I repeatedly kick my legs until my feet are free and I slowly realize that the gravel beneath me now feels like a smooth, cold surface.

As I crawl across the cold smooth surface I slowly realize that I am on my bedroom floor struggling through what feels like bedsheets that impair my movements. I continually grasp for air and strain to catch my breath. I know that somehow I am no longer in imminent danger; however, a bigger part of me tells me to continue to fight my way further away from the fire or possible next explosion. Breathing becomes a bit easier so I am able to exhale as I lay with a heavy heart still traumatized by the death of the man and the baby. I look for clues to confirm that I am possibly having the worse nightmare of my life; conversely, the agonizing pain throughout my body states just the opposite.

Still having trouble stabilizing in the reality realm, I drag myself across the floor through a puddle of something wet. I continue to move in the direction of where the light switch will be if I am indeed in the safety of my home. After struggling to free myself of the entanglement, I gain the strength to pull myself up far enough to reach the light switch.

To my surprise, I am in my bedroom and it looks like someone has been murdered in here. Oh my God, what is happening?!? There is blood all over the bed, covers, walls, and the floor. I am immediately taken back to the state where I am fighting for my life. With little consideration for the abrasions all over my body, I force my body to comply with my heart's need to protect my daughters. In excruciating pain I crawl down the hall to the girls' bedrooms, praying the whole way. "God, please let them be ok."

Although the girls are resting peacefully and I can see that they are okay, I spend about five minutes lying in the hallway watching them sleep.

Watching my daughters sleep allows the time for me to calm my nerves as I try to make sense of all that has happened. Although the lines between delusion and reality are still a bit blurred, my heart's pace has slowed to what feels like a regular beat, so I slowly return to my room to clean up this mysterious disarray.

My body won't comply with my desire to clean for very long so I sit in my bathtub with cool water running over my bloodied body and sob uncontrollably because I know that at least a portion of the experience is somehow real. Even after the blood is washed down the drain most of my body is bright red, blistered, and still aching from the fire. The ibuprofen and the burn gel that covers every spot on my body that I can comfortably reach help with pain management. Intellectually, I realize that I must have gone to sleep in my bed and woke up in the same vicinity, so I must have been dreaming. However, I also know that at least a portion of the dream was somehow real and, although I do not understand what or why, my wounds are evidence that I was in some sort of accident.

Although I'm able to towel up most of the blood on the floor, I'm too weak to add fresh linens to my bed. I lay atop my mattress wrapped in Dear's quilt, staring at the ceiling with tears freely rolling down my cheeks while horrid visions of me, the man, and the baby burning in the fire occupy my thoughts, making sleep impossible. I can still smell the stench of charred flesh and hear the tormented screams as we helplessly burned in the inferno. Who pulled me from the fire and why me? How'd I get there? How'd I get back?

Still needing a dose of reality, I pick up the phone and call Vanessa. "Hello?" Vanessa answers in a whispery, inquisitive voice. I speak with such urgency that she can hardly understand what I'm saying. For a brief moment Vanessa thinks that I am calling from the hospital or the side of the road, truly needing emergency assistance. She desperately struggles to wake herself and soon understands that we are discussing what she determines is a dream, so she reassures me and promises to call after several more hours of sleep. I truly need her to help me figure this out RIGHT NOW, but I reluctantly agree to wait for her call back.

I am much too afraid and anxious to go back to sleep so I muster the strength to make it back down the hall to watch the girls sleep. I sit outside of the girls' bedrooms under Dear's comforting quilt choking down as much water as I can handle in an attempt to quench the fire in my throat. As usual, Tia is laughing in her sleep and tossing back and forth on top of the covers in search of a comfortable position as her naturally curly hair covers the majority of her face. I glance into Kali's room and smile as Kali is peacefully resting in her usual position with her naturally curly hair neatly pulled away from her face, in a ponytail holder. Kali is just as calm and steadied when she is awake and has been this way all the years of her young life.

In an effort to escape the awful thoughts of what I think may have been a dream, I try to focus on happier times, remembering the girls as babies. Kali's birth was quick and she remained quiet until the doctor tapped her gently on her bottom. Conversely, Tia refused to enter conventionally as she forced her way into the world via a cesarean delivery, kicking, screaming, and swinging her little frail arms as though she were already defending her place on this earth. Kali and Tia look very much alike, but their personalities are totally opposite. Thinking about the difference between Kali and Tia reminds me of the distinct differences between Alex and me. I would never knowingly sleep with someone else's husband, especially the husband of my sister. My mind is racing in so many directions that going back to bed would be useless. I continue to drink ice-cold water, which seems to be the only thing that soothes the fire in my bones, as I apply burn gel to my wounds.

The comforts of gospel music flowing ever so softly from the speakers soothes me as I eagerly anticipate the rising of the sun and Vanessa's call. Each direction of my mind's eye invites an emotional waterfall, and each tear is filled with a terrible memory. I'm too tired to fight the stream that pours down my cheeks, so I force myself to embrace each feeling as I mentally replay the terrible trip down the road to death.

Reality or Nightmare

I have just about finished cleaning as much as I physically can when the doorbell rings. Realizing that it is very early on a Saturday morning I immediately consider and even hope that Kevin has come home and couldn't get in because I had the locks changed the day after he left. Although subconsciously I know that this thought is unrealistic, I check my appearance in the mirror and move as fast as I am able towards the door. I still feel the effects of the accident, and right now I would welcome Kevin's arms as my safe place to land. He will take one look at the burns on my body and surely want to nurse me back to health. Perhaps this tragedy is what we need to pull our family back together. I take a deep breath as I say a quick prayer, "Lord, please... thank you, Father," before opening the door, relying on God to know my heart's desire without verbalizing the request.

I open the door and am quickly disappointed when I see Vanessa standing there in her jogging suit. I try to hide my disappointment, but Vanessa recognizes the loss of excitement in my face and responds, slightly offended. "Good morning to you, too". I smile as I make every effort to hide my true feelings and I truly can't explain my let-down because Vanessa does not know that I secretly want my husband back home. She would consider me weak for the mere thought of taking him back. Her continued lecture brings me out of my head. "I came over here because it sounded like you needed someone to talk to, but I can go back home and get back in my bed if I'm not welcomed." I quickly apologize and try to explain what happened to me, which is difficult because I'm not sure what happened. Vanessa recognizes my emotional need and the blisters on my hands as she helps me to the couch and puts on a pot of coffee. I would usually put on my façade, but I do not possess the strength, and besides, I am getting pretty tired of wearing the happy mask over a painful soul.

Vanessa and I have been friends forever and have always shared our most intimate secrets, but today is much different. I tell her not only about my trip down the road to death, but also everything leading up to this trip. I tell her about how I often walk around in a daze, not realizing how I moved from moment to moment or day to day. I even tell her about my thoughts of suicide. Vanessa is not only surprised but disappointed that I have suffered alone through this pain for so long. As tears pour from my eyes, I tell her how I lost everything in about a thirty-day timespan and how I was too embarrassed to admit that I had failed in so many areas of my life.

Vanessa seems a bit uncomfortable with the downpour of tears and it's probably because she has never seen me cry this hard. She tries, but is unsuccessful at her attempts to remind me of my strength and independence. She also insists that she did not set me up on a date and that I was just dreaming, which makes me mad because I know that what I experienced was somehow real. Real enough to cause burns all over my body and I still smell the burnt flesh that's etched into my nostrils.

As Vanessa continues her attempts at convincing me that I was dreaming I can see her lips moving, but my thoughts are fixed on the screams as we were all perishing in the massive burning ball of metal and glass. The thoughts of their torment keep the tears flowing. Although I do not know what she is talking about, Vanessa must have said something she thought offensive because she starts apologizing and passes me the box of tissues from the table. My focus shifts as I sneakily use my sleeve so that I can save the tissues in case Mother comes over and needs one.

Again, I have lost touch with reality and haven't a clue what Vanessa is saying, but feel compelled to turn on the TV. Before Vanessa can complain about me not listening to her, we both notice the story on the local news. "A father and his son were killed early this morning in a fatal accident. The car exploded on impact after going off the road and down a steep embankment.

Onlookers report that the fire was too severe to attempt a rescue. Two eyewitnesses report that the car was swerving prior to leaving the road and they saw another adult in the vehicle. The father was found hovering over his child's car seat in what looks like an attempt to protect the child from the fire, it seems. No other bodies have been located and only a miracle would allow someone to walk away from an accident of this level." A big part of me is relieved that my dream or whatever I experienced was real, but reality immediately sets in, which causes me to scream uncontrollably, "that poor family... the baby... why, Lord, why?!?" Vanessa tries to convince me that I must have fallen asleep with the TV on and somehow heard this story reported on the news while I slept, which in some way became real. But I know that she is wrong. I cannot explain it, but I was the third person in that car this morning. I do not know the father nor son, but I do know that I was there and the thought of witnessing their death makes me sick to my stomach.

As I hobble past my bed towards my restroom I am just within range as my insides rush past my lips and splash through the water that is peacefully resting in the low-profile porcelain lavatory. I empty my soul into the toilet for about twenty minutes. Vanessa, being a true best friend, holds my hair while toweling down my face and the back of my neck with cool water until my stomach has no more to give. As she is helping me to the bed she notices the bloodied walls, bed and covers, and the stains that I was unable to remove from the hardwood floors. She asks, "What happened in here?" as she collects the bigger pieces of my favorite statue and places them in the trash receptacle. The look on her face tells me that she is at least now considering that something more than a dream happened.

As I talk she takes a closer look at the burns all over my body and insists that I need more medical attention than the burn gel and ibuprofen from my medicine cabinet. Her private physician arrives within the hour and provides proper treatment to my second and third degree burns, as well as bandages to the many lacerations that Dr. Walton has stitched closed. The only question that the doctor asks is if I am safe, as she looks around at what appears to be the scene of a massacre of some sort. I assure her that I am not in danger as she finishes her exam and we both try not to notice the cleaning crew that Vanessa called in to make the room look brand new again. Vanessa is so focused on her plan of action that I'm a little frightened.

It's as though she has had to use the service of a private, unnamed doctor and what seem to be secret, professional cleaners before.

The cleaning staff do not speak or give eye contact, they just clean. When they are done they use a special light to insure that they have cleaned all traces of blood and/or flesh from every inch of the room. Before leaving, the doctor hands me a bottle of generically labeled pills certain to help me rest through the pain. In less than an hour the doctor and cleaning crew have performed their separate tasks and are gone. Vanessa sits on my bed with her back against the headboard, props a pillow on her lap, and insists that I lie down and tell her the story again. I am happy that she wants to hear because I need her to help me figure out what happened. She brushes softly through my hair avoiding the burned patches of scalp and listens intently as I cry with every detail of the horrific story.

Every ounce of proof states that I was in a terrible accident and was somehow a witness to the man and his baby's terrible death. How else would I know the intricate details of the position of the bodies? Intellectually, she knows that my words are my reality; and even though she can't explain what happened, she believes in her heart that I was a involved in a horrendous event… whether a reality or nightmare.

Unassuming Angel

onday mornings are often difficult to manage; however, the pain tearing through my body makes this Monday morning more difficult than usual. Although I've tried, I am unable to hide the fact that every inch of my body severely aches. The girls accept the explanation of me falling down the stairs, but I doubt that an adult will fall for this story with the many bandages covering differing degrees of burn blisters and stitched lacerations. I would love to hang onto the covers until the last minute; however, I cannot move as quickly as procrastination forces me to, so I have to get up with the second notification of the alarm after hitting the snooze button. To hide most of the bandages I wear a long, loose-fitting dress and squeeze my swollen, bandaged feet into a pair of flat sandals. I drop the girls off at school a bit early so that I have time to hobble into the office, get coffee, and take my seat in the conference room before the others arrive. Any movement draws attention to my apparent discomfort and I don't think that I can talk about the accident without having an emotional breakdown, so I have to make every attempt at avoiding a conversation in this direction.

As planned, I make it into the office before anyone else arrives, and am sitting with my hands on my lap under the table so that the bandages are hidden. The meeting is quite interesting; I advise the team of three possible client accounts in which we will all benefit. After the meeting I sit pretending to read through my emails on my tablet as the others leave. I can hardly believe that I made it this far without any questions; now if I can just make it to my car I will be in the clear. All is well until my cellphone rings and Urijah calls me to his office to discuss strategies for the new potential clients. I am tempted to tell him that I have left the building, but he can see me sitting in the conference room from his office so I have to go. I take a few deep breaths before standing, and then slowly make my way in the direction of his office. Once he notices my difficulties he comes to my rescue and helps me down the never- ending hallway, which is not easy because anywhere that he touches hurts. By the time I am seated he has asked me "What happened?" several times. My mind races for possible fictional answers; however, one look in his eyes and I am unable to lie to him. I want to tell him the truth, but I'm not sure that I know the truth. He gently holds my bruised hands with an inquisitive look on his face as he waits for me to gain enough courage to speak. For some reason I feel comfort in his presence. I think that I overlooked and confused the brightness of his angelic light for my excitement at having purpose again in the workforce or our grandmothers' connection in Heaven. The truth is that he has a comforting angelic glow about him. Talking to him is easy and not once does he accuse me of lying or imagining the whole thing; conversely, he seems to believe me. He agrees that somehow my experience was real and thanks God for allowing me to live through the terrible ordeal. He says that his world would be devastated without me in it, which is a surprise because I never knew that he cared… ***His World Devastated"?** …* Hmm … interesting, I think as he speaks.

Urijah insists on driving me home, and once there he comes in to ensure that I make it to my bed safely. I am initially shy about him helping me to get undressed, but his gentle nature and Dear's sweet voice in my head reassuring me of his pure intentions allow me the courage to permit him as he helps me into my pajamas. Once I am tucked comfortably into my sanctuary of down-feather goodness he sits next to the bed and talks to me between holding my hand and weaving scriptures throughout his prayers: "No weapon formed against Jonnie shall prosper" and "Legion, you have no place here". I know what 'legion' means when used in this context. Did all of Kevin's sinful activities with Alex leave a legion of evil spirits in my house?

I begin to quietly pray under my breath, while searching for a connection with Dear, as I tell him parts of the adventure that I may have forgotten to mention the first couple of times. He patiently listens to my near-death experience in the burning inferno seven or eight times and never once does he complain. Instead, he helps me to try to make sense of how I got there, why I survived, and everything in between. Although he states that he is not religious, he understands when I talk about Dear's gift of discernment and seems to believe me when I tell him of the audible conversations between her and God when she was here on earth. Through our hours of conversation, none of my supernatural-speak seems to alarm him. He is as comfortable with this conversation as if he has first-hand knowledge of the subject, but he didn't grow up going to church, so I'm confused. The longer we talk the more I'm convinced that he has to be an angel and his humble spirit merely magnifies this fact. I feel a type of love that I cannot explain. Although not the type that usually attracts my attention, he is naturally good-looking; however, the longer we talk the more I realize his beauty, and I am completely interested in knowing every intricate detail about him.

Urijah has a transparent glow that I've noticed before, but did not understand what I was seeing. His eyes have a light behind them that he seems to try to hide, but his spirit won't allow. His lips beautify more with every melodic phrase, and the glow beneath his beautiful skin illuminates, making it almost impossible for me to lie here listening without touching him. I feel like the pressure cooker that Dear used to prepare pot roast when we were kids. The love is so overwhelming that I can't help but cry; however, the emotion behind these tears is different than I've ever experienced. The water that flows through my body and out of my tear ducts seems to have a cleansing effect. With each moment I feel lighter and somehow brighter on the inside, which magnifies the darkness of the world that I have become accustomed to enduring. The only words that I can muster are, "I swear you must be an angel." Urijah does not confirm or deny my assumption; instead, he maintains his focused look as he stands, pulls back the covers, and whispers something under his breath while moving his hands over my body without making physical contact. It is as though he is wiping something away without touching me. Without gaining permission, he then walks around my room and even in the master bathroom, still speaking too low for me to understand, but the feeling that radiates from his being is heavenly and comforting. The paint on the walls seem brighter without changing color, and my hardwood floors have a glow beneath them. For the first time in my life I feel a love almost too powerful to grasp. A love that is too unadulterated for comprehension in the natural realm. Is Urijah an angel? He pulls the covers back over my body, takes my hand, and looks into my eyes, penetrating my soul as though he is connecting to a goodness that I forgot I possessed. Our souls are connected via the gateway of our eyes for about two minutes, and then without deliberation he tells me that he will see himself out.

Although he has been here for hours I feel as though he is leaving too soon. I fight back the emotion until I hear the door close and then I cry as though I am releasing several years of built-up pain, anger, resentment, hate, and all the other negative entities that I allowed to take up residence within my being. With my mouth wide open I silently scream out the torment that accompanies every bad thought. For every undeserved slap across the face; for every negative word spoken against me; for every unwanted touch; for every time I was made to feel less than; for every time that I refused to cry because crying did not change the hurt... Instantly I feel differently about tears. I never realized, but I have waited for these tears for a long time. I welcome the overdue healing tears as I lie facing the ceiling which is illuminated by all of God's glory. I lie with my arms outstretched across my pillows and my palms in an upward position, as though in a state of surrender to the goodness that is upon me. I don't understand all that is happening in these moments; however, I somehow feel weightless and delivered from some of the unmerited heaviness of my history. I don't know how to process what I feel for Urijah and the mercy that I've been shown on this unassuming day. Today was another ordinary Monday that started like most, with the exception of the pain-riddled body that I dragged out of bed this morning. Who is this young man with such a deep soul and an obvious influential connection with God Almighty? I have no method of acceptance for the magnitude of feelings that overload my limited emotional structure. "Urijah is so beautiful" is all that sits at the forefront of my mind. I would never have guessed that he would not only open the door to a world that I've been searching to find, but also carry me through the threshold via his angelic wings.

I lose track of natural time, but it feels like hours that I've been silently pouring out the gloom of my existence in exchange for my newly acquired glow. I would lie and bask in this amazement for weeks if I could, but the day is fading and it's time to get the girls. As I get dressed I realize that my physical pain has lessened and I'm able to move a bit more freely. I slowly back out of my room so I can see the yet glistening glow for as long as possible. I pray that it's still here when I return. Although unexplainable, thanks to Urijah I know that I am now on a path of healing. As I drive, I thank God for His greatness and for sending one of His unassuming angels to rescue me in the midst of being condemned to fiery Hell, with no return to any level of salvation in sight.

Flaws

It's been almost three weeks since Urijah tucked me into bed and took me on the journey to new mental, emotional, and most importantly, spiritual heights. Miraculously I awoke the following morning free from any pain, burns, or lacerations. I have always believed in God's power, but now I know first-hand how capable God is at completely healing the physical body, as well as the mental psyche. I am thankful that he left a few scars neatly tucked away inconspicuously on parts of my body to remind me that the accident was definitely not a dream. Equally, I can still feel God's presence through every inch of my room, which serves as an ever-present reminder that Urijah must truly be an angel and was instrumental in my deliverance.

I sashay around on a bed of clouds ever since that glorious day singing and greeting everyone within earshot, which is unusual because I am naturally an introvert. Mother notices something different about me, but I won't taint my beautiful memories by inviting her into my world of bliss. I share highlights of my miracle with Daddy as a testament that God's healing power is real to hopefully inspire him to believe just a little bit harder. I also had to tell Vanessa about Urijah and my deliverance when she came by to check on me because my wounds were gone. Again, she does not want to believe, but has no choice since the evidence is so telling. If not for my battle scars, she would think that she somehow witnessed parts of my nightmare. I just smile and confirm that I, too, confuse the lines of reality and fiction these days. However, the healing that happened on the inside and sprays outwardly onto everyone within reach makes the experience undeniable.

Although I still live in my head a lot, the thoughts are lovely and I feel compelled to share my inner joy. Most people confuse my shyness as condescension, so I understand the apprehensive responses from the office staff when I sing my "Gooood Mooorninggg" greetings their way as I saunter through the doors smiling from ear to ear while secretly scanning the office for my first glimpse of *him*. My mornings grow brighter with every anticipated Urijah encounter, making the snooze button almost obsolete because I'm awake well before the sound of the alarm, daydreaming about possibilities. Will he ask me to join him for lunch today? Will he confess his true feelings? Am I imagining all of this? Will he finally ask me out? I'm excited these mornings and this is a welcomed lovely feeling. I find myself looking for reasons to make my way into his office and even create problems just so that I can be in his company. I don't want to be presumptuous, but he also appears to feel the sweetness in the air. Not one morning has passed without one of us finding a reason to spend time together. I am certain that the staff notice something, but he is the boss and I am bringing in most of the profits these days, so to my knowledge they mostly keep any assumptions to themselves. Besides, we are a most unlikely pair and I would not believe an attraction existed if I were not living in this wonderland.

Because of my sweeter disposition I've bonded with most of the ladies in the office and have been invited to the Administrative Assistant, Evelyn's 58th birthday party. Because he is here I am also floating through the place on the wings of what feels a lot like love. I never thought that I'd know a day without the threat of pain lurking somewhere in the not so distant future, but these days I don't feel the tinge of anticipated danger that usually sits dormant in the pit of my stomach waiting for a reason to come forth. Joyfulness has taken me hostage and I willingly submit to its hold. The sting from the despair caused by Kevin has even dissipated.

Kevin was the love of my life, or so I thought, but the love that I feel for Kevin is elementary when compared to the magnitude I feel when I think about Urijah. He introduces me to a masculine sweetness at a much higher level with every encounter. Although I'm older, he seems more experienced in his ability to demonstrate a selfless love in a rare, pure manner. It appears that his love has never been tainted by disappointment and therefore is still in an unpolluted form. The power behind his protective words of concern is almost overwhelming when he speaks of going to any limit necessary to shield me from anything in the world that could bring me pain. He even jokes about respectfully putting Mother in her place because he disapproves of her harsh words aimed in my direction.

My heart reaches through my chest and gives him a hug every time he tells me that I deserve so much more than I was dealt via the hand presented by life. No one has ever expressed these thoughts because everyone sees my world as perfect and considers that I have no reason to complain. He obviously sees the real Jonnie when he looks in my direction, and for this I am most thankful. Besides Dear, I don't know that anyone has ever seen me for who I really am; a lonely woman, afraid of failing, wanting to be loved unconditionally. Urijah sees past my wall of strength, which is probably why he feels the need to protect me even from my own self-inflicted ill-intensions. In such a short time we've grown an irresistible bond and yet we have never physically touched romantically, at least not outside of my fantasies. The man said that his world would be devastated without me in it… and he doesn't even really know me… Wow! I've never known a man to express himself so freely and sincerely at this point in a relationship. Thoughts of our many moments cause a beautiful cleansing flood to move towards the exit of my tear ducts as I pick at the cucumber salad sitting on my plate attracting flies.

Even seeing Kevin, Alex, and their girl-toy fondle each other at the dinner table, while Mother pretended to ignore the vulgar behavior last Sunday did not disturb my utopia. I almost feel pity, because they may never know this level of adoration. My thoughts are interrupted by Urijah's touch as he gives me the professional- type hug and asks me to share what has me almost in tears. I smile, return the hug, and wipe the joy-filled water that's trapped by my bottom lids. I want to tell him of my love for him, but Mother taught me that a lady never makes the first move. With Mother's lessons ever so present, I whisper "I love you" in my inner spirit as I assure him that my display is prompted by joyous thoughts. He returns the smile that says, "I love you back," and sits by me with a plate of carbs that he devours in 9.5 seconds. Realizing that I am not judging him for what and how he eats makes me once again thank God for my inner healing. Our magnetic attraction keeps us in the same vicinity through most of Evelyn's birthday festivities. It is as though we came together as he brings me another bottled water, force-feeds me cake… insisting that a few carbs won't harm my fit physique, or I wipe crumbs from his chin. Kevin was attentive; but again, his best efforts are elementary when compared to the way that this young man dotes over me and my every anticipated desire, and we are not even a couple… yet.

I can't believe that I secretly have such strong feelings and neither of us has made a verbal confession regarding the blanket of emotions that hover in the air above us begging for acknowledgment. Intellectually I recognize that inviting him into my world would be a major adjustment for us both. He is much younger, which means that he lacks the life experiences that I've known. He is just beginning his career, has no children, has never been married, spends his free time playing some type of sport, and I think he lives in the family home that his grandmother left him when she died. Conversely, I have had two major relationships, have two little girls, am in the midst of a divorce, spend my free time dodging bill collectors and dealing with life, and live in the dream home that I may lose soon if I don't find a way to convince Kevin to release my frozen assets or find a way to bring in the money necessary for the lifestyle that I created. Even though he is my employer, he is so inexperienced in every area of life when compared to my cup-running-over, maximum-capacity, drama-filled life. Nevertheless and despite his inexperience, he handles me as though he has the manual to all things Jonnie. I would never want to go back to a world where he doesn't exist. I can't believe that I was blinded to his true beauty until he tapped into my spiritual vein on the day that my deliverance began.

The sun is setting lovingly amidst the skyline, which indicates departure time. Urijah walks me to my car and is preparing to say goodbye when one of the party-goers interrupts our conversation with what sounds like business so I sit patiently pretending to look for something in my purse, giving me the excuse to wait for a proper goodbye. I'm really not listening to their conversation until I hear the man asks Urijah how the little lady is handling her new role as a mother. Then I notice that he seems a bit uncomfortable as he answers, "Oh, uh, she loves it…. Really tired, but she's adjusting," before cutting the conversation short and making his way to my car window.

"New mother?" I ask inquisitively before noticing the almost smug look on his face, which seems to say, "I owe you no answers." Like an avalanche, my world crashes right into my lap as I toss my purse on the passenger seat and start the engine. He notices the weight of agony across my brow and says that he will tell me all about the situation later. I can do nothing more than stare at him with my jaw clenched as I fight back the flood about to happen. He asks me several times if I will be available later so that he can call, but a calm and collected sentence is not within my reach and I don't want to cause a scene, so I remove my foot from the break allowing the car to roll slightly forward. Urijah walks slowly with the movement of the car, hanging onto the window asking if I'm ok. I don't even have the words to ask him to step back so I continue to cautiously pull forward, forcing him to eventually back away, all the while asking if I will be available later.

Since when does he need permission to call? Is he playing a game? Finally, he gently grasps my wrist, motioning for me to stop the car and look in his direction. His angelic glow has dimmed and the only words that come forth in the form of a whisper through my clasped jaws are "I'm done!" before I drive away with a stream bursting its way down both cheeks.

The little lady? New mother? He'll tell me all about the situation later!?! He knows all about my divorce, Kevin cheating with Alex, Mother and how hurtful she is, my two daughters, and almost everything else that makes up the crazy world where I exist… except my financial hardships. How dare he make a fool of me? He has a little lady at home with a situation? How silly I must look to the office staff and their families! I am hurt and even more than that I am pissed and completely crushed at the thought of him with a wife and child! Having more children was not on the cards for me, until I met him. Imagining the strength of our worlds uniting to create a love child is a beautiful vision. I am positive that I have not been imagining the fire between us and all the while he's had a SITUATION!?! What the hell???!!!??? Why do I allow myself to open up to possibilities? I opened up to the possibility of Mitchell, and that was tragic. Kevin was another possibility that I should have left unexplored, and now Urijah! Ughhh! I could just scream!

As I tear down the freeway with my bleeding heart beating irregularly I receive a text message from him that simply states, "Done?" I'm partially happy that he cares enough to reach out, but still I won't justify his question with a reply. What does he expect? He has a little lady at home adjusting to motherhood! No wonder he hasn't asked me out or physically crossed any lines, besides the gentle touches on the arm or the professional hugs. I should have known that he was too good to be true. Once home, I head straight for the comfort of my bed, but ever since that beautiful day my bed is much too peaceful a place to entertain self-pity and depression. Therefore, I opt to lie on the floor in the back of my walk-in closet on top of a makeshift resting place suited to lots of crying and evil thoughts. Of course I have my phone right by my side because a big part of me wants to hear from him again. I never respond to his text because thoughts of him playing house with the new mother and their bundle of joy infuriate me further. I think that he should reach out to me again, if I'm as important to him as I thought.

A weekend in an empty house leaves a lot of free time for me to fall further away from the righteous path and lean towards the darkness that I know best. Although his angelic glow dims a little more with every remembrance of the conversation that brought about the abrupt change to my world, I still am unable to lay in my bed while feeling sorry for myself. I feel conflicted as though evil and good are trying to occupy the same space, so I spend the weekend in the back of the closet wrapped in Dear's favorite quilt, staring at the ceiling. I try to cry myself to sleep but the pain is too severe. I have never felt so wounded. I mentally go over our every encounter trying to identify when I became disillusioned about the obvious flame between us and I'm certain that I did not imagine our magnetic chemistry. Equally, his presence and prayers changed my world for the better, making me forever grateful for his involvement.

Although not as bright, the walls, ceiling, floors, and even my bed still possess a glow that I wish would just go away. I desperately want to return to my world of gloom, but I've been touched by an angel, making my usual hiding place uncomfortable. There is no escaping him because I carry the battle scars that were healed when he personally appealed to God Almighty on my behalf. I'm so confused… Why would God bring him into my world only to snatch him away moments later? Why hasn't he called? Do I serve a cruel God?

Days of deliberation and a puffy face later, I conclude that, no matter his faults, Urijah left a brightness in my world that refuses to completely dim. I need this job, so I return to work on Monday in my proper place as his subordinate, anxiously anticipating our first interaction. To my surprise, Urijah attends our Monday morning meeting via conference call and, due to a family situation, he will work from home until further notice. I wanted to look in his eyes while I asked him questions that I mentally composed while laying in the back of my closet, but this luxury is not afforded me due to his family situation.

I have difficulty focusing during the meeting because of the various zigzags my mind takes through my thoughts of him. I can't decide on my level of love for him; however, I know that I could never hate him. My world feels shattered, and yet hearing his voice reminds me of all the goodness he brought into my life of despair. No matter his flaws, he made my days brighter, and my nights bearable, and now I don't know when I might see him again. Pride caused me not to respond to his text and now pride sits proudly in my lap laughing in my face. How many times must I make a foolish decision based on pride's guidance? When will I learn that pride is not a good advisor?

His voice calling my name via the speakerphone pulls me out of my head. "What do you think, Jonnie?" My name flowing across his beautiful lips causes an array of emotions, which prompt unwanted tears to form. I pull myself together, answer his questions, we converse about the Langston account, and he asks me to keep him posted on the outcome. Although our conversation is not of a personal nature and includes the rest of the staff attending the meeting, I can hear the concern in his voice and feel the blanket of love return to its proper place, hovering in the atmosphere. Is this his way of asking me to call him? By the end of the meeting I side with being glad that I met him because he has more than my heart; he has a part of my soul. I mentally agree to hear him out if and when he makes contact again, no matter the situation. I can't explain the feeling, but he introduced me to a world that I'm not ready to leave.

In his world I experience an unadulterated love that forces me to wish him every happiness, even if that happiness is not with me. Right now is when I realize that I've been expecting perfection from myself, as well as others in my life, and this expectation leads to inevitable failures. No matter my heartbreak, I choose to go on loving Urijah even if that love has to be from a distance.

We may never know a physical connection; however, our spiritual bond supersedes any that I've known. I will move forward remembering him as the angel who flew in on his illuminated wings and rescued me from the wounds of the burning inferno. I learned more about God's grace and mercy as Urijah appealed unselfishly on my behalf when I did not exercise the strength to go to God for myself. Urijah serves as a refreshing reminder that God still loves me and even knows me by name. "I love you, Urijah" rests in the center of my thoughts, along with the ball of questions waiting for answers. I will never be able to dismiss all that Urijah is to me, even as I accept the fact that angels have flaws, too.

Power of the Tongue

My, how time flies when your life is at a standstill. It's been two weeks since I last saw Urijah and I miss him. I miss his smile, his laughter, his gentle touch and being close to him. I can hear the confusion in his voice over the speaker phone and I can tell by his brief responses that he is at least a little upset. I want us to go back to how we were before, but not at the expense of opening my heart to be hurt again. Not loving him is impossible so I will secretly continue to love him from a distance. Hopefully my spirit will connect with his in a higher dimension and give him the message to reach out to me again. Emotionally I just can't open up to any more negativity; so therefore, I attend the Monday morning meetings and leave immediately after for a client meeting or any other excuse that sounds good. Hearing his voice is becoming more bearable and the tears have subsided; although, I'm still unable to sleep in my bed. It's been almost forty-nine days since I was in the terrible accident that caused the death of the man and his child, and the memory is fading when compared to the tragedy that I live every day. My life has returned to its pre-Urijah days for the most part. Three days after the accident I could not eat, sleep, or focus on anything other than going over that cliff and fighting for my life in the midst of that burning inferno that took the lives of two innocent beings. Being estranged from Urijah is a different kind of pain. It's pitiful and my soul feels empty because my utopia has disappeared. Additionally, the constant calls from the many different bill collectors, the stress of hiding from Mr. Repo Man, watching local television because the cable is disconnected, and piecing meals together from the frozen mysteries I have been able to find in the back of the freezer, have me focusing less on the loss of the precious lives in the burning inferno and more on my miserable reality.

For a while I was on the path of healing and on the road to enjoying life at a higher level, but then I realized my happiness was based on how I felt in Urijah's world. I'm unable to maintain the level of high necessary to keep me smiling through my tormented life without him, so regretfully I've returned to wishing for my own demise. My newly discovered love for life totally disappeared when I escorted Urijah out of my life without hearing his explanation. No matter what transpired during the past month, my life is at a standstill and my heart aches more than ever because I now know how it feels to lose a pure, unspoken love. Ten days have flown by and yet gone nowhere. What happened to my love for life? I gained and then lost so much more in such a short time! How can that happen?!? I try to focus on Urijah's encouraging words as I search for the true meaning behind my trials, but I'm lost to this elevated mindset without him. Besides, he is probably bouncing his newborn angel on his lap at this very moment and, although spiritually I wish him well, naturally, my heart can't process any further pain. Therefore, I decide to move forward with my plan to end my life as soon as I gain the courage and develop my plan of action.

I am tired of thinking about everyone and everything else. The girls will be fine. Between Kevin and Daddy, they won't allow Mother or Alex to taint them too much and, besides, I will be able to keep an eye on them from Heaven… if I make it there. I realize that killing myself is not an option, because God has stopped my repeated attempts by making my body reject every version of poison concoction I created and attempted to swallow. I guess that I will have to put myself in harm's way. Why couldn't I just die along with the man and his son…? Or perhaps instead of them. I would have gladly taken the child's place, although I didn't feel this way when I was staring death in the face. So little time ago I was happy for life, apologetic for ever wanting to take my own life, and thankful for another chance to make things better. Well reality hits, and although I feel terrible that the desire has returned, again… I think I want to die. Alex would tell me to take my destiny in my own hands, call Urijah, and put our world back together. She always tells me to go after what I want, but I wouldn't even know where to begin, which is probably why she has my husband in her bed.

The guilt and confusion weighs heavily across my chest so I take advantage of the time that the girls are in school and return to my makeshift bed in the back of my closet. Laying in the back of the closet with the door closed blocks out not only the light, but also the sound of the doorbell and telephone calls from the unwanted. Today is Kevin's evening with the girls, so I don't have to re-enter the world until my appointment with a client tomorrow afternoon.

This time, I ensure that my hideaway is void of any noise so that outside influences do not invade my dreams. The house is silent while I lay and plan how to put myself in places where I am certain to meet up with the grim reaper. My first thought is to walk the streets at night in a bad neighborhood. I guess I can look in the paper, the Internet, or just watch the news as a means of locating the worst neighborhoods. Perhaps I can get into a really bad fight with Ms. Eloise. She will be forced to pay someone to kill me if I slap her in public, and I would satisfy one of my fantasies before leaving this earth. She had Alex put in the hospital for hitting her at the house with no witnesses outside of me, Daddy, and the help. Surely she will have someone cut my brakes or something worse if I blatantly disrespect her in public. Maybe I will slap her in her office or at church, but then I would look bad and I don't want that. I don't want to damage my reputation. I just want to stop my tormented life. I know! I can put on Kevin's old ski mask and rob the local grocery store or the bank, and maybe I'll get shot in the process. At least we will have fresh meat for the week or some of these bills paid if I get away with the crime.

While laughing to myself at the many crazy thoughts circling my mind, I find myself in the back isle of a mini-market. What the hell am I doing here? I don't have money to waste at a mini-market. Everyone knows that their prices are much higher than the grocery store. This is crazy! I've obviously done it again; Preoccupied with life and living in my head while out and about not realizing what I'm doing or where I'm going. I don't even remember driving here. Anyway, I'd better get out of here before they start watching me. As I walk towards the door I realize that I do have a craving for chocolate, but I don't have any money with me; I don't even have my purse. Maybe I left it in the car. I rush out of the door to get in my car, but I must have left my keys in the store somewhere because I don't have them either. My heart begins to race! When did it get dark and where did I park? Okay, I have to calm down because I am starting to scare myself. Last week I lost the car and the girls helped, but they are not here. I have no purse, no keys, no money… I must have left everything. I search the small parking lot for a short while then decide to return inside to look for my keys. I can push the panic button on my key, which will help me locate my car. Surely the clerk will understand and help me. I can't believe how forgetful I've been lately. Maybe while I was in the store my automobile was repossessed. This would be embarrassing. I can't call Daddy because he's been in the hospital for weeks and I'm tired of calling Vanessa because I don't like her seeing the person I have become; desperate, depressed, broken, and needy. Perhaps I can call Kevin, but where would I tell him to come because I don't recognize this little store?

As I return to the counter for assistance, the cashier is nowhere in sight. I hear people speaking in another language from the back room. I call out, but they obviously do not hear me so I walk towards the voices. The voices are coming from the other side of a closed door. I politely knock and call out, "Excuse me. Is anyone available for the front counter?" No one answers so I return to the counter and wait. Surely they have not left the store abandoned. I stand at the counter for about ten minutes looking for a bell to ring for service, a phone, or sign of any other life inside or outside the store. Not one bell, phone, or person is to be found, except for the dirty couple sleeping outside… Yuck! They look up at me and appear to want to say something, but I guess my snarl and rolling of my eyes discourage them, so they retreat to their warm embrace next to the dirty trash receptacle. Maybe this is my opportunity to take some food and walk to the nearest phone booth and call Kevin, but how would I explain food from a mini-market, needing a ride, the whereabouts of my car, or any of this? The problem is that I don't recognize the neighborhood, there are no street signs on the corner, and I can't remember anything about this situation. All that I remember is that I was looking forward to a quiet evening away from the outside world in the back of my closet. I have to interrupt the gentlemen who I hear in the back; that's all there is left to do. As I get closer to the door, I grow more and more embarrassed at the thought of having to admit that

I am lost, my car was probably repossessed, I have no money, no identification, and I need to use a phone.

For some reason, my knocks on the door separating me from the sounds on the other side bring tears to my eyes because I have again allowed myself to get in a position of neediness. The voices are elevated and sound angry, so they clearly do not hear me. I push the door open just a crack and call out, "Hello…" and no one answers. I find myself through two sets of doors and deep into the back room in the midst of about twelve men screaming at someone on their knees with a bag over their head. I try to run, but my feet will not move. I have not been noticed and clearly need to get out of here before anyone sees me. Without much warning, the person on their knees jump up and run in my direction. One of the men grabs the runner, throws him to the concrete floor, and snatches the bag off his head. Just as clear as day I see that this is Congressman Willerger. As I think, "Be invisible" I wonder, "What the hell has he gotten himself into now?" He is always in the news, under investigation for his involvement in something underhanded and crooked. Whatever it is, I don't want to be involved, but my feet still won't release the spot. This reminds me being stuck in my spot as I was forced to watch Kevin and Alex' vulgarities. The gunshot interrupts my thoughts, causing my bladder to release its contents down my legs, into my shoes, and across the concrete floor. The man who threw the Congressman to the floor has just shot him in the head. My body responds with the loudest scream I have ever known and all of the men aim their guns at me and pull the triggers. I can feel each bullet enter my body as though in slow motion. The initial numb sensation turns into a burning, sharp, piercing penetration through my flesh, finishing with the exploding of each organ that is hit, while inside of my body. The final infiltration is the bullet that tears through my skull, ripping out the back of my head. My feet finally release the spot where I stand. As my body hits the cold concrete I can see one man standing over me with his semi-automatic gun cocked and ready to load the final shot into my riddled remains. I lay there choking on my own blood whispering to God, "Please don't let him kill me. I'm sorry, God. I'm not ready to die."

I see that Congressman Willerger is dead and realize that I will soon follow, so I say my final prayer. "Lord God, please forgive me for all of my sins. I apologize for not appreciating the life that you gave me. I took my life for granted and wallowed in self-pity way past its welcome. Please take care of Tia and Kali and give them the life that I should've had. If at all possible, please allow me to make it out of this situation, for you are the God of miracles. If not, please let me see Dear soon. I love you, Amen." Dear always told me that "death and life are in the power of the tongue, and they that love it shall eat the fruit thereof," (Proverbs 18:21). This means that words are very powerful and God has given us the ability to speak positivity or negativity into our lives. Through my foolish words I chose death and at this moment as I take my last breaths I wish that I had spoken positivity into my world. All my life, I spoke that I would have a beautiful life as an adult, and for the most part I did. Death brings about a clearer view into my world. My worst days were better than a lot of other people's best days. Thinking about the homeless couple outside brings me shame, but it is now too late as I exhale for the final time, realizing that I did not really want to die, but rather I carelessly allowed words to flow from my mouth over the most powerful tool in our possession: the tongue! I'm afraid that have misused the power of the tongue for the last time.

Death by Decision

The heaviness of my history has disappeared as I float freely, enjoying my transition. Although not truly a plan that I had hoped to complete, I must be dead to the natural because I feel alive in the spiritual. For the first time ever, I have no fear, no worries, and no apprehensions. I'm weightless. I feel weightless and free from any pain and all suffering. As I look down upon my physical body lying lifeless on the cold concrete, I know that God loves me. I thank Him for his grace and mercy, and for allowing me to exit a cruel, ruthless world not worthy of a lonely heart longing for love. I won't focus on the negative; however, I am a bit bothered that the men who shot me are wrapping my body in plastic as though I am trash and are gathering the Congressman in the same fashion. Before I can dwell on their purpose, I'm distracted by the bright light shining in the distance and am compelled to go in that direction. The music playing is the most beautiful sound ever to bless my atmosphere. The melodic magnificence in the air causes a flow of love resembling the feeling that resonated through the air on the day of my deliverance; only this current love is much greater. I glide upward without another thought about the troubles I leave behind.

My love for my daughters has intensified, but I am so distracted by the thought of me finally making it to Heaven that I refuse to look back.

Besides, what's the use? I wasn't much good to my daughters as I lay in the back of my closet amongst a blanket of depression, anger, fear, and self-pity. I embrace the fact that I'm dead and no longer a part of the disappointing world. Once I make it to Heaven I will ask God to grant me the job of their guardian angel so that I can still guide and look out for my girls. Right at this moment I am excited to see Dear and finally look upon the face of the Almighty God. I have a whole bunch of questions for Him, but mostly I want to show honor. I can see what appear to be the gates to Heaven in the distance. I have never seen such glory, but before I can get close enough to confirm my assumption, I run into Dear. I mean literally... I run into Dear, who is descending swiftly in my direction and knocks me back amongst the clouds. Once I realize what hit me I attempt to hug her, but hugging a glorified body that doesn't want to be held is difficult, to say the least. I am confused. I have anxiously awaited our reunion, but I never imagined that she would not greet me with open arms. Why isn't she happy to see me? Before I can ask what's going on she speaks in a harsh voice of contempt, "Go back! It's not your time to be here!" What? Dear has never raised her voice at me and now she not only yells, but her tone is deep with a growling, raspy texture. She must be reading my mind because she does all of the talking, answering me before I can ask the many questions running through my mind. The roughness of her voice scares me. "You are not welcome here before your time! You have a work left undone, now go back and finish! You have to earn the right to be amongst the Holy ones!"

She is scaring me so I do the only thing that I can think to do. I scream for the Almighty, "God! Father GGGodddd!" and when He doesn't answer, I call for the One who died for my sins, "Jesus... Hey, Jeeeesssus! Please answer me." Surely he will be merciful and allow me to stay. Dear must be upset because she wasn't expecting me so soon. I wasn't expecting to be here so soon either, but we have to make the best of the situation, right? I refuse to go back to a world that discarded me like unwanted trash and I definitely am not going to Hell, so Heaven is my only option. For the first time in my afterlife I feel really afraid. Where will I go if not with Dear? This is not at all what I expected and if things weren't bad enough, I notice a burning firestorm where earth should be. I can hear screams of tormented souls in the distance and it seems that the anguished shrieks are ascending out of the consumption of fire below. I can feel the Father of lies pulling me downward when Dear instantly appears in front of me, takes my hands, and speaks in the lovely voice that I remember, "Dear child, your work is not yet complete and therefore you are not welcome here yet. It is blasphemy to take your own life and even worse to try to trick the Death Angel by causing your death at the hands of someone else. Life is a dance, but not all dances are worthy of your choosing. Death by decision is not your dance. You've been allowing life to dance all over you. *You* have to choose when, where, how, and if you will participate at each situation. Choose the dance wisely." I'm even more confused now than when she was yelling at me. What does all of this mean? As quickly as she appeared before me, she's gone. "Wait a minute! I don't understand. Deeeaaaarrr," I yell for her. I see her in the distant air above me to the left of what must be God, judging by His size and the magnified glow all about Him. To His right must be Jesus because He has an equally blinding shine and they both have their backs to me.

Even turned away, their glory is too much to look upon without shielding my eyes and bowing in adoration. I now see Dear facing me with the look of love in her eyes and all around her angels begin to materialize. The one closest to her resembles Urijah, but I can't be sure because each angel holds a beauty almost too pure to behold. They are numbered as the stars in the sky with a radiance shining much brighter than the sun, which is beneath them in a position of honor. Dear whispers sweetly and loudly, "Choose the dance, JJ," before turning away and standing with her back to me. As if choreographed, the angels also turn away one at a time, with the Urijah lookalike turning last, and then finally the sun dims giving way to the inevitable darkness that follows. The only light available is at a distance originating from the burning void, and I'm determined to stay as far away from that hole as possible. I drift in a confused state for what must be an eternity until I hear the agonizing cries of Mother. I have never heard her cry so I anxiously rush in the direction of her screams, "Oh, my baby… God, you didn't have to take my baby!" What would cause my classy mother to carry on in such an undignified manner? All questions are answered as I get closer and notice Mother, Vanessa, Sheila, Urijah, Kevin, Alex, the girls, and Daddy in a wheelchair hooked to an oxygen tank, at my funeral. I recognize many of the faces, but the most outstanding is Urijah's as he sits amongst the office staff looking off into the void with tears streaming down his cheeks. I want to hold him, but I get distracted by the caked-on make-up around the bullet wound through my forehead, my protruding lips stitched together so sloppily that the thread is showing, and my puffy face demanding unwanted disturbing stares. This body does not look at all like the one that I paraded around when I sported it through this earth. I worked hard to maintain a perfect appearance and the last visual that everyone will remember of me looks like a cheap, discarded whore. Why are they having an open casket memorial service? I look terrible! The make-up is not even close to my complexion. Damn her!

I'm sure that Mother insisted on an open casket to bring me shame one last time. I hope that they don't allow my daughters to see me like this. As usual, Tia seems content as she smiles and looks in my direction; conversely, Kali is quietly crying uncontrollably. Why don't they take her out of here? Vanessa is holding her, but Kali clearly can't handle my death and needs to leave. Perhaps if Mother wasn't stealing the scene with her fake declarations of love, someone would notice the little girl on the front row having a nervous breakdown. I can't believe that Mother is causing such a scene. She didn't even like me, but now that there is an audience she is falling apart? I never would have guessed that she'd act in such a manner. She is such a phony! I wish that I could appear for just a few minutes and tell everyone how she really feels about me. I would let them know that she never loved me or even wanted female children. No one is in a position to put her in her place. Vanessa is obviously trying to be supportive by allowing Mother to grieve in her own way. Daddy is too weak from his illness to regulate Mother, Kevin is too guilt-ridden and probably trying to figure out what he is going to do with two little girls, and baby sister Alex seems to be in shock about the whole affair. I kneel before Kali and touch her on her little hand in an attempt to soothe her pain by taking it from her, but I'm not able to relieve her sorrow. I feel every intricate detail of the unbearable agony ransacking her young heart. What have I done? My selfish desire to leave my terrible life before my time has left a motherless child to face this world alone. Even though the church is filled to capacity with people paying their final respects, Kali is alone. Being alone in a room filled with people is a terrible feeling that I recognize intimately.

I spent my life surrounded by many people, yet still alone, and now I've left Kali to duplicate my hellacious youth. I'm convinced that I deserve to spend eternity in the burning void and am willing to accept my fate until

Tia reaches out and wipes the tears from my face with her little hands. "Mommy, it's ok. Your crying is almost over. God showed me," she says in her small voice. Tia sees me? Oh my God, thank you! I gently caress her face and tell her how much I love her and her sister. Not knowing how much time I have before she's unable to see me, I speak quickly, apologizing and asking her to tell her sister how sorry I am for the choices I made. I tell her that I love them both so much and I promise to stay with them as long as God allows.

In a twinkling of an eye I find myself in what must be Urijah's home because he is changing the diaper of a newborn baby boy in a partially decorated baby's room. He then places the baby in the crib and puts a blanket over a sleeping lady who must be the child's mother. He kisses her softly on the forehead so as not to wake her and then goes to sit alone with his head reclined backwards in a dark, silent room. He is apparently deep in thought, staring into space as the tears begin to flow down the sides of his face, finding a resting place in his ears. I want to hold him. Now that I am in the afterlife and probably on my way to Hell for blaspheming against God and leaving two young children alone, I have nothing to lose. Coyness has disappeared from my usual collection of emotions, so I'm going to hold him. I stand behind the chair, wrap my arms around his neck, rest my head against his, and inhale the moment. I have no physical body so I am unable to feel how soft his hair must be against my cheek, the firmness of the muscles bulging from his chest, or the security of his arms, but I do feel the strength of emotional love between us. I'm not sure how much longer I will be allowed to roam the earth, but for now I just want to hold him a little while longer before returning to Tia and Kali. As I hold him he begins to speak to God in incomplete sentences: "God please… Show her… Help her… Amen". What does he mean? Is he talking about me? Does he know what I did or that I'm lost, because I feel lost. After holding him for what feels like five minutes, I thank God for the time, kiss him softly on the lips, and move in the direction of Kali and Tia's love. I can no longer see Urijah, but I hear him say, "Choose the dance, Jonnie." What does this mean? Could that angel have been Urijah? I want to go back to him, but I feel the distress amongst my daughters' emotions so I continue in their direction.

I find Kali and Tia both sitting alone in one of Alex' guest bedrooms. Kevin and Alex are downstairs watching a movie, while my precious children have been ordered to stay in this room because the movie is not appropriate for children. Kali is entertaining the emotions of abandonment, confusion, rejection, and other negative groupings unfamiliar to her young world. Although unsuccessful, her baby sister Tia tries to console her. Tia is trying to convince Kali that I will be back when she points at me and says, "See... I told you." As hard as Kali tries, she cannot see me and scolds Tia for making believe that I'm in the room with them. I'm angered when Alex yells up for them to be quiet because their banter is disturbing her movie. As though I'm watching footage of their young life in fast-forward motion, I'm swiftly moved to Mother's kitchen table as they are being made to eat sauerkraut and corned beef hash. Tia refuses to eat, while Mother holds my baby's nose and force-feeds her, causing her to choke. I am livid, but because I chose to misuse the power of my tongue, I can do nothing but watch in disgust. Why are they with Mother? Is this my Hell? Kali is doing her best to swallow the pickled cabbage without tasting it because she wants to please Mother, but even this method fails and causes her to vomit across the table. Without a second thought, Mother slaps Kali from the table. This is a scene from my childhood. How could I have left them here to her vices? Oh God... I have to help them. Softly I hear Dear's sweet voice, "Choose the dance, JJ." What in hell does this mean? I then hear Urijah repeat his earlier plea, "Choose the dance, Jonnie." How? How do I choose the dance to get out of this situation and what does this mean? As Mother is in the restroom teaching Kali a lesson, Tia grabs my hand and says, "Mommy, you have to choose to fight. Come back... go back and come back to us. OK?" My scream of fury causes three of the double-pane picture windows in Mother's formal living room to explode as I leave her home in search of relief.

During my exit I see Mother mistreating Daddy, Kevin and Alex on vacation enjoying my insurance money; while leaving the girls to Mother's cruelties, Vanessa arguing with Mother in her quest to see the girls, and Mother pretending to be distraught as she uses the free press to further publicize her brand. Mother has interviews with all of the majors, Oprah, Dr. Phil, Dr. Oz, as well as the locals agreeing that I put myself in harm's way in an attempt to cause my own death. They label my death as "death by decision", stating that when I left the house that day, I parked my car in a bad neighborhood, and purposely walked the streets forcing someone to rob rape, shoot me several times, and then leave me dead in a ditch. This is not what happened! Mother exploiting my daughters in front of the cameras for her financial gain sickens me further. Her stock has gone through the roof as she sails even further to the top of her world on the back of my bad decision. My mistake was misusing the power of the tongue, not parking in a bad neighborhood and walking the streets looking to be murdered… Or is this what happened? Wait a minute. I remember being shot the same time as the Congressman. Why are they reporting so little about his passing and magnifying my 'death by decision'? If they would only look, they would see that the same gun used to shoot him, fired the fatal shots to my body.

The media reports me as the distraught daughter of a celebrity who secretly suffered due to the many problems with finances, marriage, death of grandmother, loss of job, etc. The last thing that I wanted was to air my dirty laundry. Even after death I would not want Mother to benefit by shining a bad light on me or my family, but now the details of my failures monopolize the evening news on every channel. My life was not that interesting… was it? Had I known, I would have written a book so that I could leave the proceeds and a legacy for my daughters.

I have traveled to three of the four corners of the earth in search of relief, but no matter how far I go I can still hear the tormented cries of Kali and the pleas of Tia asking me to come back. I wish I knew how to get back to them. I don't understand why God would do this to me. He is supposed to be a merciful God. Didn't I suffer enough during life? Dear knows how disappointing my life was and then she turned her back on me, leaving me alone in this afterlife. My days and nights all seem to blend together, but it feels like I've been stuck in this realm for a very long time. I can feel a pull towards the burning void, but that's the last place that I want to go. The screams pouring out of that dark, smoldering hole are horrible; equally, the smell is unbearable. I avoid that corner of earth with all my might. Just when I think that all hope is lost, I remember my beautiful experience with Urijah on the day that my deliverance began. Traveling home is easy. I think about where I want to be and I appear in my bedroom. I don't know why I didn't think about coming here sooner. The beautiful glow still remains. God's love is present and I can almost smell Dear's home-made soup cooking in the kitchen. I walk through the house realizing that I made the wrong choice. I didn't recognize how blessed I was and therefore I chose to leave. I now realize that I should have fought harder to overcome the depression.

While traveling in this afterlife I saw some terrible sights, which confirmed that I was truly blessed and had little reason to complain when compared to others. I vividly remember families living on the street with their next meal nowhere in sight and a young man fighting for his life on the operating room table, while I looked for every opportunity to abandon the gift of life that I had. I feel the heavy burdens from each person I encounter. The most intense of the burdens come from the children unable to do more to change their family's situations. Each child has dreams bigger than they may ever realize, but their mental planning for a better tomorrow makes today bearable. As I walk through my dream house viewing each of my collections, I am unable to shake off the shame. I could have provided shelter for many of the homeless, but I didn't realize how much I had and how blessed I was. If I had another chance, I would choose to handle my life differently. Not that I would move strangers into my house, but I could do more than wallow in self-pity. I wonder if God can still hear me. "God, if you are listening, please allow me another chance."

The sound of my front door opening pulls me out of my thoughts. Vanessa has had a key since Kevin moved and has finally decided to use it. I watch as she slowly walks through the house in deep thought. Why is she here? Maybe she is here to pack my things so that Mother can give them away to charity. I wish that she could see me like Tia can, or at least hear me. I follow her for a few minutes as she walks through the house with her hand sliding over the furniture and finally stopping at the pictures on the wall as tears stream down her face. Vanessa has a tough exterior, so I never thought that I would ever see her show this type of emotion. In one sense it is comforting to see that she cares so deeply; conversely, I wish that my actions were not the cause of her sorrow. I don't even remember causing my own demise, but I remember hoping to die so I'm sure that I somehow caused my death. I can do nothing more but watch as I apologize for my actions and tell her how much I love her.

Vanessa is the sister that I always wished for and now I have caused her visible pain, which hurts me. Am I doomed to an eternity of watching my loved ones suffer? She sits back in my favorite chair as though she is trying to feel any essence I left behind and begins to cry aloud. I kneel before her and go through the motion of wiping her tears. Of course, I do not have a physical body, so my attempts are in vain; nonetheless, still I maintain my position at her feet as she sobs and speaks aloud. "God, I miss her so much... Where is she? Please bring her back to us!" What does she mean, "Where is she?" I was buried what must be days ago. Her pleas are so heartfelt that I am also crying and praying for another chance at the life that I threw away. "God, I promise... If I just had another chance, I would choose life! I would choose the dance! I will figure out what Dear and Urijah means and choose that direction. God please..."

I lay my face on top of Vanessa's bony feet as I continue to pour out to God and this time I can almost feel the water gathering underneath my cheeks, if I had physical cheeks. She must also feel something because she abruptly sits forward and wipes the top of her feet, right through my face... Wow that was weird. She examines the residue of water on her hand and then looks up towards the ceiling as though she is looking for a leak. Somehow my tears are on her hand. After a few minutes my tears have evaporated so she figures that she must have imagined the wetness. She seems to be deep in thought as she is now leaning forward with her face buried in her hands. Within a couple of seconds she has returned to her deeply saddened state as the tears drip through her fingers and fall freely to the floor. "God, please... if you can hear me, please give me another chance. I won't waste my chance... I promise."

The weightlessness of the afterworld disappears slowly as I empty my heart to God, as well as to Dear. "Dear, please help me if you hear me!" The weight of the situation gets heavier as I notice the collection of tears that Vanessa and I have caused to gather atop my hardwood floor. For a split second I almost feel the superficial concern about ruining the floor with all of this water, but I regain my focus on the importance of the moment. I wrap my arms around the bottom portion of her legs as we both continue to plead for my return. I'm perplexed about her wanting me to return from the grave; nevertheless, I pray with her. Like a radio station slightly out of range, I experience bouts of clearly feeling her legs against my body; however, as quickly as the pressure of her legs against my chest appears, it disappears. I want to talk to her so badly that I ache in the pit of my stomach. I attempt to press against her more firmly so that I can ease the internal pain caused by my broken heart.

In the midst of us both baring our souls Vanessa screams and jumps up. She runs towards the door and then stops to look in my direction. "Jonnie?"

she asks inquisitively. "Jonnie, is that you?" She sees me? "Vanessa? You can see me?" I ask. She screams and runs over to me yelling, "Girl, where in the hell have you been?" as she grabs me. Oh my God... thank you! Initially I think that she sees me like Tia could, but when she grabs me I realize that I once again have a physical body... because it hurts. After hugging, crying, and both of us excitedly trying to talk at the same time, we take a breath and she tells me that everyone has been looking for me for days. As she speaks, I realize that she thinks that I either secretly took a trip or have been hiding in my home all of this time. This is all wrong! I try to tell her my story about being shot with the Congressman, dying, my meeting with Dear, roaming in the afterlife, visiting Urijah, the heaviness of true hardship in the world, not being let into Heaven, seeing, feeling, and hearing the torturous screams coming out of the burning void, experiencing my funeral, the torment of my daughters at the hands of Mother, me choosing the dance, etcetera, etcetera, etcetera.

Vanessa has that same look of disbelief on her face when I tell her about me surviving the burning inferno. Because I'm starving, she orders food and we talk for hours; both of us telling very different versions of the missing time-span. She assures me that my murder has not been on the news; there is no talk about my choosing death by decision; the girls are safely in Kevin's care during the week, and have spent the past two weekends with her and her family. I have to find a way to get her to believe me. I know... I have to tell her more about what led to my death by decision. I tell her about me wanting to commit suicide. I show her my makeshift bed on the floor in the back of my closet. Although some of my confessions shock her, she maintains the look in her eyes that states 'she thinks that I am crazy'. As we sit on the couch I search my mind for proof of my experiences. I wish I had paid closer attention to street signs while in the afterlife so that we could go help the homeless families. I don't even know how to get back to the store where I was murdered.

Vanessa continues to discount my experiences as dreams until I feel a sharp pain in my head. As I rub my head I remember that this is one of the spots where my skull was penetrated by one of the piercing bullets. I quickly grab her hand and place it through my hair over my injury. As she pulls her bloodied hand away she notices blood running swiftly through my hair and down the side of my face. I attempt to run to the washroom for towels, but

I am too weak and fall as soon as I stand. I feel myself fading so I begin to pray, "God, please allow me to stay. I promise that I will learn how to choose the dance. I deserve a better life than I've accepted! I also deserve to leave a better legacy than death by decision. God please help…"

Angered and Thriving

Waking up in a strange location connected to wires coming out of beeping machines is a bit startling, to say the least. I slowly regain consciousness and am thankful to see Vanessa here standing next to my bed with a smile on her face; however, she has tears in her eyes and a worried look on her face. I can see her mouth moving, but cannot hear the words racing past her lips until she has obviously repeated herself several times. I'm in what appears to be a hospital, but I don't recognize the décor. If I understand her correctly she found me in the back of my closet close to death caused by an overdose of pills and several gunshot wounds. Her lips are moving so fast that it's difficult to keep up, but she says that I lost a lot of blood and have been in a coma for a couple of days.

Because she knows that I do not want Mother or her audience in my business and wasn't sure what she would say if she did notify them, Vanessa discreetly had me transported to a private hospital by the same medical team who repaired my brutally damaged body after the explosion that caused second and third degree burns to over half of my frail physique. She didn't want to believe that I was in the car accident which claimed the innocent lives of the father and son and now she is in disbelief about finding me with gunshot wounds because there is no evidence of a gun being discharged in my closet. She states that she had been to my house several times before that day and had searched every corner for any evidence of my whereabouts and I was not there. I know that I was not there because those men dumped my body in a field somewhere.

Once I'm finally able to fully comprehend her words I learn that I've been here for four days, lost a lot of blood, and have a bullet still lodged in my skull that will possibly cause some type of pain throughout the rest of my life. In an attempt to salvage my job, Vanessa went to my employer and explained that I may be out for a little while longer due to family situations. She also told my family that I was out of town attending a work conference. She is so amazing and has associations in places I never knew truly existed. Through my recent experiences I've learned that her family is not only wealthy, but also powerful in a secretive kind of way, which explains why Mother treats Vanessa so well. I apparently underwent a surgery to repair the damage caused by the bullets bouncing through my organs. I'm happy to hear that Vanessa has the support of her mother, who has been right by her side to ensure that I receive the best of care.

Judging by the name on my wrist bracelet my true identity is even concealed from the staff, with the exception of the doctor who now stands over me with a smile on her face explaining how close I came to death. I am so aggravated with these people. I *was* dead! Just as I'm preparing to tell her my story, the doctor states that I did not have enough blood flowing through my veins to be alive and my body resembled a corpse that had been dead for weeks. She tells me that an army of angels stood two deep around us on every side in the operating room, as though they were standing guard on assignment to ensure that I made it out of surgery safely. The Doctor further explains that we were enclosed by a band of angels facing us with a second grouping standing behind them facing outward. There was an identical grouping in the same formation above, as well as beneath us and they were all connected by the bond of their wings and their determination to complete their assignment from God. She states that once they made their presence known, their glory was too bright for her to see with her physical eyes until she yielded to God and one of the angels touched her pupils, allowing her to see through spiritual eyes.

The doctor's personality is much softer than when she bandaged my wounds after the accident; like she truly believes me and now has her own unbelievable story to share. "Based on the clock in the operating room, my staff and I were in there for thirty- three hours; however, the clock and calendar right outside the door indicated that they were in surgery for thirty-three minutes," she states confidently. The doctor shushes me and asks that I allow her to finish when I ask her to explain the conflict of time. Besides, I don't know if she truly understood the time conflict; however, growing up with Dear I learned that God's time greatly differs from our time. "The chief Angel blew a gentle warm wind over your exposed organs, causing the blood to replenish as he guided my hands through every intricate movement as we repaired the damage caused by the ordeal you underwent. As I operated I saw what appeared to be some sort of war going on all around us between the angels facing outward and numerous spiritual enemies. Although they were not physically labeled, in my spirit I was able to identify the enemies as demons of fear, guilt, despair, anger, ineffi-ciency, self-pity, depression, rejection, double- mindedness, grief, fatigue, bitterness, insecurity, doubt, sensitivity, withdrawal, control, perfection, retaliation, escapism, pride, heaviness, confusion, strife, jealousy, paranoia, competition, judgment, impatience, self-accusation, and religion – just to name a few. Instead of dying when they were struck by one of the angels, they would divide and two more would arise in a much bigger and possibly stronger form. It appeared that the evil spirits were winning and, without realizing my actions, I allowed the demon of fear to penetrate the lines of defense by way of my mind. This process repeated a couple of times, until the chief angel told me to denounce the spirit of fear and placed a helmet of protection over my head, which permitted me to continue my mission. The Chief Angel then began to minister to your spirit as though you were awake. He spoke with a gentle authority, telling you that you would have to resist the demons that have taken over your world by way of your mind. He spoke in a heavenly language that I somehow understood as he prayed for strength on your behalf. Most of the demons were defeated; however, a few escaped. The Chief Angel advised that they would regain their strength, gather others, and attempt to return to our world at a later time by way of our minds. He explained how they would enter our lives again if we lowered our mental and spiritual defenses again. "The Devil is tricky and will enter your life at any opportunity, so stay meditated on positivity, brightness, love, and God," the Chief Angel said, "before we returned our attentions to your physical body. I was able to remove all fragments of metal from your body, with the exception of the bullet lodged in your skull that the Chief Angel insisted I leave behind as a reminder of your afterlife experience."

The Doctor speaks of her experience for a great while as she granted permission for her own tears to flow freely down her face and onto her expensive blazer. She stops me every time I try to tell her of my afterlife adventure, finally advising that she saw my experience through a vision and knows first-hand of my afterlife experience. I can tell by the expression on her face and the words flowing through her lips that she not only believes my current story, but also that I was pulled from the burning inferno. "Somehow and for some reason you've been blessed with multiple chances to complete your mission. You have work left undone and a testimony to share," the doctor states. Before leaving my room and telling me that I should be able to return to my life in a couple of days, the doctor warns me to stay meditated and not to waste the opportunities given. She stops at the door prior to exiting and states, "Prior to the introduction to your unbelievable world I was agnostic, but now I am more than a believer; I know that God, as well as the Devil, and angels of all levels exist. I purposefully neglected to share how the angels ministered to me because I'm still overwhelmed, but perhaps in time I will also share my story. Most importantly at this point is that *you* choose the dance and then share with others what that means," she says in a confirming voice. I am a little foggy about everything that has happened, but her words bring about a warm sensation throughout the room that we all feel as I honestly respond, "I don't know how… yet."

As promised by the doctor, I am rejoining my previous life within a couple of days and working diligently to put the pieces back in place; however, this time I have a different attitude. The vivid memories of the afterlife have faded, but periodically return in small, quick flashes. The words 'Choose the Dance' play repeatedly through my thoughts at all times and when I think about Kevin, Alex, Mother, or anyone else that ever caused me pain, I get angry. My return home was met with a final warning from the electric and gas companies, a water bill too high to be real, and a reminder that the cable has been disconnected for a while now. Additionally, I have missed several meetings with potential clients, which could prove detrimental to Urijah and his small company if neglected any further. The ringing of the house phone startles me because I'm surprised it is still connected. Unlike before and without much thought, I answer the phone and make arrangements with the finance company that holds the pink slip to two of my vehicles. When I place the phone back on the hook I feel good about making the choice to deal with the caller on the other line. I'm opening the windows to air out the house when I say aloud, "Whew... I'm glad I chose to deal with that dance."

To my surprise, the meaning of "Choose the Dance" rushes to me as though I just mentally attended an accelerated seminar on the subject. I don't have all of the pieces to the puzzle, but I do have a clearer under-standing. When Urijah hired me I negotiated that the company pay for my cellular bill, which includes unlimited access to Internet radio; thank God, because the silence in the house is deafening. I turn Pandora to my Fred Hammond and Smokie Norful station and allow angels to fill my home and minister to my spirit, as I anxiously look forward to hugging the girls for the first time in what feels like a lifetime. I am energized by the thought of being a better mommy, which I decide is one of my missions to complete. God blessed me to have two of the best daughters ever granted and I am no longer going to ignore a blessing of this magnitude. I wasn't a bad mommy before, but now as I clean the house I search my mind for ways to be more present. I vow to have more pajama party days; I will listen more, and dance with them when they ask. Besides, who says that mommies can't be silly? The growling of my empty stomach reminds me that I can't seem to get enough to eat since my return to this realm; however, the pantry is bare. For the first time this angers me. My usual go-to feelings of some form of sadness are not present. Why should I be over here nursing a demon of self-pity while Kevin moves on with his life intact? The thoughts that consume my mind form a plan of their own and I go alone with every detail because I am sick and tired of being an idle, sick and tired, lonely and abused, tossed-away-after-being-used woman. No one has the right to mistreat another person! Thinking about how I allowed so many individuals to take advantage of my good nature fuels a fire in me that I never knew existed. I feel tingly, I feel rejuvenated, I feel happy, I feel... I feel... What do you know...? I have given myself permission to feel something other than being a victim. I've never known this type of joy, mixed with the powerful feeling of making a difference by taking control of my life. I can almost see the angels in the room rejoicing with me as I scrape the last of the peanut butter from the sides of the jar.

Just as I am refusing to worry about the absence of food in the house Vanessa rings the bell and stands at the door with enough food to last for several weeks. We put away groceries as she confesses to her lack of faith in my recent ordeals, but states that she clearly sees a difference in my persona and feels the difference in my home. With a smile plastered across my face I tell her that death was a good lesson for me, but now I'm alive and happy to rejoin the living! Not ten minutes after leaving, Kevin arrives with my two little angels. I hug them with more vigor than ever before, almost forgetting the deeper importance of this reunion until Tia puts her little hands on the sides of my face, looks me in my eyes and says, "Mommy I knew you'd find your way back to us." She remembers? I look in her eyes deep enough to see her soul as I try to figure out if she truly knows what she is saying, as she stands before me smiling. She then looks around the room and says, "Mommy, the angels are beautiful… and I will help you choose the dance, ok?" Tears of joy leap from my eyes! Not only does she remember, but she can also see angels in our home. Tia, and I have a privately beautiful moment until I notice Kevin and Kali watching inquisitively and I pull Kali into our hug-fest. I am a bit ashamed to admit that until this very minute I have usually desired the company of Kali over Tia because Kali's personality matches mine. Kali is my first-born and had a few years to explore my world without the distraction of Tia as she found a quiet place within my solemn universe of depression. She has always mimicked my feelings and therefore she can accompany me to the most elegant situations while maintaining her calm composure. Conversely, Tia has always been so active and full of energy, making her presence at a sit-down dinner impossible for everyone involved. I thought Tia had somehow inherited her Aunt Alex's personality, but this is not the case unless Alex can also see into the spiritual realm. Tia seems to have her own special relationship with God. For the first time I understand Tia a whole lot more. I guess that I, too, would find sitting still at a dinner party difficult if I were being entertained by angels. Wow! This realization adds to my believable but unbelievable experiences.

Thank God for the faith that enables me to keep seeing His amazement! Lord, I thank you for both of my daughters. As though to purposely interrupt the beautiful embrace that the girls and I are sharing with the angels, Alex pushes the front door open and abruptly asks, "Kevin, are you coming?" The expression on Kevin's face says that he wants to join our uniquely heavenly family huddle; however, his looks of regret are jolted out of his atmosphere as Alex grabs his arm, "You hear me? Because I can call Talia to come and get me if you want to stay for family dinner and whatever else follows!" Kevin snaps back, "Calm down, Alex," as he squats down and calls the girls over for his goodbye hugs. He holds the girls most endearingly as he stares at me, and tears of remorse form in his eyes. I almost want to look around to see if someone standing behind has his attention because he hasn't looked at me like this in a long while. He then stands, sends the girls over to hug their auntie goodbye, walks over to me, reaches in his pocket, and puts a folded stack of money in my hands. He places the money between our palms as he gently caresses my hands and tells me that he is glad I'm back. He looks as if he wants to take this moment a bit further, but this is impossible with Alex hanging in the background, yelling for him, and insulting the stale air in my home, "You need to open up some more windows in here and let this stale air circulate." Kevin wants to ignore her but can't, as he firmly demands, "Alex, be quiet," and they leave the house bickering. I'm perplexed. Is there trouble in paradise?

After finishing their homework, the girls and I cook whatever they want for dinner, get in our pajamas, and watch Madea movies in my bed until they both fall asleep. I set the Blu-ray player to repeat because the cable is off and I don't want an abrupt stop in sound to awake us. The movie is now watching me as I mentally replay the many images of my life, while noticing the glow still illuminated behind the paint on my ceiling. My emotions are multifaceted. I am happy with the outcome of my experiences because I gained so much knowledge and have begun in a new direction, but I'm mad at Kevin and Alex for the roles that they continue to play, no matter how much I've benefitted. A small, sweet voice joins me in what I thought was a private moment, "Daddy still loves you, Mommy; may I brush your hair?" Tia then gets up, grabs the brush and some hair accessories. Anyone who really knows me knows that playing with my hair is one of the fastest ways to lull me into a deep slumber. She positions herself against the headboard above my head as she plans her hairstyle masterpiece. I allow my mind to drift to earlier this evening. Kevin and I shared a beautiful moment until Alex interrupted. The more I meditate on this thought I am determined that I can have him back if I want. For a brief time Urijah and I found our way into each other's hearts and I was certain that we would find our way into each other's arms; however, fate had different plans and blessed him with a child and its mother... whoever she is to him. Besides, I know Kevin and, although we were not perfect, we were comfortable. How dare Alex take that from us!

Before my thoughts go too far I realize that I am in danger of returning to my comfort zone of allowing myself to be the victim and inviting self-pity and depression back into my world. I instead get angry and become determined to change my world. I'm not sure if Kevin knows that he handed me over $700, which is enough money to pay some of these bills and put gas in the car so that I can visit Daddy tomorrow. The fact that he handed me any money says a lot and the gentle way that he caressed my hands says that he still loves me and maybe even misses me. I won't allow my feelings to slip into a rejected state, so I become determined to change my world. However, my determination is fueled by fury, but takes a turn for the better when I include a plan. I fall asleep thinking about the many paths I can take in an effort to change the direction of my life, and this feels a lot better than crying myself to sleep.

Even though I am asleep, I feel alive! My situation has not changed much, but the way that I view my situation has changed greatly. I refuse to be the victim any longer. I am still wounded and mad that Alex took my husband, but for the first time ever I have a plan of action in which I look forward to pursuing. Life is still tough, but I am determined to move forward. As Tia repositions my head so that she can reach the back, I am awakened just enough to give her a loving caress on her ticklish little feet and thank my Father for allowing me to see my problems from different vantage points! I am still angered, but now I have a plan and I'm thriving!

Dinner for One

I t's been a long time since I could afford to eat at *Le Chet' Marie On The River*, and I feel a bit guilty for using the $200 bonus award monies to treat myself to a night out without the girls. Although Urijah's advertising firm is flourishing and realizing the highest revenue in its short history, I understand why he is not yet in a financial position to offer me the income that my experience and expertise dictate. He recognizes that even through my absence his firm continued its success due in great part to my 98% close rate. Urijah often grants me electronic Bonus Bucks, which I turn into gift cards redeemable at local vendors. The amount of the Bonus Bucks varies based on the potential profit margin the company stands to gain. During my absence a lucrative deal closed resulting in me receiving a $200 gift card. I have used all of my other Bonus Bucks for the girls, the house, or towards car repairs so I feel as if I have the right to treat myself, especially since Daddy is better and once again sneaking me groceries or money. Nevertheless, dinner for one still seems a bit awkward.

I long for the company of my husband or Urijah, whom I really miss. Kevin is somewhere with Alex and their girl-toy Talia doing God knows what, I'm sure, and my interactions with Urijah have been limited to short blurts via conference calls. He hasn't even reached out to see if everything was ok since I returned to work. He is no doubt busy with his new bundle of joy these days, but I thought that he would have at least called.

Being alone in public brings about a humility that I could do without, but I wanted to come here, enjoy a great meal, and be alone with my thoughts. Besides, I miss the phenomenal food and atmosphere. If I had enough money for two on the gift card I would have invited Daddy. The treatments are working and he has returned to work. He was nothing like I saw in my afterlife; thank God! He is still not completely cancer-free, but I have faith that he will be. Thank you, God, for Your Mercies! Healing! Growth! And the Bonus Bucks!

The last time I was here Kevin and I sat at this very table and fantasized about having sex in one of the elegant stalls in the ladies' restroom. We often spoke about our fantasies, but never acted on any of them because I am very conservative and afraid of getting caught. Eventually, I saw with my own eyes that my conservative nature did not hinder Kevin from experiencing his fantasies. For some reason I was granted a front-row viewing as he pounded my baby sister, Alex, from every direction in our marriage bed. The thought still pisses me off to no end!

As I sit waiting for my medium rare filet mignon to arrive, I can feel my eyes swell with the hurt that bleeds from my heart without permission, and this is not what this night is supposed to represent. I refuse to spend my one night out on the town reliving painful moments. I refuse to invite self-pity to join me for dinner. That spirit is no longer welcome in my world! I have become so lost in my thoughts that I do not notice the maître d' kneeling by my side preparing to catch the tear waiting to escape. His voice is a deep, silky baritone as he speaks, "Allow me to wipe away the sorrow," and he gently catches the falling tear, as though he is a professional tear catcher, without causing havoc to my perfectly positioned make-up or dirtying his stark white handkerchief. Something about him causes an instant and unexpected fire in my Victoria's Secret that catches me off guard. I am afraid that if he makes the slightest suggestion, I will be living out my every fantasy with him this very night as retaliation against Kevin, and maybe even to spite Urijah for his untold mysteries. My God, he has to be the sexiest man I've encountered in a great while, but wait! He is the maître d', the waiter! What am I doing? Just as I am talking myself out of the fantasy he hands me a single, long- stemmed rose and looks deep into my eyes as though he can see the hurt in my soul. As he is about to speak, Alex walks by, laughs, and says, "Running out of options, sis?" and Kevin is following behind her like a lost puppy in heat. What are they doing here? Why would he bring her to my favorite restaurant? Isn't sleeping with my lesbian sister in our marital bed sting enough? To make matters worse, the hostess seats them two tables away with Kevin facing in my direction.

The maître d' interrupts my anger: "My name is Cornelius, let me know if you need anything. Anything at all." I find myself lusting for him. I can feel the moisture against my inner thighs. What is going on? I have never lost control in this manner. This is not normal! Or is this normal and I've forced myself to act abnormally all these years? I would go to the powder room, but Alex just headed in that direction and I do not want another encounter with her. Once the maître d' leaves and Alex is out of sight, Kevin approaches my table and asks that I excuse Alex's behavior, and with tears in his eyes he apologizes for any pain that he caused. "I never meant to hurt you, Jonnie," he says in his most sincere voice. I know this man and he is telling the truth, but why now? He softly grasps my hand, apologizes for bringing her here, and tells me that he will always love me before returning to his table.

I guess that I should be careful how I toss around my wishes. I longed for my husband and here he is; however, he is not alone. I should have specified my desires… Jeez! Throughout the evening I find myself flirting with Kevin through equally exchanged gestures across the room and I'm immensely more excited each time Cornelius approaches. The heat in the atmosphere is so intense that when Kevin walks towards the restrooms and motions for me, I follow without hesitation as though I'm in some sort of trance. Did he just enter the woman's laboratory? Is he going into the woman's washroom? He is and so do I. I find him in the third stall sitting on the toilet with his pants unzipped, exposing his saluting manhood beneath the sexy boxer briefs that I purchased. He is so sexy and the look in his eyes tells me that he wants to be forgiven. I stand frozen, considering all that is at risk. My reputation in the community as a good Christian woman will be shattered if we are caught in an unseemly position, but in the same instant I also remember Alex and her nasty attitude towards me since I caught her in my bed with my husband, as though I did her wrong. Instantaneously, my alive and thriving attitude transforms into revenge and overtakes my desire to maintain my perfect image. I enter the stall, close the door behind me, hike my pencil skirt up around my waist, and straddle Kevin like never before. Technically, he still is my husband and I have every right to make love to my husband, right? In the ladies' room at *Le Chet' Marie On The River* is pushing the limit. Nevertheless I have always allowed my idea of being a lady to interfere with the fact that I have the right to choose my own dance, but 'the lady' won't stop me this time baby! I'm choosing to dance right on top of Kevin's lap! I can't help but to wonder if this dance is one that God would support, or am I heading down a dark path? I don't want my over- thinking to hinder these long-overdue thrusts, so I push rational thoughts out of my head and let my disgust for Alex lead me through this experience. It's a good thing that the stalls are completely enclosed. We slow down just enough each time we hear someone in one of the surrounding stalls, but thoughts of Cornelius fuel my desires so I never completely stop moving, and Kevin's kisses tell me that he enjoys each new angle of my inner being. The amazement beaming from Kevin's eyes ensures that this is the first of many more escapades. Although I'm not certain where my current actions will lead us, the image of his unzipped pants exposing his saluting manhood beneath the sexy boxer briefs pushes me in a forward motion and I anxiously consent to the momentum.

Once we reach what feels like a seven-to-one climax ratio I give Kevin the all-clear sign, wipe my lipstick from behind his ear, and whisper for him to leave the garage door unlocked if he wants a continuation later this evening. He has a puzzled look across his face as he pulls himself together, gives me one last sensual embrace, and exits cautiously. After what Ms. Eloise refers to as a quick 'ho bath', I adjust my clothes, return to my table, and finish my half-eaten meal. Unbeknownst to Alex, Kevin and I continue to exchange glances throughout the rest of the evening. Thoughts of my crossing the lines of virtue spark tingles throughout my body. I lick my lips seductively as I play with my champagne glass, causing Kevin to shift himself several times as he pretends to listen to Alex. To my surprise, someone paid for my meal so I keep my gift card for another night of admiring Cornelius, and perhaps the next time I can meet *him* in the ladies' room. As I'm leaving with my rose in hand Alex asks aloud, "Do you need us to help with the check or did your new boyfriend get you his discount?" For the first time I feel a new confidence as I smile and say, "I've been well taken care of, thank you." If she only knew the details of how well and by whom, she would vomit.

Alex has always harbored a sick competition with me although she would never admit this obvious fact. I usually sit on the sideline refusing to participate in her silly competitive games, but this time I'm allowing myself to suit up in the name of retribution. Whereas I usually maintain that God fight my battles, this time I'm up for the challenge and possess a willingness to fight to win. Again, Cornelius interrupts my negative thoughts and walks me towards the door. "I hope to see you again." To my surprise, I suggestively respond, "Oh, you will." I'm not sure what has gotten into me, but I sort of like it. I'm sure that I will do a lot of praying and soul-searching tonight, but for now I am just going to replay the many delightful images dancing through my thoughts as I enjoy my drive home. I would stop by to visit Daddy, but I'm sure that Mother would read the guilty pleasures written across my face. Dinner for one certainly had its benefits on this hot, unexpected, romantic night! I'm not sure if thanking God is out of line, but I say it aloud nevertheless, "Thank you, God!"

Full Circle

It's been three weeks and a lot of mixed feelings since my night at *Le Chet' Marie On The River*. I find myself feeling guilty for feeling good about something that was so bad in so many ways, but the smiles prompted by the images which won't leave my thoughts are uncontrollable. I don't think that Dear would be proud of my actions that night, but I am proud of the confidence it took for me to follow through. Although I've repented several times and feel a little bad for Alex, the repeating thoughts of the episodes are welcomed and bring about a refreshing enhancement to my daily life. I find myself smiling outwardly for no apparent reason, but soon after wondering if Dear is sitting with Jesus shaking her head in disappointment. Nevertheless, Dear loves me and will somehow keep me on the right path, like she did in my afterlife experience.

The rose given to me by the professional tear catcher still sits atop my closet shelf hidden from the world, as though it contains a secret I care not to publicize. Just a glance at the *Le Chet' Marie On The River* gift card turns any frown upside down. I look forward to going again with the hope that Cornelius will be assigned to personally handle all my needs. The night was so breathtaking that I don't want to spoil the magic by speaking about its amazement. I haven't even told Vanessa because I think that her ability to believe the unbelievable is still on overload after all that she has experienced through my ever-changing world. Besides, where would I begin? Shall I start with Kevin, Cornelius, or Alex and her nasty comments? Oh, and by the way, I had sex with Kevin in a very public place while Alex waited for him at their dinner table and my food got cold. She would never believe that I continued eating a meal that was left unattended, so I know that she would not believe that I stepped out of my box to enjoy life… perhaps a little too much. The whole evening was and still is so overwhelmingly delicious. The mere thought of Kevin's eyes rolled back, while I straddled him causes renewed excitement. I will hold this night close to my heart while I relive specific details and share these moments with no one. I hope that I am choosing the right dance.

Tonight Daddy is being recognized for his positive contributions in the community with a formal dinner and recognition ceremony thrown by the Mayor's office. Mother actually founded *Leisurely Connections*, but Daddy's signature is all over anything positive about the company. Mother was dead set against putting money or any type of contribution back into the community, but Daddy insisted, and for years he has been acknowledged. Even through the toughest moments of him battling cancer, he ensured that the Community Reach program continued. He insisted that his illness should not hinder his continued contributions to the community, which speaks to his deserving this night of gratitude. This is the first year that his efforts have brought about this level of recognition and the smirk behind Mother's façade of a smile states that she is sickened at the thought of him receiving any notoriety at all. What's even more disturbing is the joy I gain by watching her discontent. The dinner is semi-formal and I typically would buy something new to wear for the event, but since buying a new article of clothing is not even a consideration I find myself rummaging through each of my closets for something a little sexier than I usually wear and perhaps even with the tag still attached, which wouldn't be too unusual.

Kevin has been a part of our family for years so I'm certain that he'll be there with Alex. Besides, Alex is the type of rebellion who would want to show off her new man to the masses, even if her new man is her sister's estranged husband. She gets some kind of perverse joy out of shocking others with her outlandish behaviors. It's as though reactions of disgust ignites her craving to push the envelope a bit further each time. I, on the other hand, spend most of my day concerned with how to please others so that they will continue to favor me. So, although my goal is to be an unexpected sexy that will heighten Kevin's regret for leaving, I won't go too far up the sexy scale. Besides, no matter what I wear, Alex will find a way to pull any attention in her direction, even if the attention is negative. Everyone will expect her to show up with one of her girlfriends, but she will show them to never underestimate her unpredictability, while I sit alone and embarrassed for us all. Ms. Eloise will handle the whole situation elegantly, as per usual. She will act as though she has her family under control and pretend as though she personally blessed the union of Kevin and Alex, when the truth is that she does not like Kevin and has never had Alex under control because Alex is just like her. Alex is truly her mother's child.

The night is upon us and Daddy is beaming with pride as he takes his seat onstage, while Ms. Eloise smiles as though she has a small pocket of throw-up sitting on the back of her tongue. Why can't she be happy for Daddy? He is the reason that investors did not pull out years ago when the company was in financial trouble. Additionally, his relationship with the media continues to bring positive press and a national customer following. I hope she finds a way to get it together. Perhaps she should go to the restroom and spit out the hatred that is clearly caught in her throat, but now would not be the right time to exercise the legion she possesses. Of course, Daddy's focus is on giving God the glory for anything positive in his life and being thankful for the challenges that make him stronger in the Lord. For some reason he really loves Mother and is constantly reminding us to be thankful to God for our mother. Just like Dear, daddy is a saint and I feel that he deserves a wife better than Mother. I haven't told him that since I was nine years old and got my one and only spanking from him for speaking disrespectful words against Mother. Anyway, tonight is about him and the focus is all positive.

Dear's presence is never far away and the proof is in this multicolored, sexy gown that was waiting for me in the back of the closet with tags still attached. It seems as though Dear led me right to the dress that fit my newly found curves perfectly. I grow anxious as I await Kevin's arrival. I have not seen or spoken to him since we had sex in the powder room at *Le Chet' Marie On The River*. Because seeing Kevin is too painful, I've arranged that he pick up the girls from school on Fridays and drop them off at school the following Monday when it's his weekend. For the past three weeks I find myself regretting that decision because I miss him and would love to run into him. Where are the damn teacher conferences when you need them? The absence of the past three weeks should make for an interesting reunion, even if from a far. My dress is a long, slinky, wraparound with splits up to my mid- thigh on both sides. My cleavage is also nicely accented and my leg muscles are delightfully displayed through the sheer stockings I found for ninety-nine cents on the shelf at Walmart. Who knew that nice stockings did not have to cost twenty-six dollars? I have wasted so much money over the years being what Kevin used to refer to as "a snob".

My personal recession and my afterlife experiences bring about many revelations and I am thankful for now being able to find the many blessings in the silver linings. I have several pairs of heels that match, but chose the five-inch, multicolored sling-back pumps with the woven material across the toe. I always match my bra and panties and tonight is no exception as I slip into my lacey crotchless panties and matching push-up bra in Kevin's favorite color. I chose these panties in case I need quick access for another restroom trip… A girl can dream, right? ☺ Just the thought of a repeat of the *Le Chet' Marie On The River* incident causes excitement, but I'm torn. Should I allow myself to feel this way about Kevin? He *is* my husband, but also my sister's boyfriend and being with him would probably hurt her feelings and potentially hurt me all over again. I am not sure if Alex has any real feelings for Kevin or if she's toying with him because it is convenient and presents the thrill of another self-proclaimed game that she is winning. Anyway, I pray for strength as they enter the room forty- five minutes after dinner is underway.

Alex always makes an entrance and tonight is no different. She has on a dress that exposes her entire back, which means that she is without a brassiere so her breasts are a bit saggy; as saggy as perky breasts can get. She has always been blessed with perfect breasts, but hopefully this will change when and if she has kids. Ms. Eloise does not hesitate with her comments, "Alex' dress is so short that if she were to bend over everyone would see her woo who… and dinner is almost over. I hope they ate before they got here". Kevin has his hand on Alex' bare back, which causes instant jealousy on my part; however, he immediately removes his hand once our eyes meet. They both speak and Alex and mother exchange a few unpleasant words as they take their seats at our table. Kevin is positioned almost directly across from me, while Mother is to my left, which makes it convenient for her to lean over and scold me for not bringing a date, "Why didn't you bring a date? You're embarrassing yourself parading around town alone like you're desperate… when you're not disappearing for weeks on end. You're a pretty girl. I'm sure you could have found someone to bring with you besides Vanessa!" I want to ask her to stay out of my business and tell her that I was not disappearing, I was dead!, but of course I respond with a polite and respectful, "You're right, but I knew that Vanessa would want to be here to celebrate Daddy." Showing her respect is often difficult, but Dear, Daddy, and God all insist that I respect my parents, so I must obey. Besides, I don't want my days to be shortened on her account.

Immediately, Kevin makes eye contact and is trying to tell me something. I don't read lips well, so I'm at a loss and I don't want Vanessa to see us. Throughout the night she periodically leans in to ask if I'm ok because she knows of the pain that I experienced when Kevin left. However, she doesn't know the whole financial mess that I'm in, just that I'm on a budget because of our legal separation and that our funds are frozen pending the legalities. I can see that Kevin is doing something under the table. My speculation is that he and Alex are fondling each other and then, to Ms. Eloise's disdain, a ringtone plays from my phone. "Why isn't your phone on silent?" she scornfully whispers. I scramble to stop the never-ending text tone as everyone within earshot looks at me a bit irritated. I know better, but never thought that I would receive any type of notification since I walked away from Urijah. I stop the noise as quickly as possible and then realize that Kevin has sent me a text message that reads, "What happened 2 u?" I quickly tossed a convenient lie out on the table: "It's my job." For the remainder of the evening Kevin and I exchange text messages as follows:

Me: when?

Kevin: I left the garage door unlocked? Me: what? Why?

Kevin: U told me 2… Me: No I didn't!

Kevin: Yes u did. That night, remember?

Me: Ohhhhh. So you did?

Kevin: Did what? Left the garage unlocked? Yes!!

Me: Wow…

Kevin: I've waited 4 u every night

Me: You have? No you have not

Kevin: Yes! I have… But I guess u chickened out

Me: No… so you seriously have waited for me?

Kevin: Yes & that dress is hot on ur body! I'm excited. It's a good thing that I don't have 2 stand up anytime soon

Me: Why? You're really excited? Hard?

Kevin: Yes. U r so gorgeous & u r owning ur sexy n a new way now. Btw, I love the curves… may I touch?

Me: Really? You think? Thx & maybe…

Kevin: Yes! I'm sure someone else also loves them curves…

Me: :-}

Kevin: I'm just thankful that u r speaking 2 me again

Me: God is good to me so I have to forgive and move forward

Kevin: U surprised me the other night. I didn't think u would

actually follow me and don't forget about me while you're moving forward

Me: Well, I'm full of surprises lately

Kevin: U were like a wild animal, unleashed

Me: Really? Wow… lol

Kevin: I have thought about u a lot since that night & each time I bcum xcited

Me: What have you done about that? Kevin: Handled my bizness

Me: I bet you have

Kevin: Mostly n shower, but always alone!

Me: I'm sure… :-| smh

Kevin: Really… only u can extinguish the fire u ignited that night

Me: :-}

Kevin: I want 2 talk 2 u… soon

Me: Well… leave the garage door unlocked

Kevin: I have… 4 the past 3 weeks

Me: Well, keep doing it and perhaps I will surprise you.

Kevin: I will!

Kevin: How will I no?

Me: How will you know what?

Kevin: When u plan 2 surprise me?

Me: When I show up!

Kevin: Wow… I'll b waiting

Me: you'd better be!

Before I realize how much time has passed, Daddy is being announced and heading up to the podium to make his speech. I can't believe that Kevin and I have texted the entire evening without anyone noticing us both texting. Ms. Eloise leans over several times during the evening and tells me that it would be ok to leave if my job needs me. She would love for me to be called away from Daddy's celebration. Alex is so oblivious to our actions because she is in her own world flirting with the lady at the next table. She totally missed the fact that Kevin spent the evening looking under the table at his phone. As a matter of fact, she is too conceited to ever suspect Kevin's attraction to me again; or any other woman for that matter, as long as she is within eyeshot. Kevin is her only experience with a man and, boy, does she have a lot to learn.

I am on such a high tonight. Urijah was the last man who sparked these types of feelings. The night of sex with Kevin in the restroom was more about revenge, but now I am starting to love him again. I really wish Dear were here to offer some of her great advice. I really miss her! Although there are two little girls who never allow for a dull moment in the house or my life, Dear's absence is forever present. On the ride home Vanessa asks, "What is going on with you tonight? And I know that you were not texting your job, so don't lie. The atmosphere doesn't light up with joy when your employer calls." I am so glad that she asks because I am dying to tell and her asking was just the invitation I needed. I tell her the whole story while she intently listens. To my surprise she says that she is glad that I am smiling again and tells me that my loyalties are to me, not Alex or Kevin, and then she asks the ultimate question, "So when are you going over there?" I am so not prepared for this reality. I have toyed with this man all night, but can't really see myself sneaking into Alex's house through the garage… And if I did, then what? Alex is so angry at life and would welcome any reason to kick my butt, which she definitely would do if she caught me in her home with her man, even though he is my husband. When we arrive at Vanessa's house she convinces me to let the girls spend the night, and tells me to call her if I need any type of backup. Vanessa has always been like a sister to me and possesses a lot of characteristics that I wish to have. She is outspoken and confident.

Vanessa and Alex got into a physical altercation in my parents' backyard right before my welcome home from college luncheon began, and Vanessa beat her tail. No one attempted to stop the fight too soon because Alex was being disrespectful to everyone and crossed the line with Vanessa. Vanessa is the only person who I have ever known Alex to fear. Even Dear said, "Sometimes you have to allow them to take their lumps," and she and Ms. Eloise stood there and watched Vanessa punch Alex in the mouth repeatedly until she stopped calling us 'bitches' and apologized. What made the day much more powerful is Vanessa not allowing Alex to leave my celebration "because that would be rude," Vanessa told her. Wow! I had never seen Alex under so much control. Vanessa apologized to us all, but said that she could not stand idly by and watch Alex's disrespectful nature any longer. Alex eventually made peace with Vanessa and they have been good ever since, because Alex no longer test Vanessa. So when Vanessa tells me to call her if I need any type of back up, I know that she means business. As we are sitting in the car talking, I receive another text from Kevin: "The door is unlocked... chicken?" I show Vanessa the text and without another thought I decide, "I'm going!" Vanessa smiles and gives me some words of advice: "Don't get caught" and "Don't put more on this than what it is. This is you having sex with your soon-to-be ex-husband. This does not mean that you are getting back together and I don't want you hurt, so leave your heart out of this." She gently squeezes my hand and tells me that she loves me before getting out of the car. Her words of advice are timely because I do still love Kevin and a big part of me wants us to put our family back together.

On the drive to Alex's house my mind races and my body follows with anticipation. However, Vanessa's words of wisdom ring continuously and cause Mrs. Revenge to take over my every intention. I don't know what we will do once I arrive. How will he know I'm there? Will we leave and go get a hotel? I don't know the plan, yet I continue to drive. Kevin moved in with Alex once he left our house because our finances are tied up in litigation, so he says. I was kidding when I told him to leave the garage door unlocked; nevertheless, I'm here. As I park in front of Alex's garage my heart is pounding and my hands are shaking. I take a deep breath, go to the side garage door, and just as he texted, the door is unlocked.

I am now standing in a dark garage in five-inch heels and a slinky evening gown. I climb into the back seat of Alex's S550 Mercedes-Benz because it is cold in the garage, and then I wait. I am reaching for my phone to text him when the door to the house opens. My heart drops to my feet! Oh hell… How will I explain being in her car, in her garage, in the dark? What am I doing??? Then I realize that Kevin is standing in the doorway looking into the dark garage. He is about to close the door because he doesn't see me in the back seat so I take the little flashlight on my keyring and shine it in his eyes. His smile illuminates through the darkness as he shuts the door behind him and walks towards the car. He looks so sexy in pajama pants, a wife-beater, and bare feet. He climbs in the back seat with me and without hesitation we embrace in a passionate kiss, which leads to groping, heavy breathing, nibbling, and then the ultimate penetration of flesh. He is pleasantly surprised when he learns that my panties are crotchless, which increases his excitement causing him to take a closer look. He kisses me in places and angles that he never has before. I'm sure that Alex has taught him some of her tricks, but instead of becoming angry all over again I am quietly thankful for how Alex's lessons are to my benefit. He has me in ways I never thought possible, especially in the back of a car. I never knew a headrest could be so useful. At one point I find myself wanting to cry because we never experienced this type of passion during our marriage, but I hear Vanessa's words, "Leave your heart out of this," so I get it together and physically enjoy the moments. Periodically I am the aggressor and his response to this type of control fuels my power. I do everything that I want to do to him, which does not include giving him oral pleasure, but there is always next time. We were in Alex's car for a little over an hour so she must have been asleep already. Once she is sleeping she usually doesn't wake until the next morning because she is a very deep sleeper, so I guess Kevin feels that we are safe. When we are done he walks me to my car, passionately kisses me, and watches me drive away right after he tells me that he loves me. He is either very bold, arrogant, or really does love me. I'm floating on air, completely satisfied, and a bit confused as to where we go from here. I won't allow myself to feel guilty for sleeping with Alex's boyfriend because he is still my husband. I've loved that man since I was in my teens. He was my first love and grew to know me as intimately as his next breath, so I'm not letting go until I'm ready. No matter how the situation appears or where he currently resides, he is legally, mentally, emotionally, and as of about thirty minutes ago, physically mine. He pursued me and I willingly opened up to his every intent. If we are ever caught, Alex will just have to accept the facts because she initiated this sick competition that I appear to be winning. At least I feel like the winner this night. Perhaps karma is justice because right now I feel justified! From my vantage point, we've just come full circle and I refuse to bow out gracefully.

In the Midst of Darkness

The past two months have been the best months or the darkest months of my life; the verdict is still pending. On one hand, I have never felt more alive and free to do as I please. On the other hand, I keep waiting for God to smite me for enjoying and even creating darkness in the midst of the light that followed me back from the afterlife. At least I am no longer depressed or feel like life's victim. Conversely, I have become the villain in a lot of ways. I have made love to Kevin in every part of my sister's home and mostly while she was asleep in another part of the house. My need for revenge, love for my husband, and perhaps even the sickness of wanting to beat Alex at the game that she created has taken over and leads me down a murky path that I'm not ready to leave. I so enjoy the renewed attentions of my husband and the amazed look on his face every time I pull a new trick out of my bag. I don't know if I can ever stop this newfound activity I'm learning to enjoy more with each new experience. It's like I get a rush with each new high and I'm becoming a junky to my new drug of choice. I am confident that this is not what Dear meant when she told me to choose my dance, but I am enjoying myself.

The girls are spending the night with Vanessa and her family and I'm feeling a little adventurous, so I drive towards Alex's neighborhood. I don't have plans to see Kevin, but I don't want to sit in the house alone so I go for a drive; even though I shouldn't be wasting my gas. While sitting at a stop light close to Alex's house I text Kevin, "get rdy". He responds, "get rdy for what? I'm in bed". I immediately get angry! Is he denying my visit? I was sort of kidding, but now I am going, he can't stop me, and he'd better be ready for me. It's only 10:30 and he rarely goes to bed before midnight, so he must be having a romantic night with Alex. The thought of him sexing Alex severely pisses me off because, in an effort to get me to go downtown the last couple of times we were together, he told me that he and Alex no longer have sex. If this is a lie I'm not sure how I will respond, but he will have to answer. I know the game in which I'm involved and I'm prepared to follow the rules, as long as I'm privy to all of the information. I told him, "Lying to me will be detrimental to our friendship" and he was adamant the passion which fueled their fling was dead. He was almost in tears as he explained how he sits on the sidelines watching while she and Talia exclude him. He seemed so sincere when he told me that I was his reason for getting out of bed these days. He talks about coming home, but I'm not ready to go back to our life. I still don't trust him and I'll be damned if I allow him unlimited access to my loins while he jeopardizes my health by sleeping with my freaky sister.

Although I don't comply with his repeated requests, I often consider visiting his lower extremities, so now I'm mad at the thought that he may be allowing Alex to please him and lying to me about their encounters. It's as though I have to be better at whatever Alex is doing to him at this very moment and I'm truly feeling up for the challenge, so with each trick of my imagination my anger deepens. I'm steaming hot! I'm heated with anger and strangely enough, passion. So much so that I find myself parking on the side of Alex's house, slipping off my heels, and climbing the balcony that leads to the custom French doors of her master suite.

Alex loves the fresh air blowing across her face while she sleeps so I know that the doors will be open. I peek through the window and to my surprise, Kevin is in the bed working on his laptop with folders of paperwork between he and Alex while she sleeps with that mask across her eyes. I am very relieved that he and Alex are not in some hot lovemaking session. The relief overtakes my common sense and before I give much thought to the situation I get on my knees and crawl through the French doors past Alex and around to Kevin's side of the bed. As he is intently typing and obviously deeply focused on his work I reach my hand under the covers and gently caress his manliness, which initially isn't so manly. He about jumps out of his skin, which disturbs Alex's sleep just a bit. The fear across Kevin's face and his repeated half-attempts of rejection fuel my determination to get what I came to receive – *my way*, despite what he says he wants. Besides, I spent years catering to his desires and now I just don't care about what he or anyone else wants. I am choosing to be selfish, but I am not sure that I'm making this choice for the right reasons. If he had asked me to climb up the balcony, sneak through the French patio doors, crawl past Alex, around the bed that they currently share, and perform services on him while my sleeping sister lay next to him, I would have accused him of losing his mind for even thinking that I would stoop so low. However, the fact that this was my idea makes the thought intriguing and exciting, so I go full steam ahead with the dance that I have chosen at this time. Within no time, the laptop is in the bed between he and Alex, and he's no longer resisting. Conversely, he has slid down in a full horizontal position facing outward, which makes my mission more accomplishable. I put my head under the covers and caress his manliness with gentle vigor. I've done my research and passion has set my body on fire, so he is getting my very best efforts.

His continued growth and pulsation are stronger than I've ever known, which increases my eagerness to caress his parts like a soldier returning home from a long war. He struggles to enjoy my attention in silence while blocking Alex's attempts as she periodically reaches to connect a part of her body with his. Quite possibly she is slightly awakened with each sound he struggles to stifle. The torment of anxiety, coupled with gratification displayed across his face, increases my dark sense of satisfaction. At this very moment, I feel that I am gaining retribution for them cheating on me in my bed. I don't think that he should be able to enjoy my company without sacrifice or risk on his part. Although I still love him, I am still angry at him for his betrayal of our marriage and he must pay for his infidelities in one way or another.

Once I am satisfied with the level of torture and gamble I have created for Kevin and just before he reaches complete gratification, I remove my head from beneath the pricey down comforter my sister has adorned the king-sized bed with, and turn to crawl back out the same way I entered. To my surprise, Kevin slides out of the bed and attacks me from behind, right there on the opposite side of the very bed in which Alex sleeps. My first instinct is to fight him off out of fear of waking Alex, getting caught, and her kicking my butt for disrespecting her in her house and in her bedroom! I left my purse, phone and any resemblance of a weapon in the car so I am truly vulnerable to any attack she would offer; equally I am not a fighter. I can almost hear her voice aloud as if God is trying to warn me of the inevitable danger just moments away. However, as Kevin rips my lacy La Perla lingerie away from my mid-section, my apprehension takes a back seat to pleasure and I allow myself to fall into the whirlwind of excitement, indulgence, and risk that is fueled by the darkness of my attempts at revenge.

As Kevin is busy whispering "I love you" in my ear I am busy pushing my torn red La Perla panties under the bed that he and Alex share in the hopes that she may later find them and know that he is cheating on the 'Almighty Queen B' – in her home! Our explosions leave puddles of evidence atop her handwoven Persian rug, which excites me, causing continuation in various positions. Like heated young lovers, our infidelities expand to her walk-in closet and I purposely pull several of her expensive outfits to the floor and use them as my mattress as we exceed previous records of release. In the name of passion, Kevin goes along as I rip the closet rods holding her pricey ensembles out of the wall causing two racks of her neatly positioned clothes to meet the floor... probably for the first time. Finally, just for kicks and giggles, I squirt, which I did not know was possible, on her brand new Christian Louboutin Interlopa 165 fringed suede knee boots. I wish her luck getting my signature scent out of all those fringes.

Once we are finished, Kevin walks me to the front door, out to my car to ensure my safety, kisses me as though we are teenagers, and stands in the middle of the street waving as he watches me drive away. This reminds me of when we were dating. We were head over heels in love, and neither of us was shy about showing our feelings. His display of emotion causes conflict in my spirit. For the first time in my life I have hate in my heart for the man whom I have truly loved for most of my adult experience with romance. Hate is not a foreign sensation for my heart. I've prayed for relief from the suppressed disgust that I feel for Mother ever since I can remember, but I never thought that I could truly hate Kevin. As I drive home I find a sick sense of delight just thinking about the hidden panties under the bed, the oral sex performed on my husband while Alex lay next to him, and the acts he performed on me next to the bed where Alex slept. I've never known such intensity! I'm curious how he will fix the mess we made in her closet, and if he will notice my essence sprayed across her very expensive boots.

I feel powerful and proud of myself for taking control of my desires. I now understand a little better why he cheated. It must have been the rush, but now that he is free to have sex with Alex whenever he wants, I find him in bed next to her, working. In my immediate opinion, what Kevin and I have done in her house over the past few months is much worse than her sleeping with my husband in my bed. Specifically because they made a bad judgment call in a weak moment and what I've done was purposefully calculated and meant to hurt my sister and cause pain to my cheating husband – two people whom I really do love. As I pull into my garage, this thought brings me sadness and Kirk Franklin's *Hello Fear* playing through the speakers does not help me rid the sudden conviction. As the song embraces me, I sit in a dark garage listening to every word with tears streaming down my cheeks and hitting me in the perfect spot to water my darkened heart. I can't form the words necessary to ask God for forgiveness since I know that I am not done with this particular type of sin. The pay-off is too great which makes my remorse minimal. I'm mostly proud of the woman I'm becoming since my close bouts with death, and I'm not yet ready to place this situation in God's hands. I've always prayed my way through tough situations as I hoped for a better tomorrow, and now I'm tired of hoping and I want to take action. Even though what I initiated was wrong, I feel a sense of power that I've never known. Honestly, at this very moment I feel strong and in control of my life. Just the thought of the amazement on Kevin's face as he allowed me to wreak havoc on Alex's belongings makes me feel like superwoman. I allow Kirk's words to speak into the atmosphere and hope that God interprets what it is I would say if I could create the remorse necessary to pray myself out of this darkness. When the song is over I wipe my eyes to clear my vision enough to maneuver around the bikes and over the skates, making my way into a cold, empty house. While soaking in the tub enjoying the massaging jets as they play a medley over my tired body, I plan my next move. I laugh sneakily, thinking about possible outcomes. I decide that I will need an unsuspecting participant as I pray that I don't become completely lost in the midst of all this darkness.

Does God Love Through Darkness?

I t's 3:33am and as I lay in the bed rummaging through my mind about the next phase of my plan I realize that Kevin is still getting the upper hand. He disrupted my world and now I am helping him to do the same to my sister, but what price is he paying? Why should he still be standing and smiling every time I see him? In the name of sisterhood I have to alter this path that we are on so that he is not winning. Throughout most sleepless nights I mentally search for ways to equal the pain Kevin caused, realizing that I may not be able to recover from severe destruction to his heart. The broken sprinkler head outside my window is causing a puddle, which serves as another reminder of the many things that I can no longer afford to fix. Listening to the water outside my window also bring about the pleasant reminder of the gift card for *Le Chet' Marie On The River* and my beautiful encounters the last time I was there. I quickly jump out of bed and hurry to the computer in the hopes that they have an opening soon. To my surprise there is a recent cancelation, so I type in my information as quickly as my fingers will move and hit enter. Someone must be smiling on me because this place is impossible to get into on the same day, especially on a Saturday. The reservation is at 5pm, which is much earlier than I would rather have dinner, but I refuse to let such a small inconvenience create a detractor in an otherwise exciting moment. Perhaps I will even be lucky enough to be served by that sexy maître d', Cornelius. Throughout my usual Saturday rituals my focus changes from the evil I wanted to bring to Kevin to the thrill of seeing Cornelius again as I pray that he is working today. I am tempted to call to see if he will be there, but pride won't allow me to dial the number. Besides, they probably don't give out that type of information for safety reasons. I leave this evening in God's hands and hope that he continues to smile on me – even though my recent actions don't deserve his favor.

I'm so excited about having dinner at *Le Chet' Marie On The River* that I arrive at 4:05pm for a 5:00pm reservation. I let the hostess know that I am here and have a seat in the bar area. I have to be careful not to have more than one drink because I don't have extra money, so the $200 gift card will have to cover the whole evening. The time seems to crawl as I periodically glance around looking for Cornelius, to no avail. Although I can't see into the restaurant area, I can see other maître d's walking by, so he must not be here. Well, worst-case scenario I will have a great meal and make it home in time to catch a nine o'clock movie on one of the local channels or perhaps I will see what Vanessa is doing and hang out with her and her family for a little while.

I am looking around so much while the hostess is walking me to my table that she asks if I am expecting someone else. I want to tell her, "Yes, I'm looking for that sexy Cornelius," but of course I give her a puzzled "What do you mean?" innocent look as I take my seat. I am honestly disappointed and escape inward to my thoughts until he interrupts my inner world with that deep sultry voice: "It's lovely to see you again." To my surprise it's him… Cornelius and I cannot contain my emotions. As my smile takes my entire face captive, my night improves from that moment forward. He shows me so much special attention that at times I feel as though I am the only customer in the restaurant. I thought that I may be imagining his attentions until I learn that he was scheduled to be off work at five, but paid his peer to allow him to handle my table personally. The deal is sealed when he asks if he can take me elsewhere for dessert. Without a second thought I remember the lemon pound cake that I made earlier and invite him to my house for dessert. He agrees to bring the movie if I add coffee with the pound cake, and allow him time to go home and freshen up first. I have just enough time to get home, tell Vanessa all about my evening thus far, and freshen up before the doorbell rings.

When I open the door, the maître d' has been replaced by an even sexier man with the prettiest lips, breathtaking smile, and amazingly dreamy eyes that radiate through my tough, high-class demeanor. I'm melting inside and it's a pleasant thought that Kevin is not the cause. In his hands he holds a single red rose decorated in fresh greenery and baby's breath resting beautifully in a crystal vase, along with a bottle of the sparkling wine I ordered with dinner the last two times I dined at *Le Chet' Marie On The River*. The gifts are impressive, but even more impressive is that the rose is from a nearby florist that closed hours ago, not from the restaurant where he works. I'm not sure how he got the rose at this late hour, but I'm sure he could have gotten it at a discount or even free from his place of employment, but he spared no expense. His effort has not gone unnoticed. I invite him in and he enjoys a generous helping of my home-made lemon pound cake as he sips coffee and I sip sparkling wine. The conversation that fills the atmosphere is so beautiful I forget that he is a waiter, and the best part is that he makes me laugh. Not just "Ha, ha" laugh… but 'the laughter that flows from your stomach until you almost pee your pants' laugh. I have to excuse myself twice to go to the restroom. He seems very comfortable with being in my home as though he is used to being in luxury. He handles my imported crystal glasses and antique dishes with the utmost care. I am nervous as he insists on helping me clear the table until I see him navigate his gentle strength without one mishap. We retire to the family room to watch the romantic movie he brought as the fire sings an inspiring love song in the hues of red, orange, and yellow from the fireplace. I get so lost in his moments that I have to keep reminding myself that he is but a waiter. How could he be so refined? I have a feeling that what I see is but the surface of this hunk of a man. This is the perfect night… and then I receive a text from Kevin.

"Leave the door unlocked"

I politely excuse myself and respond, "tonight is not good for me"

Kevin replies, "It will be! I'll b there soon" I again reply, "no. not tonight"

Kevin doesn't take my rejection well and immediately replies, "aft last night, you don't get to tell me no. It took me forever to clean up the mess we made, but it was worth it. I need more of you!" If you are too sore I can be gentle.

How dare he make demands on me after all that he has put me through? Does he honestly think that I am sitting around waiting for him to call me when he decides to play? Revenge recognizes an opportunity and pushes me to respond without much thought.

"Not tonight. I'm tired... turning phone off & going to bed"

I changed the locks when Kevin moved out, so he can't get in unless I leave the doors unlocked. I know that I haven't heard the last of Kevin tonight so I put my phone on silent, apologize for the interruptions, and go unlock the garage doors. When I return to the couch I sit even closer to Cornelius. The dancing flames ablaze coupled with the romantic mood pouring from the actors on the big screen help to create a plan of action. I hear a truck park in front of the house and realize that this must be Kevin. Without thought, I place my finger under Cornelius's chin, turn his head in my direction and kiss him as though we have done this type of thing for years. When he responds favorably I straddle his lap facing him. As the kisses intensify I hear the garage door gently close and Kevin tiptoe across the kitchen floor. Cornelius's back is to the kitchen so he is none the wiser, but through my loosely closed eyes I can see the pain on Kevin's face as he stands frozen, watching me attack Cornelius with gentle nibbles to his lips, ears, neck, chest, and every section of skin in those areas as I maintain a steady rotating motion on top of his lap. Unlike me when I caught Alex and Kevin having sex in our marriage bed, Kevin is not frozen for long and quietly leaves the house the way that he entered. I expected to hear his truck speed away, but all that I can hear is Kirk Franklin's *Hello Fear* playing loudly in my head as I take advantage of this unsuspecting gentle stranger. The conviction is clear as God's love embraces my heart, and for the first time in a long while, I feel remorse. Just as quickly as the hatred of Kevin began... it has ended and the tears flow as the kisses stop. Here I sit on this man's lap and the tears have graduated to a full-blown, unexplainable sob. I try to excuse myself, but he sits me next to him, holds me tightly, and encourages me through his tender words, "just let it go, babe. Let God work."

Who is this man? Have I been entertaining an angel while acting like a whore? This thought brings about more shame and regret for the darkness that I have allowed to overtake my intentions and spark my every movement for the past several months. Instead of choosing to let God heal my hurt, I chose to fight my own battles and seek retribution in my own manner. As I try to explain the tears to Cornelius, he assures me, "I recognize God's work. There's no need to explain." He goes on to quote scriptures and tell me that God's love can heal even the deepest wounds. He says that I wear my pain like a coat of armor and that it's time to leave the heavy covering at the altar for God to rid. He speaks to me as though he can see my life's pain displayed across my forehead – and this is a little frightening. He locates a face cloth and Dear's Bible in her room, and returns to wipe the sorrow that pours down my cheeks as he reads from God's Word. My repented heart greets the sun as it rises and shines across my puffy face as a sign of God's grace and mercy re-entering my world. I attempt to explain to Cornelius that I am not the woman who jumped on his lap and attacked him. He lets me know that he has witnessed another one of God's miracles and all that happened was necessary for my continued healing and deliverance. What does he know about my deliverance? Was he one of the angels standing with Dear in Heaven? I don't remember everything about my experiences in the afterlife, but I often see brief flashes as a reminder that it was all real! Cornelius continues to hold me and stroke through my hair as he tells me that God is going to work even bigger miracles in my life.

We move to the kitchen and I sit on my knees in the chair in a childlike position watching him as he cooks us breakfast. I feel full, but force myself to at least taste the food. I am full of God's love, His Word, and forgiveness. I excuse myself and take the best shower since Dear was here with me. As the water runs over my head and down my face I am thankful for life and another chance at making honorable choices. I get out of the shower and put on my comfy sweats and oversized T-shirt... you know the kind that I would never wear to impress a man. Equally, I'm not wearing a stitch of make-up. For some reason I feel as though I have been in a revival all night as my soul rejoices. I feel as though I do not have to be anyone other than myself with Cornelius, and right now I choose to be regular ol' comfortable Jonnie.

Cornelius has used Dear's bathroom to shower and change into a pair of Daddy's sweatpants he found in the back of Dear's closet. This man must be of God because I have not allowed anyone to go into Dear's room since her passing, and at this moment I am glad that he has gotten comfortable and intends to stay for a little while longer because I do not want to be alone.

It's 5:00am and I have decided not to go to church this Sunday morning. I lie across my bed and, as though he has read my mind, he tells me that I do not have to be alone. He is a perfect gentleman and quietly prays for me as I rest peacefully on his chest, looking up at the glow in the ceiling, thanking God for His compassion and forgiveness. One last tear escapes as I decide that I will call Kevin when I think he is awake and apologize for choosing to purposefully hurt him. Choice is a powerful, God-given tool and not only have I chosen to ask for Kevin's forgiveness I am choosing to enter the next dance in my life with the angel wrapped in maître d's clothing, no matter his financial status.

The phenomenon of Cornelius happening at this time in my life proves that God does love through the darkness, because I had no plan to stop seeking my own retribution. I traded in the spirits of self-pity and depression for the spirits of anger and revenge. After all God allowed me to experience, I still chose to walk in darkness, and yet He loves me enough to rescue me from myself. I am thankful for my adventures through the darkness because each step of my evolution has been a necessary means of getting me to this moment. I decide not to place too much judgment upon my own head, because a harsh sentencing will hinder my next steps towards my complete healing. I lie here listening to the healthy rhythm of Cornelius's heart as I realize at this moment I'm entering the next season of my deliverance. The God that I'm learning to know is not the God that I've had in a box all of these years. The enormity of His Grace and Mercy is more than I can comprehend, so I stop trying to make sense of his Love and just accept it! I whisper in my spirit repeatedly the only praise that seems to fit, "I love you, Father... I love you, Father..." as I realize I may never be able to understand a love pure enough to embrace me, even in the midst of my filthy darkness. Thank you, Lord for Your Agape love! Amen.

Shattered Italian Crystal

Never before have I been so in awe of another human being as I am with Cornelius, the maître d'. I thought that I had reached my peak understanding of who God is and His capabilities in my afterlife experience; however, each moment with Cornelius opens me up to know a greater God for myself. Whether we are cooking, laughing, playing cards, watching movies, reading to enhance our spirituality, or just holding each other, God is ever-present. Not because Cornelius is preachy or religious, but because he is positive, encouraging, and inspires me to see God in all that I do. I find myself accepting my mistakes as moments of growth and I now understand that I will never be perfect. Realizing that I will never be perfect may sound like a ridiculous realization; however, childhood taught me that life leaves little room for mistakes. I find myself striving to be perfect, while mentally highlighting my imperfections as I judge myself for not being the image of perfection. Whew... The thought alone is exhausting.

Repairing self-esteem issues is not an easy process, but Cornelius seems to be up for the challenge as he assists me in my continued growth. He remains patient when I spout negative, self-damaging comments and then once I'm calm, he gently points out the blessing in the less than perfect moment. He encourages me to relax and states that, when I feel the need to be perfect that I should instead, strive towards excellence, not perfection. Completely relaxing around him is not easy because I don't want to show him too much of who I really am in case he is not up for a project of this capacity.

On the outside, I appear to be a woman who most would desire to be close with, in any capacity; however, I am still a work in progress and quite ashamed of some of my dealings. The other day I dropped one of my expensive Italian crystal glasses and, as I watched the shattered Italian crystal race across the kitchen floor, I instantly began to cry. I take good care of my things and am not clumsy, so why am I dropping a pricey piece of Italian crystal? What is wrong with me? I can't afford to replace this right now and I hate not having the entire set on view in my dual see-through, glass display cabinet. I often walk through the house in the quiet of the night to look upon all that I've accomplished, which reminds me that my life was once a dream fulfilled. I feel as though a woman of my means and status should have plenty that displays her success, but I won't if I destroy my belongings. The bill collectors calling, the empty gas tanks, disconnected cable, and now the shattered Italian crystal pull me towards the realization that my success is fading and this thought scares me. Looking at my collection of things provides a limited view into my past successes, which gives my life meaning and reminds me of my ability to succeed, so of course I cry as another piece of the fruits of my labor dissipates.

The Italian crystal exploding across the floor seemed to yell up to me as it faced its destiny, "Loser! How could you fail me, when I've brought you so much joy?" Cornelius acknowledged my reaction without judgment as he asked me questions that led me to think about why breaking glass would bring me to tears. Through our discussion I discovered that I equated the loss of the glass with the loss of my prosperity. The shattered Italian crystal represented me taking another step in the wrong direction and this reality is very upsetting. Cornelius patiently listened and validated my concerns; however, he then helped me to realize everything else that the shattered Italian crystal could represent; growth, ridding unnatural detachments, the building of my patience, seeing the object as just that... an object... etc. By the time we finished our discussion I had come to the realization that the shattered Italian crystal only represented what I allowed. The freedom of this realization was so powerful that I could have busted up every piece of

Italian crystal in the house, and believe me, there is a lot. However, I decided that the growth of the moment was more invigorating than destroying my house. The shattered Italian crystal glass was just that: a broken glass. No more, no less, just broken glass.

Kali, who is most like me, noticed the missing piece of crystal as she and Tia sat at the table after school eating their snack. Kali was almost in tears as I explained that I had dropped the glass. Looking in her tearful eyes made me realize the damage created by the spirit of perfection, so I anxiously explained the lesson I learned from the shattered Italian crystal. Both of the girls seemed to grasp the idea of us having the authority to relinquish the unnatural connection to inanimate objects a lot faster than I did. Tia could not articulate her thoughts very well, but I could feel the relief for us in her spirit as though she was saying "It's about time you two got it." Kali was almost as excited at the realization as I was, as she grasped the idea that it's just glass. She sat taller in her chair, as though she accepted the growth in the powerful realization that she has control over how she allows things to affect her. She asked, "So, Mommy, I can choose how I respond to life's mistakes?" Her question was so profound and brought back Dear's words, "Choose the dance". "Oh my God, thank you! I think that I'm starting to get it," I thought over and over as we finished our conversation while snacking on apples and carrots. The atmosphere was light and joyous in the days that followed. Kali corrected herself every time she would begin to speak negatively about herself, "It's a mistake… now, where's the lesson." Thank God that she is recognizing her God-given power as a child!

Seeing Cornelius is always refreshing, especially after a few days apart. As I tell him about the girls and the lesson they learned when Kali noticed the missing glass, he smiles and nods as though he already knows the story. His being able to read my spirit is a little unnerving and I often become afraid that he may leave or that life may take him away like it did Urijah, so I have not shared my financial difficulties. He just thinks that I'm really frugal with money. I hope that God continues to cover the personal secrets that need not be shared at this point in our relationship. Cornelius and I share a unique connection and therefore he again reads my spirit and assures me that he will be here until I no longer need or want him. I am sure that I will always want him, so my fear subsides, until I think about my beautiful time with Urijah.

I was certain that Urijah and I would somehow ride off into the sunset hopelessly in love, but he was planning his ride with someone else. Thanks to Cornelius, I am no longer angry at Urijah, but I would love to ask him a few questions. Why didn't he tell me about the baby and his wife, girlfriend, or whoever she is? Urijah is a beautiful person and I will probably always have a gentle love for him, but we're in different places in our lives; we always were, no matter how much I wanted otherwise. I guess that I will always have affection for him because of the positive roles he played in my spiritual growth, but life dictated that our love remained at a non-physical level, and the bigger part of me is ok with this fact. Besides, the age difference mirrors our individualized life experiences and I'm not sure if we ever really had a chance of happiness in the carnal arena. I occasionally wonder what Urijah is doing outside of bouncing a newborn on his knee or managing a thriving advertising business from home. The fact that my love for him has not totally disappeared is evident to my heart every time I hear his voice over the intercom. He has a way of directing a question to me just to hear my response. I know that he still loves me; however, life got in our way. I hope that he recognizes my love with each client added to his roster, as his profit margins grow thanks to my efforts. All the while, he's home nursing a newborn that's not my child. I would have had his child, if only he would have asked.

Oh well, I'm ready and willing to move forward in my world because the momentum in my life continues to increase as I eagerly take the journey with my current co-pilot, Cornelius. Cornelius is different. He plays a bigger, more dominant role in all areas of my world. Not only am I in awe of his mere presence, I honor, respect, and even desire to submit to him. He seems to be from another place; a place of knowledge and royalty, as odd as this seems because he is a blue-collar, working-class man. I'm sure that he lives paycheck to paycheck, which I can really appreciate right now that I'm working a lower-level job and have limited access to my funds, due to my pending divorce. Kevin had been giving me extra money to help with the girls and our living expenses, but I am sure this has stopped after the stunt I pulled on top of Cornelius's lap. Wow… I really didn't think about the consequences of that move before taking action. Although I've put myself in an even deeper unfortunate financial position and I'm certain that Cornelius won't be of much help on his nominal income, I don't regret inviting him into my life. It's been only a short while, but I feel like our spirits have known each other before; perhaps in another life.

Cornelius often speaks as though he's blessed with the wisdom of the Archangel Michael, and is not the least judgmental as he reassures me that "… all things work together for my good …" when I start to judge myself for the dark moments I created. Although we spend our limited amount of free time lounging around the house, at the park feeding the ducks, or working out in his home gym, I'm never bored by his company because his essence is intriguing. His interpretation of God's amazement is refreshing. I always thought I had to be perfect to dwell in God's presence, but Cornelius states, "He loves when you praise Him, so honor Him with thanksgiving and He will take care of the rest." Who knew *I* could create an atmosphere of worship? Wow.

I used to love Sunday mornings because I can feel God's presence when the praise and worship team sings, but my praise is no longer restricted to just Sundays. Cornelius and I sing, pray, and honor God with our worship when we are together. What I like most is that there is nothing ritualistic about our actions. We give thanksgiving unto God as we feel led. There is no set rule on which action must come first or how we worship… we just worship, and when we are done praising God, Cornelius reassures me with his warm embrace. In his arms I feel that everything is going to be alright. As a matter of fact, whenever he is in the vicinity I am content. It seems that I finally have met a man who satisfies my spiritual, emotional, and physical realms. Although we are both very affectionate, we have not made love yet. I am very attracted to Cornelius, but I want to put distance between the 'dark' Jonnie who made love with Kevin throughout Alex's house, mostly while she slept, and the 'enlightened' Jonnie who will give herself to Cornelius one day soon, hopefully.

I explained the pain that drove my anger as I apologized to Kevin for setting him up to find me grinding atop Cornelius's lap. He not only understood, he graciously accepted my apology and told me that nothing could damage the love that he holds for me in a protected place deep in his heart. He agreed to give me the space that I requested as I get my life together. I was certain that he would yell, curse, and call me at least one unpleasant name, which is why I asked to meet him in a public place for my confession and apology. Conversely, his mild demeanor and gentle caress of my hands led him right back to the private place in my heart. At that moment I realized that no matter our sorted history, I still love my husband and not even pain can destroy his place in my universe. Even as I move forward towards Cornelius. I have not had much experience in the romance arena and therefore I am tempted to run back to my familiar place in Kevin's arms. However, Cornelius offers an unknown path of intrigue that I am anxious to travel.

In addition to our busy schedules, our time is further limited because I'm not ready for Cornelius to be here with the girls. Kali and Tia are just getting used to their new mommy and I'm not ready to share our moments of laughter, love, and adventure with anyone. As Cornelius introduces me to a God bigger than I ever imagined, I teach my daughters how to live a humble life through God's grace, free from judgment. Periodically, Daddy even joins us for our discussions about God's love. The atmosphere in our home is once again bright and glorious. I am constantly joyful and learning to hang onto my joy through tough times. The girls are thriving and finding their own inner peace. I truly believe that Kali is starting to see herself through the eyes of God, which lends indication that I'm finally doing something right as I teach them about His grace and learn more about God's grace, mercy and love for myself. Tia usually adds to our conversations by speaking from a place of wisdom which far exceeds her young age.

Dear always said, "Tia has an old soul" or "That baby has the wisdom that only God can grant," and for the first time I see what Dear saw. Tia has always been a happy child, but her joy has increased and her conversations are more confident. Kali's timid nature is changing and she laughs more as she sheds the self-judgment she learned by watching me be so hard on myself for anything that resembled failure... She is finding her place not only in our home, but also in her world. Three days after my incident with the shattered Italian crystal, she dropped our last glass of juice on the kitchen floor, which is usually a crime punishable by my negative words about her carelessness and her own self-berating, which invites the spirit of low self-esteem into our home and hearts. Conversely, as Italian crystal shattered and juice raced over the floor we all froze in silence, until Kali erupted in laughter: "I guess I should have shared the juice with Tia," she stated between uncontrollable bouts of hilarity. "God does not like ugly," she continued until we joined her joviality and helped her clean the mess.

We are learning to find the blessing in every situation, even in the midst of shattered Italian crystal. Kali apologized to Tia while the laughter continued even after the floor was spotless. We each survey the floor for any missed pieces of glass or sticky juice as Kali yelled, "I love my life, I love my sister, I love my mommy… Thank you, God!" and hugged me and Tia. Her sweet innocent words cause tears of joy to flow freely down my cheeks because I realize the drastic change in our home. For the first time, I am really proud to be a parent. God blessed me with the responsibility of two young ladies and we are finally on the path of happiness and healing as we all realize that perfection is no longer required. Our moments of healing are constant as we encourage each other through even the smallest discouragements. Additionally, Daddy is cancer-free and I'm convinced that his healing was expedited by our faith. Although I don't remember everything about my afterlife experience, I know that God is real and I knew that He would heal Daddy.

Tia convincingly prophesied Daddy's healing every time she saw him, so I guess he had little choice but to believe and claim his healing. Mother would try to dissuade Tia by telling her, "Although grandfather looks like he feels better, his disease is incurable and will eventually kill him, so you need to accept that he will not be with us for very much longer." Mother's words infuriated me; however, before I could speak, Tia responded, "The Devil is a liar and we don't receive that death sentence. In the mighty name of Jesus, Grandfather is healed!" She spoke with such confidence and the usually shy Kali grabbed Tia's hand and declared a confirming, "Amen! Father God, I'm touching and agreeing for Grandfather's healing." I don't know that I've ever been more proud. I need not say anything more than "Amen and thank you, Father". Mother was shocked, but became more livid when Daddy added, "I receive the healing, Lord." This moment was defining, as we all began to praise God for the inevitable healing. The atmosphere of worship became so dominant that Mother sat quietly nodding, and possibly thanking God under her breath. Before leaving, Tia hugged Mother and asked her to try to believe. She explained that doubt is a spirit that we don't welcome, and then she spoke to the spirit of doubt and fear telling them that they are no longer welcome in our atmosphere. Kali, who usually keeps her distance from Mother unless she is forced to approach, sat on Mother's lap, hugged her, and said, "I love you, Grandmother." I was so proud! Proud of both of them! Equally, I'm proud of Mother for receiving their words and expressions of love without interruption. I may have even seen a tear held captive in her right eye. On the ride home Tia whispered, "Mommy, I'm glad that you have a new friend" as she dozed off to sleep. What does she mean? What friend? Is she talking about Cornelius? The car was quiet as Tia slept and Kali looked at me through the rear- view mirror with a slight smile on the left side of her lips. Could they be ready to accept that Kevin and I may not reunite? I'm not certain where this elevation will stop, but I pray never to reach a plateau past its purpose. What I do know is that I'm thankful to my God for this atmosphere of healing. I am learning not to put a limit on God's ability. His amazement surpasses my understanding.

Prior to my life taking a turn down a terrible path, I had God in a box as my faith failed and I accepted current situations as my only option. I struggled to be more righteous than the next person, just in case there was a limited capacity to Heaven, because I'd heard that the righteous would scarcely make it into God's presence. I worked diligently to be perfect so that everyone would find me pleasant; however, in the process I did not find myself pleasant. In fact, I did not know who I was. I can now honestly thank God for my trials and tribulations because through life's challenges, I am finding myself. I am learning of God's wonder and passing on my lessons to my daughters as they discover God's unlimited power and love for themselves. Through shattered Italian crystal we are finding the blessings as we rid self-judgments and regulated religions in exchange for God's love, while we praise Him for our atmosphere of healing, growth, and love.

Until

My life is so wonderful now that I'm allowing God to work on my behalf without much interference from me, Jon Terrence Johnson. I don't get upset as easily anymore, thanks to discovering the ability to find the blessing in all that I encounter. I'm not perfect, but wait… I'm no longer trying to be perfect. What I meant to say is that I still get upset at shattered Italian crystal, but not for long, and I'm not as hard on myself during these less than ideal moments. I sleep more peacefully, the girls are happier, Daddy is healthy, and Mother is more civil than I've ever known; life is pretty good. Kevin and I have not been intimate since before the stunt I pulled on top of Cornelius's lap, but we are cordial and may even be friends again before death takes us to the other side of life's journey. I find that I no longer need an alarm to awake most mornings, and today is no exception as I sit at the computer at 3:33am working on a proposal for a prospective client. The atmosphere is serene until the phone rings.

A phone call in the wee hours of the morning is usually not a good thing, especially since Kevin and I stopped fooling around. My heart stops for half a beat until I see that the phone call is from my sister, Alex. I missed two calls from her earlier this week and neither time did she leave a voicemail, so I didn't return her call. I wonder why she is calling me.

We are not close. I don't remember the last time we spoke on the phone. Definitely not at three o'clock in the morning. My mind races through the possible reasons for her call. She would be the last person to call if something happened to our parents, and Kevin would call if something happened to the girls, unless something happened to Kevin and the girls. Without further delay, I answer the phone right before the call transfers to voicemail. "Hello?" I say, expecting to hear her usually rude tone, but, on the contrary, her voice is humbled as she explains what brought her to call me at such an unreasonable hour. "I noticed the light on in your office, and figured that you were up working… May I come in…? Can we talk?" "Oh my God, did something happen to the girls?" are my first words. She assures me that the girls are sleeping peaceably at her house with Kevin, and that our parents are fine. Her voice then becomes a bit more firm when she asks again if she can come in to talk to me. I am a little frightened because I am here alone. Surely she wouldn't harm me in my own home, unless she somehow found out about me having sex all over her house, in her car, and even in her bedroom while she slept.

Before I can call Vanessa to advise of the abrupt disruption to my early morning, Alex is knocking on the door. I quickly write on today's date of my desk calendar, "Alex Terrell Johnson came to see me at 3:33am today insisting that she needs to talk. Check my phone records and the external cameras of the house should anything happen to me – JJ". I then place my laptop on top of the calendar before heading towards the door. Prior to opening the door, I record a voice memo, "My sister Alex is here at 3:33am to see me and she sounds serious. I hope she's not here to hurt me for sleeping with my husband/her boyfriend several months ago".

I hold my phone tightly as I answer the door to an Alex that I've never seen. To my surprise, she looks terrible. She has on tennis shoes, leggings, and a big sweatshirt, as she holds up a plastic Ziploc bag containing my lingerie. My heart jumps out of my chest and runs out of the back door… probably to avoid the ass whipping that I'm about to get from Alex. Why did I leave evidence and where is Vanessa when I need her most? Damn! Once again I have created another fine mess without thinking about all of the consequences. I want to slam the door and follow my heart out of the back door, but my feet won't move. What is the deal with my feet constantly failing me? Dang it!!! I try to dial 911 on my phone, but the darn thing is locked. I can't remember the lock code to save my life, and calling the police may be the only thing saving me this morning. Alex does not take kindly to people wronging her and, right now, I am that person. Oh my God, please help me. Think, think, think, Jonnie… I stand silently in front of her trying to imagine how my face will look once she is finished pounding it into something that resembles ground beef, until she asks again if she may enter my home.

Without a word, I step behind the door allowing her access. She walks into my kitchen and I hesitantly follow her. What am I doing? She is headed towards the room with all of my sharp knives and I just had to have the strongest, sharpest knives this side of Pluto. I hate struggling to prepare a meal, so I invested a lot of money in the several sets of knives guaranteed to cut through aluminum cans with ease for the next one hundred years. The strength of those very knives may now be tested against my flesh and the knives will win because my skin is delicate. I somehow remember the lock code to my phone and send Vanessa a quick text, "Alex is here with my panties in a baggie… help". I eventually join Alex in the kitchen to find her sitting, staring at the bag full of unmentionables that she has placed in the middle of my table. Is she crazy? My daughters eat on this table… But wait, I'm in no position to make demands so I'll just keep my mouth shut. My heart has returned to my chest only to remind me how loud and fast it is capable of beating, and probably to watch me reap the rewards of my evil labors. I slowly sit down at the table with my knees bent and pointed towards the door so that I'm in a good starting position, just in case I need to run. Time feels frozen and the silence is deafening. Why doesn't she just slap me away from the table and get this beating underway so that I have time to try to hide the bruises before going to work for the mandatory Monday meeting? I decide that I will just lie where I land because running may ignite the Mike Tyson in her to rise up and mop my house with my frail body. I definitely won't try to fight her back because the inexperience in my girlie swings may infuriate her further; at the very least she would get a good laugh at my feeble attempts of defending myself. I imagine that there is nothing worse than receiving a beating while the deliverer of said beating is laughing at how you respond to her punches. Additionally, my attempts at defending against her will be silly and useless. She fought Mother… and won! I'm afraid of my own shadow, but I can't take prolonging the inevitable.

Just as I'm about to break this torturous silence with my apologies and pleas for forgiveness, she begins to speak. "Jonnie… I'm sorry". Tears roll down her face as she tells me that Kevin is doing to her what he did to me… cheating. She says that she never believed in karma until now; now that she is on the receiving end. She explains how the pieces of lingerie began to turn up, one piece at a time throughout her house, under her bed, in her closet, and even in between the back seat of her car. I wait for her to get to the part where she had them dusted for fingerprints and tested for DNA, but that part never comes. Instead, she is humble as she begs for my forgiveness for her role as a terribly selfish and bratty baby sister. Her confessions of jealousy startle me because I always view her as the prettier, more confident one. The tears' transition and grow into a full-blown snot buster once I agree to her repeated requests for forgiveness. I slowly slide my chair closer and hesitantly put my arm around her shoulders, which invites her to sob uncontrollably down my exposed cleavage. Her embrace reminds me that she likes girls and, even though we are sisters, we have never really acted like sisters, so I'm a bit uncomfortable. However, I'm not exactly sure why I'm uncomfortable. Perhaps because I expected to be wrapped up in my area rug by now, or maybe I feel guilty because I'm the reason that she is in this much pain. I enjoyed every moment with my husband when I hid the evidence I wanted Alex to find. Conversely, seeing my baby sister in pain does not bring me the joy I expected. It seems that every tear is ripping through the black walls of hatred around my heart, as my thoughts shift to providing words of comfort.

I am so confused about the way that I feel for Alex. I have hated her for as long as I can remember, but now I honestly feel for her as though she is really my sister. I begin to speak to her about finding the blessing in this fiasco, and without warning God is using me as a vessel of healing for Alex's heart. I am thankful and humbled by the words of encouragement pouring from my spirit and into hers. I tell her about my shattered Italian crystal and point out the fact that we have never embraced in this manner until now. I understand her pain, but she doesn't know to what extent. She doesn't know that I was the one cheating with Kevin in her home; she doesn't know that I am the one who caused her current pain. Kevin is the only man who has known her intimately. He took her male-to-female virginity and now she doesn't know how to move forward through life without him. She has not told Kevin about her findings because she loves him and doesn't want their relationship to end. I am in disbelief at how adamant she is about maintaining their relationship. I never knew that she was capable of loving this deeply, and I definitely never expected her love to be aimed towards my husband. I was certain that Talia or one of the other ladies would be her soft place to land once she discovered Kevin's infidelities. Conversely, she sits at my table asking for my advice on how to move forward in life with my husband. Is this really happening? I expect Ashton Kutcher to burst into the room at any moment to tell me that I'm being punked, but Vanessa comes in his place.

I forgot that I sent Vanessa a distress text a less than an hour ago, until she lets herself in to find me and Alex in an embrace. I can tell that Vanessa came to fight by the clothes she is wearing and the expression on her face, as she asks, "What's going on?" To my surprise, Alex blurts out the whole story without hesitation, as I try to give Vanessa the signal to keep quiet about the panties belonging to me. Finally Vanessa asks, "Who's he cheating with?" When Alex couldn't answer the question, Vanessa steers her in the furthest direction away from me. She tells Alex that he is probably cheating with several different women, and encourages her to move forward with the knowledge that he is a cheater and will probably never change.

Vanessa and I take turns looking for and then highlighting the positives in the midst of this tumultuous situation. We walk Alex through the 'Until' moments of this tribulation. Vanessa goes straight for the kill. "You never know how much pain you can cause another woman until you experience an aching heart for yourself". I am shocked at her bold statement in this tender moment. Even I wouldn't have jabbed her in the jugular vein with such a vicious blow so soon, but I'm in no position to judge because I helped to cause the pain. Although a big part of me would love to dig the knife in deeper, the God in me steers the conversation in a more positive direction. "We probably would have never bonded in this manner until you found yourself in the position of needing someone who understands your story, and I truly understand your story." Vanessa takes control of the conversation once again as I stand slightly behind Alex, gently caressing her, while she sits in deep thought allowing the tears to pour down her face and over my arms. "You never fully understand how your actions may affect another person until you experience the dark side of karma for yourself." Vanessa cautiously picks up the bag of unmentionables and promises, "I'll get rid of this nastiness," as she winks in my direction. She is a great friend. Whew… that was a close call.

My life was headed in another wrong direction, until I was reminded once again that God is consistently working on my behalf. I love my father so much and thank Him for another 'until' moment. My life was taking a turn down a terrible path, until God intervened and used disastrous moments for His Glory! As the morning hours pass, Alex sits on my bed talking while I get ready for work. As ridiculous as this sounds, having my baby sister here with me sorting out her life is a good feeling. We have never been in a good place emotionally and I never want us to leave. I am tempted to tell her about Urijah or Cornelius, but resist the urge and add very little to the conversation because I'm afraid that a story about Kevin may slip past my lips, so I just listen as I put the finishing touches on my make-up. She recommends my outfit, selects the perfect jewelry ensemble to match my suit, and even flat irons my hair as we laugh about childhood moments.

With an hour to spare, we stop by Starbucks for her treat of my favorite beverage before I prepare to leave for work. It's been so long since perfectly blended goodness touched these lips. I can feel my taste buds sing with each savory swallow. Before getting into my car, she embraces me as though we are sisters who have always loved each other. She thanks me for listening and helping her to her sort through her love life. She then tells me that she never knew a sister's love could help to heal old wounds until I opened up my heart just enough to allow her access. "I never knew what true forgiveness looked like until you opened up your heart and invited me in," she says as we hug. With tears rushing and two sisters holding as if for the last time, we both vow to never go backwards in our relationship. She humbly apologizes again and states, "I really did not understand the pain I caused, until love tore my heart out of its safe place." I want to tell her that I'm ok and that she will get past these moments, but I'm not ok and I'm not sure if or how she will recover. I'm not sure that I have recovered and I don't want to lie to her, so I hug tighter in place of a response. I was not prepared for this soap opera drama; nevertheless, I involuntarily landed right in the midst of love's Bermuda triangle as I watched my baby sister call my husband variations of

'Daddy'. Thoughts of their embraces are never too far from my thoughts, which cause the disgust to rise from the pit of my stomach. However, I don't want to go backwards or throw salt into her freshly opened wounds, so I resist evil thoughts and focus on the positive. We embrace once more and take a makeshift oath of sisterhood, until death us do part. I say "Goodbye" and put my key into the ignition; however, before I can start my car Alex opens my door and says, "I finally get it, so it's not goodbye... it's until. Until we see each other again, until we share another story, until I need more advice, until you trust me enough with your stories, until we share more moments over coffee or even lunch next time." I smile and return her sentiment. "Have a great day and I'll talk to you later." "Yes you will... Until then," she says as she walks to her car with the mixed expression of brokenness, indecision, and joy tattooed across her face.

I drive to work processing all that happened in such a short time-span. Loving from my drama-free atmosphere was becoming easy, until I answered the phone call that started me down another interesting path. I thought that my healing and growth were limited to me, the girls, and Daddy. I gave up on having a sister long before she slept with my husband, and now she has humbly landed on my doorstep through the introduction of her own dose of love's pain. I now have to find a way to console her past my own hurt, which is still very present. Developing a relationship with Alex means that I will have to face our demons and I'm not sure that I'm ready for this challenge. My goal is to ensure that hurtful memories remain buried; however, this is not possible given the situation. How am I to help her through her pain without facing my own? Is this truly what God desires? I am tempted to ask that He let this cup pass from me, if possible; however, in the same breath I am reminded that it is God's will and not my own to which I submit.

My tears of joy sneakily transition into pain and resentment as I recall her evilness. She has crossed so many lines and hurt me so much. Why am I the one to help her find her healing? I was satisfied living my life with her at a distance, but that's obviously not God's plan. Only God could have humbled her enough to seek my weakened shoulders and listening ears as her means of support. I sit in the parking lot in search of answers, until the administrative assistant taps on the window. "Good morning, Sunshine," she calls out as she waits for me to get out of the car. I quickly fix my make-up before getting out and heading into our staff meeting. There is a message on my desk from Urijah stating, "Let's catch up over lunch." I did not expect him in the office today and how does he know that I'm available for lunch? I haven't seen him in a long while. Nevertheless, my heart smiles... His assertiveness is sexy and shifts my mood in a direction better suited to our meeting.

My life has an ironic way of unfolding since I ask God to use me as his vessel. Although I no longer want to end my life, I would be content to forgo my pending growth if my story ended in this moment. Growing past the pain that Alex caused is going to take the patience of Job and an unselfish love such that resembles the love demonstrated by Jesus Christ. With all that has happened through our tumultuous history, I never knew my heart capacity could accommodate Alex... until circumstance dictated otherwise.

Initially, holding her was uncomfortable; however, lending her my strength felt natural as time moved forward. With a big sigh, I realize that I have no idea how to be available for Alex, while being true to myself. Halfway through the meeting in which Urijah again attended via speaker-phone, I receive a text message from Alex, "Thank you again, sis." I don't know what's next or how to respond, but I have faith that God will never leave me as I thank Him for the growth through our 'until' moments.

Touch

Due to Cornelius's hectic work schedule our time is limited. However, with the exception of the mandatory Monday meetings, my schedule is flexible, so I plan my client meetings around his availability, because I love being around his positive energy. In addition to the restaurant, he works at the elegant floral boutique, which explains how he acquired the beautiful arrangement so late in the evening on our first date. Daddy came by the house unannounced the other day and met Cornelius. I was a little nervous, but they had great conversations, which led to Daddy invite Cornelius over for Sunday dinner. How dare Daddy invite someone to dwell in Mother's presence without considering the stress that this will bring me? Besides, he hasn't even met the girls. I am definitely not ready for him to meet Mother! She is so judgmental. She will eat him alive when she finds out that he is a blue-collar worker. Well actually, he wears two blue collars, one as a waiter and the other as a florist. It's not that I'm embarrassed by his choice of professions, but more so that he has to have two professions. Who am I kidding? I am embarrassed that he is a waiter and a florist, but his pros outweigh his cons. He is a beautiful person and this is what matters, right?

The big day is here and the entire family has expressed their excitement to meet Cornelius. God help me as I check myself in the mirror once more before Cornelius arrives. He worked this morning therefore, we agreed to meet at my house so that we can ride together to Mother's house. I know that he will want to drive his Toyota Prius because he loves that car. I just hope that the little Prius doesn't feel out of place parked amongst the Big Boys; Mr. Bentley, Senior Mercedes-Benz, Sir Aston Martin, Herr Maybach Landaulet, and the rest of their friends. Even Mother's senior housekeeper drives a Lexus, so I am prepared for Mother to criticize his two-year-old Prius. Perhaps God will smile upon us and find a reason to keep her away from the windows so she doesn't see us arrive. Just as suspected, Cornelius arrives on time and, despite my subtle hints, we are on our way to Mother's for dinner tucked away as snug as two bugs in his Prius rug. Alex assured me that she, Kevin, and the girls would be there for dinner, so the whole gang will meet Cornelius at one time. I have already told the girls that my friend would join us for dinner so they are prepared for the strange man in the house. They seemed more than ok with meeting 'Mommy's friend'. I think I'm the only one who is apprehensive.

Alex and I talk almost every day since she showed up at my house at 3:33 in the morning with my undies in a baggie. She still has no idea that the lingerie was mine and I'm not sure that I will ever tell her. She has not told Kevin about her find and I'm fearful for his safety when she does. I don't think that she will actually cause him physical harm, but she is known best for getting revenge; therefore, I am confident that he will reap his karma at the hands of Alex sooner or later. She has asked me not to tell him until she decides how she will handle their relationship, so I haven't said a word. Actually, my exact words to her were, "Kevin and I do not talk about anything other than our daughters, so you don't have to worry about me telling him anything". God help us all if she ever learns the truth about Kevin and my infidelities all throughout her property. For the first time in life, I think she is experiencing how to truly love someone other than herself. Wow! My baby sister really loves my estranged husband and I truly understand because parts of me still love him. This whole situation is weird! I realize that Kevin and I have probably exhausted our chances in the romance realm, so I have moved forward in my mind, body, and heart… I think. Only time will truly tell.

I am in deep thought as Cornelius stops by *Le Chet' Marie On The River* to pick up a fancy dessert that the executive chef prepared especially for today. I guess that Cornelius is hoping to lighten the blows afflicted during the crucifixion planned for him at the hands of Mother by showing up with fancy desserts, expensive wine, and an exotic floral arrangement. He seems calm as he confidently disappears through the doors of the restaurant. I hope that he doesn't get stuck working while in there, because the last thing I want is for us to be late! I remind myself to choose the dance as I decide to relax and leave the day in God's hands.

Just as I am about to close my eyes and rest my head in a reclined direction I see Urijah. He is coming towards the car with a baby in a car seat carrier, while walking next to a beautiful young lady. This must be his girlfriend, wife, or whoever. I want to disappear, but there is nowhere to go. He is walking between parked cars headed in my direction and no matter how I try to look away, he notices me and waves. Before I can stop the motion, my hand jumps up as though she has really missed him and anxiously returns the wave. As though a sequence of motion is destined to happen, I am unable to manage my bodily functions. My lips smile uncontrollably, my heart bangs on the window to ensure that it's acknowledged, and my loins get my attention just enough to make me thankful that I wore a panty liner today. I realize that there is no escape when I notice Urijah's car parked directly behind the Prius. Just when I think that maybe he will settle for a wave, he stops at the window to continue our reunion. This is the first time that I have seen him since the birthday celebration and, although I do miss him from time to time, Cornelius holds my every attention right now. I continually remind myself why a relationship between Urijah and I would never work as I lower the window.

Urijah's first words are "I owe you an apology for missing lunch the other day," before giving me the highlights of his story. I see his beautiful lips moving, but find it difficult to comprehend his message. I had forgotten how beautiful this man is and he still glows... Wow! He then pauses and asks me to get out of the car so that he can give me a hug. Oh my God... what is he doing? Cornelius will be back at any moment and I can't let him walk up on me hugging another man. I quickly glance around before agreeing to get out of the car for a friendly embrace, although there is nothing friendly about what I want to do to him. He sucks me into his comforting arms as I release the exhale that belongs only to Urijah. Realizing how much I have really missed him makes me want to cry as I hold onto his neck like this is my last time to feel his goodness. I think I even lift one leg. Holding my composure is difficult while looking into the eyes of the man who still takes my breath away and causes my heart to beat irregularly... But wait a minute... what did he say? Knowing me like he does, he repeated himself while lifting the blanket away from the car seat just enough for me to see the beautiful little boy. "I want you to meet little Urijah." Mentally running from this reality is exhausting; however, facing the music as the facts slap me in the face is more difficult. "Little Uri... he's beautiful, just like his father."

Speaking the little boy's name is difficult because this could have possibly been my little boy. Urijah interrupts my thoughts. "His father? No... he looks just like his uncle... Uncle Urijah," he proudly states. Hold on... I'm confused because I haven't really been listening. Urijah knows me very well. He laughs as he tells me that my confused looks give me away. No, I have not been listening because all of his gorgeousness drowns out unnecessary words, but perhaps his words were necessary this time. Urijah repeats parts of his story, telling me that the little boy is his nephew and the pretty young lady is his seventeen-year-old sister, who had a baby out of wedlock. Hearing his words are still difficult but, from what I gather, his sister moved in with him once she was ordered by their father to leave their family home because she brought shame on the household. "You don't know how many times I wanted to pick up the phone and talk to you, but my family was torn apart. My sister was embarrassed, my mother and father separated because of his stubbornness and he still has not seen the baby. I didn't know where to begin, besides this story was not mine to tell" Urijah states before motioning his sister to come over for introductions. Once the sister and little Urijah were securely in the car I gave one final leap into Urijah's arms and agreed to see him later for the updated version of his life since we last spoke. He walks me back to the Prius, kisses me through the open window on the cheek, and floats back to his car. Within two minutes I spot Cornelius strutting towards the car with a lovely dessert in his hands. The two men represent opposite ends of my love spectrum... They can't be more different. However, seeing them both within minutes of each other makes me accept the obvious. 'Right now, in this moment... I love them both'.

Cornelius's proud smile tells me that he is armed with the devices he deems necessary to gain Mother's approval. His apology for the delay breaks the awkward silence. I'm sure that he mistakenly assigns the unsettled expression all over my face to the pending dinner. Conversely, worries about the dinner have taken a back seat to the awakened feelings I still have for Urijah. Holding hands or touching in some way while driving is a normal practice for Cornelius and I; however, I'm afraid that he will be able to read my heart if we make physical contact, so I fumble through my purse as I try to refocus my thoughts. Focusing on how amazingly patient he is and the many lessons I've gained with him by my side seems to do the trick, at least for a little while. Thoughts of him also bring me back to the fact that he could never afford the lifestyle I worked so hard to build for me and my family. My attorney believes that Kevin and I are close to agreeable negotiations, so I may have access to my funds again soon. Cornelius is not suited to the lifestyle that I am anxious to step into again.

Although much younger, Urijah seems to be in a better position to join me on my return to my life of lavishness, thanks in part to my efforts. Wait! I have to stop any and all thoughts about Urijah. I can only dig through this purse for so long without finding what it is that's lost.

"Are you nervous?" Cornelius's deep voice melts through my thoughts like when we first met. He is so gorgeous and sexy and smells great, and his body is chiseled into perfection… Ok, I'm ready to make contact. We are sitting at a light, so I turn his head towards me and kiss him gently on his lips. His reciprocation causes Niagara Falls throughout my body, expelling to meet the earlier flood caused by Urijah's embrace. Oh my God! What am I doing? I have never had feelings this intense for two men at the same time… like really!! Darn near the SAME time! Neither of them has experienced my body physically, but they both get my juices flowing because of our individualized connections. The feeling is great, but somehow nasty at the same time. I never knew that loving two men at the same time was possible, but it is because I do love them both. We are minutes away from Mother's home and I'm sure that the games will begin right away. However, my first assignment is to change the liner that holds the united expressions of love.

Although very different, Urijah and Cornelius have both touched me in ways never imagined. Our distinctive spiritual, mental, emotional, and intellectual touches supersede any physical connection I've ever experienced, although my intimate experience is limited. I'm open to feel love and my openness translates into juices flowing, even in the absence of physical touches at an elevated level.

My thoughts are heavy as we park the Prius amongst the Big Boys. Jazmine Sullivan passionately blowing through the speakers about being in love with another man is not helping my focus. I'm so anxious that I want to jump through the car window in an attempt to escape my current realities, but instead I turn the radio down and choose the dance of calmly sitting as Cornelius gives me a pep talk. He assures me that everything will work for our good today. He is so lovely. He should be nervous because he is about to willingly walk into the slaughterhouse, but he is more concerned with helping to get my head in the right place before facing Mother. Gentleness is his specialty and he has again made his concerns secondary to my worries.

Interrupted by the girls' knock on the window, we get out of the car and introductions begin after two big hugs for Mommy. No matter how the rest of the day turns out, my soul sings with joy because I am blessed to have an abundance of love in my life. Not long ago I was sleeping in the back of my closet... alone. Conversely, right now my major concern is how to manage the love that elevates my heart rate as it beats in several different directions. Tia and Kali's hugs bring perspective to the moment. Of all of the touches I've experienced on this beautiful day, the love and acceptance of my daughters touch me the deepest. I am now ready for this dinner. We have fancy dessert, an exotic floral arrangement and expensive wine, so I feel prepared for Mother's material expectations. Any hatred she spews in my direction will not touch me because I'm encircled in a secure embrace of love's vibrations that not even the Devil's cousin can penetrate. On this day I choose the dance of wearing love like a cloak of protection, as I relish the moments of love's touch.

Humbled

To my surprise, Mother greets Cornelius with a warm embrace as she invites him to make himself at home. "*Me casa es su casa,*" she says in a soft and inviting voice. **What the what???** Has she been sipping the cooking sherry? She even smeyeses at him. What is going on? Is she channeling Tyra Banks? Mother thanks Cornelius for "… the lovely flowers and scrumptious-looking dessert" as she pours the wine that he brought. 'Scrumptious' is not a word that I've ever heard her use and I have never witnessed her being so pleasant or doing much of anything domestic. My world stands still for a few seconds as I take in the sights of her playing a 'mother role'. Alex forces me out of my daydream as she locks arms with me and holds onto me in some way through most of the visit while Daddy tends to the staff, a duty that usually Mother insists on enjoying. This whole scene must be borrowed from a script of *The Twilight Zone*. I try desperately to pay attention to Mother's every movement, but this is difficult with my grown sister darn near sitting in my lap, Cornelius rubbing my thigh in an attempt to calm my nerves, and Kevin jealously staring at Cornelius's every soothing stroke.

From the moment she meets Cornelius, Mother starts with her inquisition. Halfway through the meal I know more about him than I learned through several months of intense dating. Mother asks questions that I assumed I knew and with each answer I grow a little fonder of him. I guess we were so busy attending to me and my troubles that I forgot to ask the questions that usually accompany a newly dating couple. He makes dealing with my troubles easier… he makes me smile… He's emotionally, mentally, and spiritually available and this is enough… or is it? I was happy with him when I thought that he was a blue-collar worker; however, today I find out that he is not a blue-collar stiff at all. He owns *Le Chet' Marie On The River*, a chain of exotic floral shops, and is part-owner of a major cruise line, but you would never know this because he is very frugal with his money and chooses to live a humble life. I'm glad to have met him when I was struggling financially, because otherwise I probably would not have given him a second look. I thought that he was a waiter! Conversely, his portfolio is as impressive as Mother's and this is good news; although I think it is better news to Mother. She's hanging onto his every word. I wonder if his financial status is why she's so pleasant. I wonder if she had him investigated prior to meeting him and was already aware of his wealth. This would explain a lot about her pleasant disposition towards him. His social experience and status would also explain why he knows his way around fine china and priceless antique treasures. My intrigue with this mysterious man has intensified.

After our lovely dinner Mother seems to be more accepting of me and demonstrates her fondness with an embrace that I've never experienced. She then gives the girls some of her favorite, usually forbidden truffles. God is truly smiling on this family today, or Mother is going the extra mile to disguise ulterior motives. In any case, I am enjoying the day and don't want my negative focus to shift the atmosphere, so I relax and enjoy this moment. After dinner we all retire to the sitting room to continue the interesting conversation, which starts off with Mother praising Cornelius for his humbleness. She all but chastises herself for living such a lavish and wasteful life as she scans the room naming the items that she could have lived without. Then the conversation turns down a path that I never expect as she states, in an almost childlike manner, "I could have been a better mother." She reaches over and gently touches Alex's and my hands as she states that she would live a different life if she could start again. Again I wait for Ashton Kutcher to jump out of the closet, until I see her fighting back the tears. I don't know that I've ever seen her display any type of remorse, with the exception of when she stood over Alex in the hospital bed. She never admits that she has any faults, at least not in my presence. Alex and I give a look of perplexity while Cornelius lends some of his usual wisdom and sums up the conversation with, "It's never too late to start down a new path."

The open wounds and sensitivity in the room shifts when Daddy plays his record collection. Before long we are all laughing as the girls dance to Ray Charles, Nina Simone, and Stevie Wonder music coming from Daddy's old record player. Doubt would usually insist that I miss such a wonderful moment while internalizing my disdain for Mother; however, not today. Today I choose to inhale as much of the moment as possible, while I enjoy the dance with the rest of the family. As I watch Mother sashay through dance partners – the girls, Alex, me, Cornelius, Kevin, and then ending with Daddy – my heart is filled with joy. This is not the mean woman whom I learned to know as my mother. I can honestly say that I have never danced nor done anything in a playful manner with my mother. Today, this woman posing as my mother is loving, full of laughter, and even the life of the party. Watching Mother's playful ways as she dances with Daddy brings the realization that this is possibly the woman whom he learned to love so many years ago. They are beautiful together! I am experiencing what I can only explain as an out-of-body moment as I review the stories in this room. For the first time I see my parents display the type of romance that would be the envy of any couple. She is submissive to the usually unapparent, but now obvious strength that Daddy possesses. Alex prances around Kevin in a seductive manner, trying to maintain his wavering attention. In Kevin's presence her vulnerabilities are overpowering, and leave her lost in her usually secure, confident world.

Kevin seems confused about which direction he should throw his affections as he holds Alex's hand while aiming flirtatious looks in my direction. His failed attempts cause the look in his eyes to turn to regret. Cornelius holds me respectfully close enough for me to feel his sincerity regarding my happiness. In this moment I feel his unselfish love. He genuinely wants me to be happy; no matter which direction I choose. He has placed my needs and growth above his own desires the entire courtship, and today is no different. He is secure enough with his own strength to know that he will be okay should my stay in his life be momentary. This realization is powerful. I've never known anyone, beside Dear to want my happiness over their own. Kali dances happily from person to person in an attempt to secure her place in each world, as Tia freely moves through the room not paying much attention to the bystanders in her world. My baby girl knows that everything will work out for the best, while my eldest tries to relax enough through her apprehensions to enjoy these lovely moments. My mind's eye watches from the sidelines as we all dance to Daddy's oldie-but-goodie records, and enjoy each other for the first time in this fashion.

I have surveyed everyone's emotional state but my own. I enjoy the attention of Cornelius, and even more so now that I've learned of his humbleness. However, I can't stop my mind from wondering how this scene would look if I were here with Urijah. Would he even know Nina Simone or Frank Sinatra's music? Would he be able to hold his own with Mother? Answer her questions to *her* satisfaction? Stand his ground against Kevin's intimidating stares? Perhaps not! Perhaps I will have to be satisfied with loving Urijah quietly from a distance. Conversely, I know how the scene would appear if I were still with Kevin because I've experienced those scenes already. Just the thought of our years of Sunday dinner together at Mother's pales in comparison to this fantastic day. Although I really loved him, I truly believe that our time has passed. Alex seems truly happy and for the first time we are developing a sisterhood bond that I want to nurture. For the first time I am truly putting her happiness above any selfish possibilities between Kevin and me. I no longer have sexual desires for him and he was once the love of my life. Besides, any time spent with him would hurt Alex and I no longer want to hurt my sister. Now look at God in that statement! In such a short time our relationship is being repaired.

As I rest in Cornelius's arms and move to the rhythms in the air, I close my eyes and see the scene in which I currently partake. Dancing, laughter, and love envelope us all. We each seem to take joy in our own piece of Heaven this Sunday evening. Even Kevin seems to delight in the fact that possibly he still has options. I am truly humbled by how fast God can work when we get out of his way. I don't know what tomorrow brings, but as I now dance with both of my lovely daughters I am thankful and humbled that God took time out of His busy schedule to shine some light on a usually dysfunctional family moment. The spirit of unity rarely visits our family gatherings. I think that we all realize the blessings in the atmosphere because everyone seems thankfully humbled at the miracle happening before our very eyes.

Distance

It's been three weeks since the family dinner where I bear witness to Mother's new attitude. I have seen her more in the past twenty-one days than I ever thought I'd enjoy. Conversely, I am starting to look forward to her visits. She is pleasant, we talk, and she has even treated me to lunch a couple of times. Paying for anything is a huge gift for her to give because she believes that everyone should carry their own weight. I suspect that Daddy may have told her about my limited finances, at least as much as he knows. I become embarrassed at the thought of sharing my financial struggles with anyone, so Vanessa and my attorney are the only ones who really know how far I stretch every penny these days. I'm sure that Daddy knew something was wrong when he saw my empty pantry. In any case, I feel close enough to touch my brighter tomorrow because Kevin and I are just days from finalizing our divorce. We had lunch the other day and he expressed how much he still loves and misses me and our family unit. I waited a long time to hear him say those words again; however, I felt nothing. All that I could think about was the devastation our reunion would cause to my baby sister. Alex really loves him and I can no longer take part in causing her pain. To prove how much she loves Kevin, Alex even stopped seeing Talia and she has been a part of Alex's life since college. I was certain that she and Talia would stand any test that time could throw in their direction. However, Talia could not fill Kevin's big shoes.

I've never slept with a woman, but I know how big Kevin's shoes are so I understand the choice. If I allowed myself to feel, I could still be prey to Kevin's magnetism, but I am no longer in the business of hurting others in an attempt to satisfy my itch. The price is too high to pay. Alex still doesn't know that I was the other woman in Kevin's life and I'm not sure if I will ever tell her. I do know that I don't want to cause her any additional pain, even though I am starving for an evening of romance and passionate chemistry.

Seeing Urijah every day does not help to curb my desires for physical attentions. There is a definite chemistry in our atmosphere but I don't believe either of us knows how to approach the possibilities of our physical longings. He once told me that he was out of college when he made love for the first time and his last girlfriend cheated on him because of his work schedule. Not only is he inexperienced, he is fearful to enter a relationship until he can dedicate the time he deems necessary to maintain a romance. As he spoke I replied, "I understand… relationships take time." When I really wanted to say, "I understand… but let's give it a try, and if we don't work as a couple, at least we can get together once a week and relieve some sexual tension." Even though my afterlife adventure taught me that life is too short and I have made forward steps in other areas of my life, I can't completely abandon my upbringing of 'staying in a lady's place'. Mother taught us that a man should choose a woman, so until he chooses to step up to the plate and take a swing in my direction… I will sit quietly on the sidelines, periodically responding to his partial displays of interest. Since Urijah has returned to the office I go in almost every day. He usually brings me something or does something special to demonstrate his love; my special coffee drink, my favorite brand of water, or a flower for my desk. 'Gifts' and 'Acts of Service' are definitely his love languages. I just wish we shared the 'Physical Touch' love language, because he is a beautiful soul and I long to be in his arms.

Cornelius has a similar, but different storyline. He has been to my office a few times and I think that he recognizes the obvious connection between Urijah and me. Of course I downplay any attraction by highlighting his apparent youth and status. I explain, "Urijah is a young man just starting his life. He's trying to do positive things for his family with the money that he inherited after his grandmother's death. He shared a special bond with his grandmother, just as I did, so naturally we have some things in common and I want him to succeed." I then shift attention in his direction by asking if he is jealous. Cornelius swears that he doesn't have a jealous bone in his body. He says that he's much too busy to spend time being jealous.

I thought that we would be further in our relationship by now, especially after the lovely day we spent at my parents' home. That evening we held hands the whole way home as we discussed the beautiful day. We were both surprised by how well he seems to fit into my family unit. We jokingly discussed Kevin's obvious discomfort as he watched another man tend to his soon-to-be ex-wife, and we were amazed at the love expressed towards him by the girls, Alex, and Mother. We were both delighted to share an evening with a family opposite to the one I had described. The sweetness in the air thickened on the drive home. Cornelius initiated red-light kisses and freeway caresses. I mistakenly mistook his advances as foreplay so when he dropped me off and said that he would call me after he checked in at the office I quickly showered, spritzed my body with love's aroma, put on my sexiest lingerie, and fell asleep waiting for his call. Our time together has decreased and I'm not sure what happened. I left my parents ready and willing to give in to my desires and I was certain that he felt the same. Conversely, on the one occasion when time and space presented the opportunity for us to fall anxiously into love's abyss, he stopped the movement in mid-motion and said, "I'd better go." I haven't had that many men on top of me, but of the few encounters, never have I had one to jump up off me and announce that he'd better go. The house was empty and I was finally ready to open up to someone other than Kevin! He was ready! We both were ready! I could tell!! I've noticed his manliness through his clothes a few times before as we exchanged kisses, but never have I noticed him *this* ready... but he jumped up and left. Since then he has allowed his busy schedule to be the excuse for the missing romance and lovemaking opportunities. I am thoroughly confused. I understand why Urijah and I maintain a certain distance; work, youth and inexperience dictate that we continue to admire each other from a distance. However, I cannot put my finger on the distance between Cornelius and me. I have been so thrown by his increased absences that I shared his actions with Mother.

Telling Mother anything is forbidden because she is so judgmental, but I was desperate and she was there. I'd hoped that she would share some of her wisdom, without the judgment and she did just that. She advised that I speak with him. "Stop tiptoeing around the elephant in the room," she said. So I stepped out of my comfort zone and asked him to explain the change in our relationship. I still don't understand his words, "I want you to be free" he said. What does that mean? He told me to get to know myself and when I am truly ready I am supposed to let him know. "Ready for what??" I asked. "And what else do I need to know about myself? I have died and come back to life for goodness' sake! I've experienced several afterlife bouts with angels and evil spirits, gone through Hell and back on this earth, struggled through financial hardship... and still struggling, suffered two major failed relationships, prayed blood and tears for anything that remotely resembles a normal family unit, found an acceptable way to exist after losing my grandmother/best friend, and I'm finding happiness after losing the love of my life to my lesbian baby sister! What more do I need to know about myself???!!! I don't want to know anymore! I just want to be happy, and being with you makes me happy. I want to be your woman... Completely yours! Making love to you is part of being yours! Besides, anything else I need to know about me I want to discover with you by my side. I don't want to be alone anymore!" I screamed at him as he stood quietly in front of me listening to my rants. Cornelius stood quietly, without motion as he witnessed a grown woman have a temper tantrum. When I ran out of words to say and life experiences to mention, he gently placed his hands on my shoulders, pulled me into his masculinity, and held me as I poured my frustrations into his opened arms. He never said a word. He just held me and stroked through my hair for about ten minutes. Once I gathered myself, he very quietly stated, "I love you and I'm not going anywhere, but I can't interfere with God's work." I'm perplexed even further, but don't possess the energy to ask for an explanation. I want some physical connectivity... more than a hug or a kiss. I want to make love to this gorgeous man holding me. Instead of debating, he starts me a bath and asks if he can take me to dinner later that evening. I'm not going to lie; the boldness of his request and the smoothness of his actions increased my desire for him, so of course I said yes to dinner and was ready promptly at 6:27 for his 7:00pm arrival.

We have spent several evenings together since my break down, but mostly in public or in the company of others. I don't know why he won't make love to me, and trying to figure out why is exhausting. I know that there is nothing wrong with his manhood, because I've witnessed him rise to the occasion several times. Alex advises me to find someone else as my sex buddy, but this is just not my style. She knows most of the intimate details of my current life, so she recommends that I choose Urijah as the man I sleep with, while keeping Cornelius as my 'trophy' and possibly the man whom I can grow old with, when he's ready. Mother encourages me to "be still and know that He is God," which is another way of telling me to be patient. She then suggests that I make the first move, which is really confusing because her advice conflicts with me living a life of the woman she raised me to be. I spend a large portion of my existence frustrated and confused. During the day, work forces me to rub elbows with a beautifully gentle soul whom I love deeply from a separate but parallel universe. My evenings are spent on the arms of a modern-day Adonis with whom I showcase a pretend idealistic life when an audience is present. However, the fairy tale halts once the curtains are down and we are alone behind closed doors. Coy, a longtime friend of mine took control of my vocals as I sat at the dinner table singing, *More, more, more,* by JoAnn Rosario. I closed my eyes and went into a soulful praise, "I need more, more, more... so much more of you... I need so much more... so much more of you..." I omitted saying "Jesus" in the song because I wasn't singing to Jesus. Unless the Son of God can help Cornelius catch the hint that my loins need extinguishing by his burning love. I laugh at this thought because I know that God will not partake in my scheme. I could feel the atmosphere shifting in my direction until Tia boldly asked me why I was singing over her food. I've been so wrapped up in my own world that I forgot that my youngest has a special relationship with the angels. I became so embarrassed when she looked at me and politely stated, "Mommy, God is not in that..." I felt so transparent to everyone at the dinner table and immediately felt my appetite leave the room.

In the still of the midnight hour I lay looking at my bedroom ceiling still aglow from the onset of my deliverance. Any reminder of the glorious day when I started on my current path of healing brings me joy, so I pray for patience as I decide to trust in God. To say that I am disappointed with my love life would be an understatement. I can see my thoughts displayed in the midst of the illuminated ceiling. I see Cornelius's and my name written in a single line for a few seconds and then the word 'distance' slides in between the names, forcing a gap of space and separation. 'Cornelius' slides to the right and 'Jonnie' slides to the left, both pushing my many thoughts out of the way until the names disappear, leaving the word 'distance' growing until it consumes the room prior to fading. My eyes remain fixed on the spiritually aglow ceiling and a remnant of other thoughts floating through the air. Leaving little time for my mind to process what just happened, more words appear. This time it's 'Urijah Jonnie' written across the ceiling in a straight line; however, before I can celebrate, 'distance' appears in the middle, forcing the names apart until they disappear and the word 'distance' takes over the room, making it difficult for me to focus on anything else. What's the message, Lord, I wonder as I desire a more definite sign. I don't want to give either Urijah or Cornelius over to distance. I love them both and want them both in my life, even if only on a platonic level. Before I can go into my prayer pleading for my continued relationships, more words appear: 'Defeat Jonnie' …….. 'Defeat' 'Distance' 'Jonnie'. The action repeats with the word 'Distance' separating 'Defeat' and 'Jonnie'. Again, leaving little time to process what just happened, more words happen, 'Loneliness Jonnie', followed by the word 'distance' separating loneliness from me. The same action repeats with the words 'Depression', and then 'Hate' and 'Fear', and 'Anger', 'Victim', 'Revenge', 'Self-Righteousness', 'Judgmental', 'Perfection', 'Heartbreak', 'Kevin', and so on… I think that I'm finally getting the message. God's grace and mercy have blessed me with growth and wisdom, and my faith in God has helped me through life's challenges. Although I'm not happy about the absence of an intimate partner, I have not traded in the comforts of my bed for the back of my closet or contemplated self- destruction. Not so long ago I would have been lying here crying and looking for an escape. Instead, I realize that there must be a reason for my forced abstinence, no matter how frustrating.

My faith in God allowed distance between me and the evil spirits who once ruled my world. Even though I've always been a dedicated church participant and strong community figure, I struggled silently with my warriors of darkness, but that was yesterday. Today I realize that my faith continues my deliverance. Although I don't understand everything about my current path, I choose to thank God for the distance. I choose the dance of praise, for without the distance of hate, judgment, anger, unforgiveness, and many of their companions, I would not have a loving relationship with my mother and sister. I don't want distance between the two potential men in my life, but perhaps they are not good for me at this time… It's too soon to tell. I don't want too much distance between Kevin and me for the girls' sake. There is a lot that I don't understanding, but I will trust God, which means that I lean not to my own understanding. I thank God for His infinite wisdom and accept distance in its many forms, because it's bringing me the right kind of togetherness. All things work together for the good… and I will be still and know that He is God as I thank Him for the blessings that arise from maintaining my distance.

Stillness

I am an active committee member on the church board of directors and tonight I will attend our bimonthly meeting to discuss church business and cast my vote for any pending decisions. Lately, I have felt a bit overwhelmed in my personal life so I'd rather stay at home wrapped in the comforts of Dear's quilt, but I must press on because others depend on my presence. Besides, staying home in an idle state would not promote the progress necessary for my continual growth. Therefore, I continue to attend the meetings with a smile on my face dishing out emotional coins from my almost depleted emotional bank. I pray that no one notices my heaviness as I search for ways of emotional replenishment. I must be honest; I *do gain* strength being around the spiritually grounded. I also look forward to seeing Deacon Hill, who is another committee member and someone whom I consider a church buddy. We have the same type of humor so he can always raise a genuine smile from the depths of my funny bone. He seems to always know what I need to hear, and exactly when I need to hear another one of his humorously wise antics. The anticipation of his gentle smile adds to the inspiration that keeps me going to the meetings, even though I should be saving my gas. Over the years Deac and I have developed a close bond and, although we have very little interaction outside of the church, I consider him a close church associate. I'm looking forward to our annual spiritual leaders' retreat because I truly need a change of scenery. Thank God that I prepaid for the week-long trip last year, because I would not be able to afford the added expense today.

As I leave the church parking lot I reflect on how the committee meeting served as a great distraction. For some reason, tonight I was more vocal and was able to utilize my advertising experience towards potential financial gains for the church. I finally pitched my advertising idea of filming our community outreach work. Our church is far from destitute, but more incoming finances allow us to broaden our involvement outside of our exclusive church community. Through all that I have endured, I'm learning that the world is far greater than *my world.* I didn't realize how blessed I was and how little I gave back, in comparison until my experience with death.

I remember the homeless family from my afterlife experience like it was yesterday and I won't rest until I find them or many like them and give back some of my God-given blessings. Tonight I shared pieces of my afterlife experience as though they were visions because I did not feel like trying to convince the board members that it was real and that I am sane. After my testimonial appeal for us to broaden our outreach, many of the board members had tears in their eyes. God's timing is amazing! I have shared my afterlife experiences with only a few people because I fear the disbelief of others, but tonight I overcame that fear. I walked the path that God laid before me, holding tightly to His hand, and spoke my truth. Although I look forward to traveling, I also look forward to getting back and launching the advertising campaign. I have always lent my financial support to the church, but now I'm giving of my talents and this feels more right than a check full of empty zeros.

As I drive down the freeway I answer an incoming call via my Bluetooth headset without checking the caller ID. I am slightly disappointed when Deacon Hill responds to my hello, instead of Cornelius. Nevertheless, I push any thoughts of Cornelius out of my mind and choose to live in the now and move forward fully engaged in conversation with the Deacon. We converse about my advertising ideas and then my testimony. The conversation is intellectually intriguing and continues until Vanessa taps on my window motioning for me to unlock the doors. In the usual Vanessa fashion, she gives me 'the look' and quietly asks, "Who are you talking to?" My pointer finger in front of my lips attempting to shush her serves little purpose because she sees the sparkle in my eyes. I say goodnight to Deacon Hill, dismiss her insinuations, and kiss two sleepy girls before they buckle in and nod off in the back seat of the car. I head home, taking deep breaths feeling renewed as the oxygen in my heart climbs towards a healthy level once again. I guess that I didn't realize how my relationship with Cornelius has impacted me because I am unsure where we are or where we are going; if anywhere. Once the girls are securely tucked into bed I spend quality time with my Father, God through quiet meditation, prayers of thanksgiving, and reading of His Word.

With heavy eyelids I concede to sleep as I realize that I have been a slave to my emotions for most of my life. When life is good, my mood is good, and so am I. When life gets tough, my mood gets low, and so do I. For far too long I have given my destiny over to the spirit of emotion, which is as fickle as the wind. I cannot control whether the wind blows north, south, east, west, or at all; however, it seems that I should be able to control how I feel from moment to moment. When I received Deacon Hill's call I instantly felt my spirit dampen because I miss Cornelius and was hoping that he was the caller on the other end of the phone; however, I decided in that very moment that Deacon Hill deserved my full attention so I rejected the emotion of depression and gave into the spirit of Now. Allowing myself to be fully available for that moment allowed me to absorb every intricacy as our conversation flowed in both directions. Weeks ago, I would have told the deacon that I had to go and driven to Vanessa's house silently wanting a different outcome. I would have then gone into her home to gather the girls and filled my emotional low with the comforts of her jovial remedies, which would have been only a substitute for the real fix. Quiet time with God is exactly what my heart needed and it is in this moment that I realize the dance that I chose. I'm proud that I did not apply quick fix bandages this night. Tonight I fall asleep feeling more whole than I've felt in a long while and my feeling of completeness is due to me exercising my God-given right to choose my dance.

Giving into the direction in which my soul pulled led me to the much-needed stillness my heart desired. I'm realizing now that I did not bow down to the spirit of emotion. Instead, I yielded to the deeper part of me... My soul! Which meant that I had to listen beyond the cries of my heart's surface ache so that I could hear my soul's desire and give into what I truly needed.

In my stillness my eyes were opened and I witnessed me willingly participating with the spirit of emotion as *we* hijacked valuable moments in trade for the pity party that followed. Tonight I realized that I have so much more to offer the world. I also discovered that I deserve a better me! I am getting a glimpse of the answers that have been here all along… I can choose my dance. I am excited to move forward on my journey as I discover more about ME! I don't have to be depressed or sad; I can choose how I feel by shifting how I think about a situation. This thought is simplistic and yet powerful!

Deac said that my words inspired him… wow, I never thought that I would be a source of inspiration for such a strong man. Thank God that I am able to recognize and then receive the lesson! Tonight, without any forethought I chose my dance wisely. Remaining in the present and choosing to pour my attentions into my conversation as I spoke with Deacon Hill taught me a long- overdue, but right on time lesson. Although I did not recognize the lesson until I sat quietly meditating; I gained another piece of me and this time I paid attention so I know how to apply the lesson moving forward. Changing how I think about a situation alters how I feel about that situation. My mind and body gave into the tug-of- war allowing my soul – my inner god – to connect with the Almighty. For the first time of my recollection, all of me is in alignment with God. In my stillness I discovered a powerful connection to my inner being.

Deacon Right Now

The five-star resort is beautiful and reminds me of the trips that I used to take with Kevin, Dear, and the girls. The inspirational music resonating gently through the lobby and hallway walls is a demonstration of the resort's appreciation for the churches continued business. As luck would have it, Deacon Hill's room is next to mine and there are adjoining doors that we eventually use to gain access to each other's room during the week-long conference.

On the plane Deacon Hill sat with two other deacons from the church and Mother Brown sat in the seat that I was secretly reserving in hopes that I could sit next to my buddy. I am not physically attracted to him, but he is funny and I really enjoy his company, so of course I wanted to spend the five-hour plane ride conversing and laughing at his quick-witted antidotes. I was so disappointed when Mother Jenkins lifted her skirt up around her waist and plopped her greasy fanny next to me. She obviously packs a whole lot of something on her bottom because she leaves a slippery butt print on the pastor's black leather chair every time she sits down in his office. I heard her tell Mother that she lifts her dress up around her waist to avoid wrinkles. Personally, I think that she's afraid she'll never get all of that ointment out of her dress. No matter her strange behavior, she always smells good so more power to her. I didn't want to laugh as she sat down with her girdle exposed so I positioned a pillow behind my head, closed my eyes, and went to sleep while Kim Burrell softly serenaded me through headphones positioned deeply in my ear canals. I periodically carefully open one eye to glance at Deacon Hill laughing with the other deacons and become a little curious and maybe even a little jealous, but I quickly shut my lid before Mother notices. No offense against Mother Jenkins, but the last thing that I want is to become entangled in one of her never-ending inquisitions about my missing husband.

By the time I gather my luggage, it's too late to ride in the same rental car with Deacon Hill, but I could feel the smile of the sun shining brightly in my direction when I learn that our rooms are right next to each other, while the other rooms are scattered throughout the resort elsewhere. "God Loves Me," I think as we walk to our rooms and Deacon Hill fills me in on the plane conversations and jokes. Without me saying a word, he knows that I am curious and offers play-by-play accounts of the conversation highlights. We have an hour before our first conference meeting and as we arrive at my room, he states, "I'll pick you up in 45." It seems that we are the only ones from our church in this section of the resort because we never see any of the others until we arrive in the lobby or conference room. As we travel the hallway to and from our rooms something begins to happen. Or maybe the 'something' happens each time he knocks on my door to gather me before the meetings or as his voice resonates from behind the podium while commanding the room as one of the keynote speakers. He is very firm in his demeanor and convictions, but shows me a softer side. I find myself becoming more and more attracted to his inner being. He is not my usual 'type', but perhaps I need to look past my 'type' because I have not had much luck with my 'type'. I consider Mitchell, Kevin, and Cornelius my 'type'; beautifully fine specimens... Whew! I lose my breath as I digress, and believe me, the mental detour is worth the loss of breath. I really loved each of them and I still love at least two of them, but I desire to invest my time and energies into someone who is able to love me back. Could it be the deacon? Even though he is not as gorgeous as Mitchell, Kevin, or Cornelius on the outside, I love to watch him speak and often find myself in a deep gaze amazed and intrigued by his EVERYTHING! The way he holds his mouth as he prepares to answer the next question or the gathering of his eyebrows as he intently listens with his pointer finger across his lips, or the way that he makes light of a heavy moment. His everything intrigues me.

Our third day is a partial day in meetings, leaving the remainder of the day for us to enjoy as we please. As the others are planning a day on the town, Deacon Hill announces that he will hang out at the resort to enjoy the amenities. I remain quiet, but plan to be wherever he is, and therefore I decline to go into town with some of the other ladies. I really do not understand my growing feelings for the deacon, but I'm willing to investigate because I can't stop thinking about him. Perhaps Cornelius's rejection has something to do with me being totally open and therefore attracted to the deacon. The beauty of his inner person grows as the minutes spent together pass. I have difficulties sleeping at night because I lay there thinking about him with an unforced smile across my face and brand new happiness in my heart. Just when I expect something firm to cross his lips, he says something sweet and melts my heart in ways that seemed but a distant memory.

We had spoken about his divorce before, but he never revealed the events in such a defenseless manner as when he sat in my room sipping chamomile tea last night. Apparently he couldn't sleep either. I am not sure if my heart intensifies when he speaks because I miss intimacy or if I recognize and relate to his vulnerability. The tension builds each time we walk to and from our rooms. The feeling becomes more intense every time he knocks on the adjoining door and waits in my room while I finish putting on my make-up or mist myself one last time with my favorite perfume, Unforgivable Woman Black by Sean Jean. The normally intolerant, timely man is patient and understanding as he stands outside the bathroom door in my room watching me finish my make-up. He struggles to maintain his thoughts while watching my every move as I line my eyes to perfection with the Evergreen eyeliner. I rush around the room expecting him to complain, when instead he reminds me that he has daughters and insists that I take my time.

As we leave the room and head down the long hallway to the elevator I can feel him looking at me as though he is seeing me for the first time. I glance his way, but quickly turn away and keep my focus forward. My quick peek reveals that his eyes are amazing and his smile shows me the truly beautiful man inside his mysterious world. I don't believe that I have ever really looked at him before, at least not in this way. As we get closer to the elevator, the conversation slows and so does his pace. I am so focused on looking straight ahead that I don't realize that he is noticeably behind me, as opposed to walking by my side. I stop, turn around and ask in a joking manner, "What are you doing back there?" Even though he does not utter a word, his eyes say it all. I know that he wants to kiss me and I want to kiss him back, but I am nervous and afraid of all of the 'what ifs'. What if, while kissing, the loose crown that I cannot afford to get fixed comes off? What if I kiss him too anxiously? What if one touch opens the door to a never-ending craving for Deacon Hill? What if his touch causes my pent-up emotions to release uncontrollably, right here in this hallway? Not only am I afraid of the unknown, but I somehow feel unworthy. Seeing my husband screw my once lesbian, then bisexual, now straight sister in our bed increased my level of insecurities. Also, Deacon Hill does not know about my financial problems, the bills that are due, the disconnected cable, or that I recently contemplated suicide quite regularly. Will he lose respect for me if he finds out how terribly out of control my life has been? I once was secure and confident and would go after what I wanted, but now I spend a good deal of time trying to figure out why Cornelius doesn't want to make love to me. If I let the deacon into my world he will know that I am not as strong and together as I appear. What would he think about me if he knew all of my failures? I love being with him, but feel so undeserving of anything more than his conversation. I think I know enough about him to know that he would deem me weak for allowing myself to choose this dance; or worse, choosing not to exit the dance floor the minute the song of self-destruction began to play. I don't want to alter his current image of me, but I do want to be in his arms. I want his lips to press ever so gently and then firmly against mine; so much so that my mouth begins to water. I want him to hold me as though he never wants to let go and then allow me to get lost in his arms as he reassures me without having to know the cause of my discomforts.

As he catches up with me I am afraid to look in his direction because my fantasy is too far gone and I fear that my desires may be transparent. I want him to take the lead and invite me to follow, allowing me to maintain my lady-like coyness. As we approach the elevator, I realize that once again I have thought my way out of a possibly wonderful situation. We are both silent while we wait for the elevator doors to open. I wonder what he is thinking. Before I could swallow the water in my mouth and ask, the elevator doors open and we both enter the crowd and stand quietly next to each other. My fantasy will remain a fantasy – at least for now.

The half-day meeting seems to drag on forever, even though the speaker is dynamic and delivers the exact message that I need to hear. I am seated with my back to the deacon, which makes the time move even slower because we cannot exchange glances. Glancing his way is almost impossible because he is seated at the table directly behind me, so I remain forward and try to focus on the insignificant conversations dancing around my table as we work on the teamwork assignment presented to each table. My disinterest becomes apparent as I have to ask each of them to repeat themselves "just once more". Mother Jenkins even asks, "Where is your mind, sweetie?" The lie that follows escapes my teeth before I even think about the words, "I'm just thinking about my mother". Everyone at the table knows Mother so the inquisitions begin. "What's wrong with her", "Is she ok?" Realizing that my lie is too far gone, I make up a story about her being sick but not wanting anyone to know. The ladies at the table abandon all thoughts about the assignment as their concerns shift in Mother's direction. Their concerns for me increase as I tell of my difficulty in caring for such a proud woman. I hear myself talking but am astonished that the words are mine. I refused to give her illness a name and continue to ask for their secrecy. Before the half-day session ends I have everyone's commitment to respect our privacy while allowing Mother to maintain her dreadful secret. My inner self asks me, "Why did you tell that lie?" as I shrug my shoulders and sneakily smile. I wonder who will be the first to let the cat out of the bag. As we are leaving the conference room, Mother Jenkins asks again that I join her and the others for a trip downtown to help get my mind off my 'problems'. When I again decline she hugs me and whispers a word of prayer and confirmation in my ear. As she prays for Mother's healing my world dims. I find it difficult to believe that I just deceived some of the church members with an invented illness – and all in an effort to hide my deepening feelings for the deacon. I guess that I didn't choose that dance very well.

My immediate thought is to ask God for forgiveness, so I do as I return to my room, slip into my comfy pajamas, and lay across my bed. In the midst of the deceit I lost track of the deacon. Perhaps he changed his mind and went into town with the rest of the group. Oh well, I guess this is my punishment for lying. I turn the TV on and fall asleep watching a Tyler Perry movie. Usually Madea makes me laugh, no matter my mood, but today my many thoughts race around the room as I stare blankly at the screen contemplating my next steps as I feel my eyelids weighing downward. I am tempted to pray for a moment with the deacon, but I can fix my mouth to ask for an ungodly moment with the deacon, so I just drift mentally until Madea's words are only heard by my subconscious. Besides, who am I trying to fool? The deacon and I could never be a long-term romantic relationship and what I truly desire is much more than just a 'Deacon Right Now' moment.

Breastplate of Strength

One of my all-time favorite things is to have someone play in my hair and to my surprise, I am awakened by the deacon gently stroking the hair away from my face. Cornelius is the last man that stroked through my hair and remembering his touch causes a warm smile to grace my lips. "It's nice to see your smile again," Deac says in a soft but manly voice. I can feel myself having a lovely moment, but usually these moments are private, so I have to wake- up and pull myself together. Or, perhaps I am dreaming and if this is the case, I want to enjoy the moment for as long as possible. I caress my pillow, groan, and force my eyelids to remain in a closed position. The gentle strokes through the front of my hair continue causing me to realize that my lovely moment is my current reality. I must have left the adjoining door cracked. I slowly open my eyes again to find the Deacon leaning over me wearing little more than a smile. A second look reveals that he is actually clothed in shorts and a nice pull-over collared shirt. I have never seen Deacon dressed so casually and was just about to compliment his attire when I realize that I can't find the words. His touch summons the warmth back into my world. I'm tempted to jump into his arms and express my gratitude, but pride and nervousness serve as calming agents so I settle for the precious smile that I can't seem to dim.

As I freshen up, Deacon takes the liberty to order room service, which means that we will stay in the room. Maybe this will be the night of passion that I so desperately need. Although I thoroughly enjoy Deacon's conversation, I can't keep my mind from periodically drifting through the possibilities that follow the magnificent meal set before us. Everything is perfect until his phone rings. After exchanging a few filtered words with the person on the other end of the phone he quietly excuses himself to his room for the next half-hour. He did not completely close the door nor did he speak in a quiet manner so I can clearly hear his side of the conversation and it is not pleasant. My filet mignon is getting cold so I finish my meal and am sitting on the couch watching the news when Deac walks back into my room and sits on the edge of the bed. He sits silently staring at the floor with tears covering his pupils. I have never seen him look so vulnerable. My only instinct is to take him a handful of tissues and sit quietly by his side until he is ready to speak. After a few minutes, he breaks the silence with some of the most painful words ever uttered. "She's in love with him and they're having a baby." At least when Kevin cheated a baby was not created and no one knew about the infidelity except for those involved and those whom we told. Deac looks down at the handful of approximately twenty tissues and chuckles as he sits back on the bed against the headboard. He pats his hand on the bed next to him so I climb on the bed and sit next to him as he talks about his situation in a slow, steady pace. Listening to him allows me to forget about being the victim in my situation with Cornelius. Deac's story unfolds in my lap and I learn more about the softer side of this strong, sweet man than I ever imagined. He tells me that he and his wife filed for divorce a year ago, but had recently talked about reconciling until he found love letters between his wife and her lover dated as far back as seven years. Even with this finding, he was willing to start over on a path of healing. However, all through counseling she remained distant and now he knows why. The tears cross the threshold of his eyelids when he tells me that they have not had sex in over a year because her body would no longer respond to his attempts. This answers the question that I could not ask but wanted to know about the baby. I guess he is sure that the baby is not his and as I ponder this thought the most unexpected event occurs.

This man of great stature begins to sob uncontrollably. Without a thought I wrap my arms around him and become his pillar of strength. I hear myself consoling him and at this moment I like who I am and I'm glad that I'm here to help him through his torturous moments. I find comfort while the deacon's head rest upon my chest, and as his tears hit my breastplate I gain a glimpse of a woman strong enough to hold the weight of a good man in the midst of his deepest sorrow. We fall asleep with him in my arms and with the exception of a few gentle kisses, the night is absent of passion. An exciting night of sex is exchanged for a night of agape love. For it is in this moment that I recognize myself as a victorious conqueror. In this moment I am proud that God chose me to be the breastplate of strength for a man as deserving as the Deacon. It was during his pain that I found more of my purpose. My pain became my testimony as I assured him that he could and would get through his moments of agony.

We remained inseparable for the duration of the conference and developed a bond deeper than ever expected. Although we leave the conference without knowing each other sexually I am fulfilled by the growing intensity of our friendship. His tears coated the breastplate of strength that I never knew existed within my fragile being. Being available for Deacon Hill shows me that I am only as fragile as I speak or think of myself. In the moments that follow our pivotal evening I can hear Dear quoting the very powerful scriptures, "Life and death lie in the power of the tongue" and "Call those things that be not as though they were", which tells me to speak it and it is already done! The conference served me well. I traded in my tears for my breastplate of strength and a stronger self-image as I stand on the shoulders of my grandmother, enveloped by the love of God!

Messenger

I 'm feeling the strength of a lioness as I take my place in line for my boarding pass headed home. Unlike the trip to the conference, I am not concerned with where I sit or who sits next to me on the plane. My focus has broadened beyond my own personal desires. God's work in my life is ever-present as I walk with my head held high and for the first time in a long while my smile is not a façade. With all that life has placed at my feet, on my shoulders, and even dumped on top of my head, I'm getting my first glimpse of my purpose. Without realizing, I allowed my spiritual being to take front and center as I ministered to Deacon Hill through my hugs, wiping his tears, my listening ear, and my words of encouragement. My focus shifted outward to helping his heart to reach a place of relief as I forgot about my fleshly desires. Even if temporary, Deacon Hill went to sleep with a smile gracing his face that night, and in part it's because I allowed God to use me as a vessel for His glory.

The thought of God using me is empowering, as well as a little frightening; however, I walk through the airport in confidence as I remind myself that the spirit of fear is not a feeling that I have to accept. Last night as we enjoyed our final night of dinner via room service Deac said that he began a new path on his spiritual journey. Although I did not verbalize my thoughts, I am also on an elevated spiritual journey. I've trained hundreds of employees and helped countless achieve career goals in Corporate America, but I've always sat quietly on the sidelines in God's army... until now. I feel as though I've grown wings out of the center of my back, earned the stripes of a fearless tiger, gained my stainless steel sword and am now equipped to fight for spiritual justice in life's army. It almost feels as though my transformation was overnight; however, I realize that with each test I was compiling my testimony. At the core of every painful trial was a triumph building strength and my new knowledge of this fact makes me smile. I own my new confidence and, although no one really knows what or when the transformation happened, the other church members see the change. For the first time, I am having real conversations with people whom I've known my whole life because my walls have crumbled just enough for others to step over. My love for Deacon grew into a true godly love... overnight! Perhaps this is the love that Cornelius feels for me and all of a sudden his actions make sense and I somehow understand.

I usually don't care to sit towards the back of the plane or in a middle seat, but today is different because my focus is of a higher level. Without realizing my seat choice, I find myself towards the back of the plane in a middle seat, right next to Sister Jenkins. I offer a genuinely kind smile as I notice her skirt pulled up around her waist as we both get comfortable. Before long the plane is ascending as I feel a spiritual being sitting in the seat to my right and without an audible announcement, I know that this is a Messenger of God. I cannot resist the urge to look to my right and find that the seat is empty as the spiritual feeling begins to dissipate, probably due to the conflict between what my eyes see versus what my soul feels. However, when I close my eyes and regain a spiritual focus, my awareness of the Messenger sitting to my right returns as I say, "Yes" and ready my heart to receive God's message. I am familiar enough with how God works to know that I am more able to receive when I decrease my flesh, and increase my spiritual stillness. Decreasing my flesh means that in this moment I have to resist fear, doubt, unworthiness, and my need for everything to make sense.

The Messenger ministers to me by showing me how God is using me. I see myself being a leader in my family; both immediate and extended family. Being a leader in any part of my family is going to be a difficult transition because I have always taken a back seat to Mother and her directions for our family, but again I say "Yes". Without a spoken word, the Messenger tells me that I will minister to the masses through verbal as well as written expressions of faith, and that I am a living testimony to how God works. Doubt tries to enter because I don't see myself as being strong enough to be a living testimony. However, as I think to myself, "God is not fear and fear is not of God", I realize that I can speak to and then dismiss the unwanted spirit of fear. The Messenger shows me that I have just chosen the dance of faith and, for the first time, Dear's words make perfect and complete sense. I see myself teaching others how to choose their dance as they walk in faith. My life flashes before me and I see my past, present, and future. I see past childhood pains, linked to present growths disguised as disappointments, and then I see future joys. Dear used to say, "Count it all joy," and now I know what she meant. When I understand how the pain is a necessary means towards my joy, I know why I should count every moment as a joyful moment. By faith, I begin to thank God for the joy that awaits just beneath the pain.

As the Messenger continues to minister I see myself standing about twenty stories tall in a field of dry land as huge tears fall from my eyes to the dirt below. With each tear that hits the ground and bursts open, the earth is watered and plants spring upward. On each plant are several vines and with each new teardrop new plants emerge, the vines are multiplied and grow upward. Flowers bloom on some of the vines, some vines produces fruit, other vines sprout leaves, and I even see thorns in the midst, but the growth is plentiful. My tears lessen as a rainbow of love pours from the core of my heart onto the growth in progress. To my right and left are others with tears leaping from their faces and out onto the earth as the fertilization process continues, based on our individual testimonies. I am shown that these are fellow brothers and sisters with their own important jobs in the ministry. I notice that we all have different-shaped battle scars and just when the vision is becoming a bit overwhelming, my brother to my right and my sister to my left take my hands and lift them towards the heavens. Without giving a reason, they celebrate their wounds and thank God for the privilege of being a vessel. We are all separate, unique, united wounded souls on the mission of helping others to heal. As my brother and sister hold my hands upward, I feel stronger and resist the spirit of feeling overwhelmed and unworthy as I suddenly gain a better understanding of my life's purpose. I feel strength behind, above, and all around me. As I glance beneath, above, and all around me I behold my feet upon shoulders of strength. I feel the support all about me from the silent soldiers who paved the way by fighting on my behalf until I was able to recognize my own calling and strength. We each realize that we all have a responsibility and mine is to inhale the lessons from each painful moment and share my experiences so that I can help others grow.

For the first time in my life, I know who I am and better yet... I know why I am. With each realization my rainbow of love thickens and I willingly increase the outpouring of my love to nourish the growth that is multiplying. With a closer look, I notice that the plants are indeed souls with wounds of their own. I am able to feel each hurt that I look upon. I am tempted to pick up as many souls as my hands will hold so that I may provide comfort; and then my attention is summoned upward. I see Dear smiling down upon me and in her smile I can feel that she is proud of my spiritual growth. The Messenger shows me that I will be able to help more of the wounded souls by being a spiritual vessel than by offering to pick up the few souls that my physical hands are able to hold. Maintaining my focus on God and His directions will allow me to be used in His way. Without explanation, I see the big picture. It's my turn to be strong for others, to be used as a vessel of healing and my strength comes through my spirituality. I finally understand that my pain does have meaning and the joy is almost bigger than my soul is able to hold. My heart is filled with celebration as Sister Jenkins taps me on the hand.

I open my eyes to find Sister Jenkins smiling gently in my direction. She tells me that they are waiting for us to get off the plane. Wow, everyone has exited the plane except for Sister Jenkins and me. She tells me that she was praying for me as I received God's message. The inquisitive look in my eyes tells her that I want to know more, so she explains that she has also been visited by one of God's Messengers. Before I am able to ask, she says that she saw the Messenger sitting on the plane next to me. She also states, "That Messenger has been with you for a while, just waiting for the right moment to deliver God's message. God has a work for you to do. Go and fertilize the earth with the ministry that God has put into the core of your soul. Thank God for all of your tests, because through our tests we gain our testimonies." I thank her and know in my spirit that now is the perfect time to offer my suggestions on her sitting without hiking her dress up around her waist.

She graciously accepts my suggestion as we look back into the emptied plane one last time before exiting. We both see the Messenger as he points at me and says, "Let go of the fear, because it's not about you". I shake my head in agreement; however, I guess I did not completely grasp the message because he points at me and firmly repeats his words several times, "It's not about you… you were sent to help others. It's not about you! It's NEVER been about YOU!!! God chose you to help others and when you chose fear you back away from your purpose – you get stuck, so don't be afraid. IT'S NEVER BEEN ABOUT YOU!"

In an instant my life flashes through my mind beginning with childhood pains and disappointments leading up to recent moments. The vision happens very fast, but I mentally capture each moment in layers as though in slow motion… I quickly receive the message. It's Never been about Me! I clearly understand that I was chosen as before I was placed in Mother's womb and at birth I began earning the lessons necessary for my ministry. God presented a baby girl to a woman who wanted a baby boy; this was the first of many obstacles I would overcome in preparing for my purpose. Seconds later I realize Mother's importance because without her there would be no me. I experienced the pain so that I can help others overcome their pains. It's never been about me… It's about God's mission. I'm merely a vessel. Oh my God! This realization is humbling, but also very empowering. As I release the blame, pain, hatred, and other negative weights from my heart I feel myself mature about thirty years in a few seconds. The Messenger nods in our direction before spreading his wings and leaving through the top of the plane. Sister Jenkins takes my hand and tells me that it is now my turn to be a Messenger for God. I simply say "Yes" and choose my dance of praise and thanksgiving as we exit the plane.

Exercising My Choice

It's been three weeks since I returned home from the conference and for the first time in my life I know how it feels to be free. My happiness shines bright and with each day I gain a better appreciation of the trials and tribulations that I endured. My meditation and time talking with God have intensified, which means that the sorrows of yesterday are becoming a distant memory. I don't want to grow so far away from the pain that I forget the intricacies of my unbelievable deliverances, but my focus has shifted. Tears of sorrow are replaced by my joyful praise because I now feel complete, but it's because of my sorrow that I am able to praise so heartily. Therefore, I need to remember every detail of how I found my way to God's grace and mercy.

My instant remedy for capturing the depth of every painful event is to write it down while it is still a recallable reality. Within three weeks I capture every intricate detail of my testimony while revisiting tortuous heartbreaks between keystrokes and tears. There were times when I felt like revisiting the emotional rollercoaster ride would destroy my joy as I navigated each carefully placed word onto paper. However, the reality that I'm here to talk about my life is proof that I made it through the storm; with the help of God, of course. Putting pen to pad was the easy part. I now have a manuscript full of my secrets, darkness, and fears ready for the next chapter of my life. Although I hear God's instructions as clear as I am Jon Terrence Johnson, I'm afraid to obey so I pray that He will change His mind and give alternate commands. God wants me to share my story so that others may grow and be healed, but I can't. I poured my bloodied soul over these pages and if anyone reads my story they will know what I've been through, what I've done, and who I've hurt. My sister is an avid reader so she will surely discover that the panties were mine; Mother will know that I enjoyed seeing Alex slap her; Daddy will know that I'm not his perfect daughter, and the world will know about my financial hardship. I'm torn on what to do with this God-inspired piece of art, so I put it in my desk drawer while I wait for further instructions from God. I'm willing to help others, but not at the risk of becoming a spectacle for all to examine.

I've been so busy working, taking care of the girls, and scribing my testimony that I haven't had much time to miss Cornelius, Urijah, or the Deacon. Of course I see Urijah every day that I'm in the office, but I'm no longer moved by his mere presence. He still has a beautiful spirit and I will always love and support him, but I no longer want to jump his bones. Instead I look for ways to build him up spiritually. Cornelius and I speak every day, the Deacon calls regularly, and Kevin says that he wants to come home with me and the girls; however, I'm so spiritually full that idle communication is kept to a minimum. Besides, my love for Alex supersedes any romantic thoughts with Kevin. The girls and I continue to strengthen our relationship, and for the first time I am able to see the forward movement in my world.

I am transitioning into the strong leader in the family, just as indicated in the vision. I now see how every hardship was preparing me to walk in my victory. I was strong for Deacon Hill, which allowed me to recognize the god within my soul. I have always been strong in my professional life; conversely, I felt weak and victimized by my surroundings in my personal world. Well, not anymore! Once I connected with my inner god and allowed my soul to rule over my flesh, I was able to put fear in its place and walk in my God-given authority over evil and darkness. Nowadays in the midst of trials I am not only finding the silver linings, but I am ripping that silver lining wide open in search of the lesson to be learned by the current trial. God promised that if I delight myself in Him that He would give me the desires of my heart, so I stand on His Word. I find that when I rely on God's promises I always find the blessing or His message in whatever is placed before me. Intellectually I guess that I always knew that I could choose my dance, but I now exercise my choice. I find myself giving words of encouragement and prayer to others and then I renew my strength through meditation and worship.

Four weeks ago a call from my attorney would have sent me into a bout of depression before I even answered the phone; however, today when I see my caller ID, I thank God in advance for the blessing before answering the phone. I am confident that no matter what the news, it will be useful so I thank God. The attorney immediately notices my upbeat greeting as she advises that Kevin finally agreed to my requests so our divorce should be finalized soon, freeing my assets. God is so great! Although I look forward to financial freedom once again, I also look forward to managing my finances differently this time. It was not an easy transition to go from being a carefree spender to looking for change in old purses, but we survived and I gained a better appreciation for money. I grew frugal out of necessity but I like knowing where my money is going so I will maintain a budget. Times are tough and the cable is off, but we never go to bed hungry. Through faith we always have enough.

I purposely pour a lot of love into my daughters because they need to feel me. Even when they are not in my presence they need to know that I'm always with them. God gifted me with two precious souls to guide and care for until they are able to care for themselves and I want to make Him proud for choosing me as their mother. I'm glad that I now realize the importance of nurturing their spiritual being, as well as their physical selves. Taking care of our souls is great preparation for my ministry. How can I water the earth with love if I don't first love me and then my family?

I learned so much this year; however, I didn't realize the extent of my growth until I wrote down my testimony. On the outside it appears that the revelation of the 'new' me was overnight; however, in reality God has been preparing me for this mission all of my life. I now recognize the testimonies that were birthed in my darkness. The pieces of my puzzle fell into place once I surrendered to God and allowed my life to be used for His glory. Choosing to inhale current moments, and accepting that I do not have to control every element of life have been the keys to my growth. I do; however, control how I manage through the situations placed before me.

This is what Dear meant when she told me to "choose the dance". When the pieces begin to crumble right before me I now take a cleansing breath so that I connect with the love within me before I take action. A cleansing breath allows me the time necessary to decrease my flesh while inhaling the positive as I exhale any negative energy. Simultaneously I acknowledge God with a whisper of his name, "sweet Jesus", which in that crucial moment reminds me of my purpose and the importance of choosing my dance wisely. Thank God for revelation!

I once heard a guess on the Oprah Winfrey Show say that we walk either in fear or in love. Thank God that I'm learning to choose to walk in love. Choosing my dance has made my time with Mother more enjoyable because I am not holding in the resentment or reacting negatively to her comments. Mother says that watching how I handle situations encourages her to work on her spirituality. I, along with the rest of the family can tell that Mother is making an effort to show more love. Although we talk almost every day, today is the first time that Alex, Mother, and I will get together since I returned from the conference.

Today Mother wants to take us to one of her favorite restaurants, which means that we will each leave the restaurant with enough food for dinner, and maybe even lunch tomorrow. We used to turn our noses up at leftovers until I made a stand to no longer be wasteful and took food home. Later that night we laughed as Mother and Alex shared my leftover meal while we watched a movie, and they wished that they had brought home their food.

We constantly find humor in our moments, which is a change for the better. I find myself being the comedian of the bunch and I never knew that I was funny. I have an hour before they get here so I pull out my manuscript for some meditation while I read over my testimony. I become lost in praise as I turn the pages of my life in review. Tears of gratitude and compassion stain the page as I listen to the little lost girl tell her story page after page. The water on the pages reminds me of the inevitable growth as depicted in my vision.

Time has gotten away from me so I grab some water and clean my face just in time for Alex's arrival. Alex knocks and then enters telling me stories about her and Kevin, as per usual. Her disposition is bubbly, which means that she and Kevin are in a good place. When she takes a breath, we hug before she pulls me to the couch in the family room to catch up on sister secrets before Mother arrives. Within minutes the doorbell rings, which is a bit odd. Mother always calls when she is turning onto my street to let us know to come out of the house. I head for the door hoping that she doesn't want me to drive because I am really low on gas. To my surprise, Mr. Repo man is here to collect both of my cars. My instinct is to slam the door because the cars are locked securely in the garage, but instead I take a cleansing breath and say, "Well, bless His Holy Name," before taking action. I decide to try to reason with the well-dressed gentleman. I explain that I am going through a divorce and should be able to bring the payments current by the end of the month. In turn, he explains his quota and his mission as he speaks with sincere authority. A part of me wishes that I had told him that Jonnie was not home and shut the door before Alex overheard the conversation that I struggled to keep at a whisper. Alex is now standing behind me asking, "How much is it?" I am embarrassed that she knows, so I tell her that I will call the main office later to fix the obvious misunderstanding. No matter what I say, she convinces me to allow her to pay the man before Mother arrives and overhears my private business. My internal voice says, "Some family leader you are... Your little sister has to pay your overdue car notes," but before I am overtaken by self-judgment I take a cleansing breath and say aloud, "Praise God," as I dismiss the spirit of shame and hug my baby sister. Naturally I am a little ashamed, but I choose the dance of thanksgiving for God's plan because I know that there is a bigger reason why this man knocked on my door two minutes after Alex arrived. I don't have the answers, nor do I know how the pieces to this puzzle will fit together, but I do know that there are NO coincidences, so I choose the dance of faith.

Mother approaches the door moments after we hang up with the finance company and the repo man is driving away. She dashes in, stating that she has to use the restroom and then we leave. Alex gets something out of her car and then we all ride with Mother to the restaurant. Alex rides the entire twenty minutes sitting up against the back of my seat with her right arm around my right shoulder. She just paid thousands of dollars for my car notes. I feel like I should be hugging her, but instead she is acting as though I did her a favor by allowing her to spend her money on my bills. I don't understand God's work, but, with each cleansing breath I choose the dance of gratitude as I hold onto her arm with both of my hands. I decide that I don't need to figure out why things happen like they do, I just thank Him for the blessings, both seen and unseen. At lunch we each share our stories. Mother catches us up on work and even suggest that we both should work with her in the "family business". I never imagined that I would hear her invite either of us to be a part of her business. Equally, I never knew that it was a family business. Alex and I both treat the suggestion as rhetorical because neither of us can picture ourselves working for Mother.

Alex is a production executive for a major production company and shares that she was just tasked to head up their newly developed print division. She advises that her company is looking for written works of all types and asks that we let her know if we come across any scripts, books, writers, etc. in need of publishing. I could not hear much more over the voice of God, again directing me to put my written testimony in her hands. I have gotten pretty good at choosing my dance of obedience, but I can't let her read my written work. Our relationship would be over and I love having a sister for the first time in our lives. We came from the same womb many years ago, but just recently became sisters. "God, please find another way," I think as I pick at my salad, take a cleansing breath, and choose the dance of silence. However, this would be the perfect time for me to speak up and accept Mother's offer to work with her. The salary would far exceed the money that I make as a consultant working with Urijah. I could also take the opportunity to help my baby sister by handing her my manuscript. However, when I put my testimony on paper I never expected anyone else to ever read it.

This whole afternoon has been overwhelming. I can't wait to get to my quiet place of prayer and meditation. I am glad that the girls are with Kevin this evening, because I really need to have an uninterrupted conversation with God. I am finding that when I don't know what to do, it's best that I choose to sit out the dance altogether, until the vision of direction is clearer. I picture myself standing on a road with many paths at my feet and right now I don't really know which path to take, so I will stand still. In this moment, I am exercising my choice of no movement at all as I strive to enjoy the present.

All Things

L ately life has kept us all busy and therefore I have not seen much of anyone, with the exception of Kali, Tia, and co-workers of course. Even though our lunch dates have dissipated, Mother, Alex and I still exchange an email or text message about once a week. Initially I was a little worried that Alex's absence meant that I was losing our newly developing friendship, but Daddy says that they haven't seen much of her either so I guess she truly is busy. The girls report that Alex spends most of the time in her office when they are visiting their dad. I hope that everything is ok because I've never known her to be so focused, but I guess that a career change which awakens your passions will bring about a new focus. Besides, we all have to mature at some point in our lives and I guess it's her time. I'm happy for her because I know that hard work and dedication will pay off, but I do miss spending time with my little sister. So much so that I sent her a greetings card just to express how much I miss her. A week later she texts a sincere 'Thank you for the beautiful card, sis. I love you'. A text reply is a little less than I hoped for, but the "I love you" tag at the end of the message warmed my heart so I forced my worries to rest as I redirected my focus to landing another account for Urijah's advertising firm. My experience and contacts in the advertising world have really proven beneficial for his company. Because of the extraordinary growth of the new company I get a strong feeling that my time to move on is near, but where will I go?

Working in a small firm and collecting a minimal consulting fee have humbled me in multiple ways. I eventually saw the ugliness of my reflection as I looked upon the beautiful souls of my co-workers; people just wanting love and acceptance as they find their way through life. I remember not wanting to drink water from the generically labeled bottle when I interviewed, even though I barely had fifteen cents in my purse or enough gas to make it home. How dare I look down my nose at anyone, but I did. I'm embarrassed by who I was then, but thankful about my growth. I grew to love my co-workers; they are my family and I will miss each of them, but I have to move out of the way of the next person destined to fill this spot. I can feel that I am close to the finale here, which causes a sense of separation anxiety. Anxiety about not seeing the ladies; not having a reason to stay busy every day; not seeing Urijah anymore; but this day has to come and it's only a matter of time. I need to wait until my divorce is final because I rely on my income and the periodic bonuses. My attorney keeps reassuring me that the divorce will be final soon. I really need Kevin to sign the paperwork and move on with his life so that I can get back to the life that I once knew. I look forward to turning the cable back on and paying off my creditors so that I can come out of hiding and enjoy my balcony once again. Daddy asked me to come and head the marketing department at Mother's company, but I'm not sure if this is smart. Mother and I are moving in a positive direction and I would hate to hinder our developing bond by trying to blend business with personal family life. Experience tells me to thank God for his guidance as I 'Be still and know that He Is God'. I have already prayed and asked for His direction and I have the faith that He will lead me in the right direction.

I took time away from work today to meet up with Sheila for long-overdue lunch and conversation with my dear friend. Neither of us has seen or heard much from Mitchell since participating in 'The Plan', but I continue to receive monthly child support checks, so we know that he is still amongst the living. As I drive I become more excited the closer I get to the restaurant because Sheila has always been a good listener and advisor. It's amazing that I gained a wonderful friend out of Mitchell's cheating. I smile to myself as I think about how amazing God is at making miracles out of messes. I'm so excited to see Sheila that I stumble over the curb and fall into her arms. We laugh as we greet each and check to make sure that I have not scuffed my shoes. I thank her for catching me and she responds, "Our relationship began with you rescuing me from a life of misery, so I'm happy to return the favor... today, tomorrow, and for the rest of our lives. We lock arms and head for the restaurant. Her happiness is obvious and she wears it well. She looks to have put on a few pounds and each one has fallen in the appropriate place. Conversely, I have lost too much weight and feel a bit conscientious because my curves are no longer so apparent. She is gracious enough not to comment about my skin- and-bones frame. Instead we hug, laugh, and catch up on all of the latest news in our lives. She and her gorgeous husband have adopted a little girl and she is a cutie. I don't think that Sheila stops smiling the entire afternoon, and her eyes sparkle when she talks about her new two-year-old daughter, Tiana. I am so happy for her. She stayed strong through years of a lonely marriage, a cheating husband, and a bitter divorce. Through it all she never lost her faith or treated me poorly, which is constant inspiration and a reminder that all things work together for my good.

God never fails! He used a situation that could have destroyed the both of us to create a wonderful friendship, and I don't use the word 'friend' loosely. We have taken turns carrying each other through the thick and thin by listening, praying, and offering words of wisdom when appropriate. Today is not much different. There are no tears shed, but she does offer suggestions on my next steps. She agrees that it's time for me to jump out of the Urijah nest. She realizes that hearing her words are difficult for me because she knows how I feel about Urijah; both personally, as well as professionally. She has some good points for me to consider, but nothing that needs to be decided right this moment.

The afternoon is beautiful and driving with the top down, the sun's warmth across my shoulders, alone with my thoughts is the perfect way to cap off my midday. My hair is blowing in the wind and I'm singing along with Robin Thicke when my phone rings. It's Cornelius and I am only too anxious to answer his call. We have yet to cross that passionate line and I'm ok because he is a great friend/date buddy. He can hear the smile in my voice and tells me that my joyfulness is attractive. We talk for our usual ten minutes before he asks if he can take me to dinner later tonight. I am only too happy to put him on hold to answer Daddy's call, prior to answering his question. I can hear the distress in Daddy's voice as he tells me that Mother has been in a car accident. She is conscious, but he tells me that I should still come as soon as I can get away from work. I tell Cornelius that I have to go and arrive at the hospital within twenty-two minutes.

My mother of steel is lying helpless in a hospital bed staring at the television through blackened eyes. She also has a broken rib, swollen face, and a laceration across the top of her forehead. When she sees me she reaches for me and starts crying. I have never seen Mother cry or in any kind of weakened state, so this whole scene feels strange. She pulls me into her and tells me about the accident in a childlike manner. I can barely understand her words through the stuttering, but from what I gather she pushed the wrong pedal. It's like she has forgotten the names of common, everyday items. Daddy can see the confusion and explains that traffic was coming to a stop and she stepped on the gas pedal as opposed to the brake. The young lady driving the car in front of her is in surgery now. The air bag rendered Mother unconscious when her SUV was hit head-on by a man driving a rather large truck. The driver of the truck was a little shaken, but he is ok. The SUV is totaled, but that's material. Right now we need prayer for the young lady who is fighting for her life.

As Daddy is praying, Cornelius walks into the room wearing his maître d' uniform, followed by Alex and Kevin. Daddy quickly explains what happened as he asks again that we pray for the young lady in surgery. I try to allow others access to Mother, but she has my hand so tightly that Alex has to go to the other side of the bed. She gently kisses Mother on the cheek as she stares into space without speaking much. I am not sure what is going on, but she is not acting like Alex. I am still learning the new Alex, so I cannot put my finger on what is wrong, but she is acting weird. It's as though she has lost her place in this world. Her confidence has diminished. It seems that she is merely existing, as opposed to living and Alex has always lived life to the fullest. I can't figure this out now, but I will talk to her later.

The doctor has checked on Mother several times and medicated her so that she is in no pain, but still no word about the young lady in surgery. Mother is resting peacefully and has finally let go of my hand. I want to be the one to tell the girls, so I excuse myself and head to their school. As I am getting into my car I see that Alex has parked right in front of me and get the bright idea to leave a sisterly love note on her windshield. I take a piece of paper from my portfolio and write:

> "Alex,
>
> I am so glad that you are my sister. We have been through so much as a family and this is just another obstacle that we will move through victoriously! I miss you. Will you have lunch with me? YES or NO ... lol (remember the note from little Christopher James). Too funny, right?
>
> I really do miss you and look forward to getting together soon.
>
> Love me...
>
> p.s. Mother will be ok.
>
> Your Big Sis JJ"

Hopefully the note will make her smile. As I am placing the note on her windshield I recall how much I hate notes on my windshield. Just as soon as I get settled, seat belt buckled, and am pulling out is when I notice the paper on the windshield blocking my view, so I have to stop the car, unbuckle the seat belt, and get out to remove the flyer that is blocking my view. Therefore I decided to leave the note on her window so that she will see the paper when she reaches for her door handle. While trying to wedge the note between the window and the rubber seal I glance at the back seat and remember the times when Kevin and I made love on that seat. I would sneak into the garage, climb in the car and wait for him to notice me wearing something sexy. Once I wore a floor- length leather coat and not much more. Another time, lingerie, and then the crotchless panties, different wigs... etcetera. We would make love for hours exploring new areas of each other's bodies, all while she slept unsuspectingly. The vision of her curled up in the corner of my couch once she discovered that Kevin had been cheating pulls me back to reality.

I secure the note and am headed back to my car when, as an after-thought, I recall seeing something on her back seat that belongs to me. I stop dead in my tracks and tell myself that surely I'm mistaken. I have to go back and confirm and as sure as I am standing here looking through my hands pressed up against her back window… there lies my written testimony! My journal! My private words! My secrets! Oh my God! What is she doing with that? How did she get it? Alex interrupts my thoughts by asking, "What are you doing?" By the calmness in her voice I can only imagine that she doesn't remember leaving my private property for all to see displayed across her back seat.

I ask her what she is doing with my private property and how she got it. Instead of answering, she becomes defensive and tells me that I should be explaining why I was sleeping with her man while smiling in her face. An argument instantly ensues and for the first time in my life, I am not afraid of Alex so I am speaking just as boldly as she once did. She throws out comments like, "Your maître d' wasn't enough for you? No wonder he won't sleep with you… He could probably still smell the Kevin dripping off you." My responses are also not nice, "You do your dirt and think that there's no consequence? You will never be all that I am, so get used to Kevin looking to supplement your relationship in his attempt to re-create what I gave him. You think that you're the only evil one in the family? Guess again, little girl."

In this moment I remember that I have to pick up the girls from school so I tell her that I don't have time to debate who's the better woman as I jump into my car. As if I hadn't done enough damage I roll down my window as I drive by her and say, "If there is ever a question about who's the better woman, just remember whom he married and refuses to divorce." I feel good about getting the last and most damaging words for about one-tenth of a second.

To my surprise, I look in my rearview mirror and see her bawling into her hands. I can tell that she is crying really hard by how much her body is shaking, and then she falls to her knees. Before I hand the parking attendant the parking slip, I see her tumble over in a fetal position in the middle of the dirty parking garage. She is screaming so loud with pain that the attendant calls for help on his radio. I have never seen anyone cry like this and she is my sister. I back up and park in the first available spot. I then call Vanessa and ask her to pick up my girls as I am running to Alex. I fall to my knees and put her head in my lap while telling her, "I'm sorry, Alex. I'm sooooo sorry." I never meant to hurt you. Please stop screaming." I scoot us across the dirty ground until we are both out of the middle of the driveway.

The fact that she not once shows any concern about getting her pinstripe double-breasted Versace suit dirty demonstrates how much pain she feels.

Once we are out of traffic and safely between two cars I hold and rock her like a baby while she belts out these sort of scream-cries so hard that she loses oxygen a couple of times. Between the scream-cries she apologizes as she professes her love for Kevin several times. "I don't know what to do with what I feel for him. I want to hate him, but I can't... I love him so much. I don't want to hurt you anymore, Jonnie, but I can't stop loving him. Please forgive me, please. I've tried to let him go, but I don't know how. He has my heart and I don't want it back. I'm so sorry, sis. I'm sorry."

My heart breaks as I listen to my sister's demonstration of pain. The God in me won't allow another minute to go by without my complete transparency. I tell her that I am not in love with Kevin any longer and haven't been for quite a while. I continue, "I let go of any romantic possibilities between us when I saw how much you loved him. I realized that me being with him would hurt you further, so I vowed never to cross that line again... because you mean too much to me. I need my sister more than I need a roll in the hay". For the first time, she looks up at me and gently laughs at my reference of 'roll in the hay' as she says, "You're showing your age, Jonnie." I smile back while continuing to console her until security guards appear on the scene. Once they are convinced that neither of us requires medical attention and we are both safe to drive, we are escorted to our separate cars and both leave the garage.

I call Daddy for an update and find that Mother is still resting comfortably and the young lady is out of surgery, but has not regained consciousness. I tell him that I will get the girls settled and be back soon. My mind is swimming as I drive to Vanessa to get the girls. I'm ashamed that I felt good about delivering the verbal knockout blow that landed my little sister on the dirty ground in the parking garage. I was determined to get the last and most harsh word; like a bully. I acted like she used to act and she was soft and venerable like I used to be. Have we switched rolls? It feels good not to be the victim, but I don't want her old role. I think that I felt good because I've never stood up to her, but this was the wrong time and the wrong way to start standing up to Alex. I can hardly wait to unload all of this onto Vanessa's lap. Once she puts a blanket over her couch so that the dirt from my clothes does not transfer, she pours me a glass of iced tea and listens to the events of the day. Before she can offer words of advice I get a phone call from Alex thanking me for the note and asking if she may bring pizza by for dinner with me and the girls, before heading back to the hospital to see Mother. Our conversation is brief once she learns that I am at Vanessa's house. They have never been close, especially after Vanessa fought Alex and won, but today life delivers a more humbled Alex who also invites Vanessa for pizza and conversation. "Tell Vanessa that I say hello," she says as we are ending our conversation.

Vanessa tells me to watch God continue His work as she agrees to join us for the conversation, more so than the pizza. I can no longer stand being in these dirty clothes so the girls and I head home. Kali has a lot of questions about the accident as Tia sits quietly in her private conversation with God. After about five minutes of repeated questions, Tia states, "Remember Kali... all things work together for your good, so no matter what happens, it is for your good. Don't worry. Everything will work out." At this point we have learned to pay close attention to Tia's words, as though God is speaking through her. Kali smiles and says, "Okay," as she dances around the room. I mentally rewind my day while standing in this expensive deluxe rainfall shower. I guess that I'm learning to trust God more because this time there are no tears, just praise for how far this family has come in a relatively short time, Thank God. I recall several moments in my life that seem grim, but worked for my good, so I tell God that I trust Him. I recognize the confirmation when Kali comes into my room while I'm getting dressed singing a song that she has created, "All things... All things, work together for my good." Tia is right behind her repeating every melodic word. We feel a sweet breeze as though Dear has entered the room. All three of us instantly look at each other and smile. We move forward with our evening with the confidence that all things are working for our good!

Preparation

Sitting across the table watching Alex swallow her third piece of pizza without much chewing causes my tummy to ache just a little. Nevertheless, Vanessa and I pick at our pizza without a word of judgment. Alex has always had a toned and curvaceous build, but now she is skin and bones and looks a bit sickly. She says that she hasn't been able to eat due to the stresses of work and her personal life, so it is good to see her eat... but my goodness! I've never seen anyone eat without taking a breath in between bites. I hope that her empty stomach can handle the spicy sauce and pounds of dough that she is inhaling. Thank goodness that it's vegetarian pizza. Before excusing themselves to homework in the homework office, Tia puts her hand on Alex's back and says, "It's good to see you eat, Auntie, you need the nourishment." Vanessa laughs and says, "That girl is older than all of us sitting here." Anyone who's been around for any amount of time knows that Tia has an old soul and is blessed with the gifts that usually accompany a soul like hers. Once the girls are settled in the other room the silence is awkwardly deafening. The only audible sounds come from my lips nervously sipping wine and Alex devouring pizza like it's her first experience with the deliciously baked cheese and veggie pie. I didn't even know that she ate pizza anymore.

My thoughts run rampant until Alex's sigh of relief breaks my concentration. "Oh my God that was good! I forgot how good pizza was," she states as she sits back and rubs her tummy. Vanessa, being the great conversationalist that she is, asks, "So Alex, what's been going on?" After this question, any resemblance of silence is gone for the next few hours while Alex talks non-stop. She tells us about how stressful work has become with her juggling two different departments while wearing several hats hoping for a promotion. She tells us how estranged she and Kevin have become since she found out that he was cheating. She has not told him that she knows, but it is hard for her to pretend that everything is okay when she knows that he has been lying to her. I totally understand wanting to forgive and move forward in the name of love, but having the hold of pride and pain not allow the forward movement. It is difficult for me to stay focused on her words when I'm wondering what she did with my journal and if she has read it. I want to ask, but I don't want to bring it up in front of Vanessa. Also, it would be rude to add to her problems at this point by asking for the journal that she stole from my house. She had to have taken it on the same day that she paid three months' worth of my car notes because she hasn't been to my home since. I'm glad that Vanessa is here to give her advice because I am not paying attention, until I hear Vanessa's voice rise, "You're what?" My heart sinks when I hear Alex repeat herself. "I'm pregnant," she says in a shaky voice lacking confidence. She sounds like a fifteen- year-old girl telling her parents about the pending bundle of joy, and understandably so... she is having MY HUSBAND's baby!

A thousand thoughts crash into my mind all at the same time. Kevin and I will never reconcile now! This baby will be a cousin and sibling to my daughters! What if she succeeds in giving him a son! I am pro-life, but something has to give. How will I explain this to the girls...? To the WORLD??? The tears trapped in Alex's eyes pull me from my selfish mind and remind me that this moment is about Alex. Vanessa is already holding her hand telling her that we will get through this together. She tells her, "**We** will raise this baby!" Vanessa's nudge under the table prompts me to take action so I reach for her other hand and reinforce Vanessa's words of encouragement. Alex tells us that she is not sure that she wants to keep the baby. Unlike me, she has never expressed the desire to have children, so her uncertainty about bringing a baby into this world does not surprise me. Alex is listing all of the reasons that she should abort the pregnancy, while

Vanessa is combating her statements with reasons to keep the child. I'm embarrassed by my next not so subtle move.

I squeeze Vanessa's knee in an effort to get her to stop trying to convince Alex to keep MY husband's baby. I forgot that she is very ticklish. My squeezing of her knee causes her to jump and at that movement Alex is aware that something went on under the table. Alex looks firmly at me and asks, "Are you still sleeping with him?" The look in her teary eyes holds a mixture of hurt, fear, anger, pride, and disgust. Vanessa is shocked and prepares to come to my defense, but I tap her gently on her leg to let her know that I have this and then I answer "No." Alex looks deep into my eyes in search of any visible untruth. She has always been able to look into my eyes and get to my secrets, but today there are no secrets. I have not seen Kevin and I'm not even sure that I still love him. I am certain that I am not in love with him and I don't want a relationship with him, but I liked having the open option. You know, like the 'break in case of emergency' option. However, her having his baby means that our romantic chapter is finished with no option for return. I would never sleep with him now that she is having his child. I know how it feels to be cheated on while pregnant and I would never do this to another woman, especially my sister. After about thirty seconds of her truth-finding stare I tell her, "Kevin and I were over a long time ago." She asks why I was still sleeping with him if we were over and I tell her that I was in a dark place seeking revenge, retribution, and at that point in our relationship a part of me still wanted our marriage to work. I take a deep breath before continuing, "At that time I wanted my family back together and I didn't want you to win, but after months of sneaking around and having sex without limitations I grew tired. Up until that time I had always been the good girl who lived within set boundaries. My time with Kevin had a lot to do with me wanting to experience life outside of the boundaries and without limits. Although I went into a dark place, I felt a sense of security because I was with my husband. I did not know how you felt about him until…" I stop just short of finishing my sentence. Alex asks, "Until what?" I can't look at her because she will see the truth in my eyes and I'm not sure how much of my journal she has read. "Until what?" She asks again, this time a little more firmly.

The look on Vanessa's face confirms that she is confused, with the conversation going on around her as I look down at the table holding my tongue because I don't want to say too much. Alex reaches into her bag, flips through a manuscript of some sort, visually scanning highlighted sections. There are colored tabs sticking out of pages throughout the document and when she locates the selection she folds back the pages and points to a section, "Until this?" she asks, pointing at the page. Vanessa asks, "What's this?" Although I am having difficulty focusing on the words, I know that these pages represent the private thoughts from my journal, although they are typed in a more professional setting. The highlighted section describes the morning that Alex came over with my panties in the Ziploc bag. The written paragraphs outlines the day she came to me for comfort when she found out that Kevin was cheating. Vanessa sees her name amongst the typed words so she takes the stapled pages from both of us and begins to read. Her mouth drops as she reads, while Alex and I sit quietly. I am sorry that Alex found out about my private thoughts this way, but I am glad it's out in the open. Private thoughts should only be shared when and if the owner of those thoughts is willing and ready to share. Alex should have never stolen my property and I don't feel like I owe her an apology.

As Vanessa keeps reading, Alex states, "I need for you to say it..." Without any clarification I know what she means. Alex wants me to admit to betraying her by sleeping with MY husband. This is the most ridiculous request, but I can see that my baby sister is really hurting and I love her, so I say it. "I did not know how you felt about Kevin until you showed up here with *my* panties in the baggie." Something about hearing me speak the truth breaks her down. Alex lays her head on the table and begins crying like a baby. Unlike my usual self, I kneel by her side and tell her that I am not going to apologize for sleeping with my husband. I don't want her to be in pain, but I won't apologize for trying to put my family back together. I was in a different place at the time and I meant to return the hurt, which is why I left evidence, but I no longer want the pain to continue. We have both hurt long enough over Kevin's infidelities, now we need to decide how we are going to move forward. I decided long before you showed up here with my 'panties in that bag' that healing my wounds should not be at my little sister's expense, while Kevin reaped benefits from both sides. Alex apologizes for stealing my journal, but tells me that her boss wants to publish it as a book. I am shocked that not only did she read it, but she allowed someone else to see the dirt in our family closet.

Alex continues to choke out words in between sob and stuttered inhales, "Reading your journal gave me a better understanding of your pain, all the while allowing me to face my demons. I am so sorry for all of the pain that I've caused throughout our lives". I'm shocked by her apology. She is but a shell of the tough, unreasonable woman she used to be. She keeps saying, "I've created such a mess through my selfishness and now I don't know how to clean up my creation." Alex goes into her bag again and brings out my actual journal. Attached to the journal is an agreement requesting permission to publish my work. Vanessa has read several pages and looks up just long enough to tell me, "This is good stuff. The world needs to read this" before refocusing her eyes on the typewritten words. Alex has cried, vomited, explained herself, apologized, ate more, and vomited again. She is now resting in one of the guest rooms. She wanted to sleep in Dear's old room, but that room is off-limits. She was not close to Dear when she was alive, so I don't think that she deserves to feel the presence of Dear's goodness that still abides in her room. Alex is too exhausted to go back to the hospital for Mother's visitation, so Vanessa and I go to check on Mother and the young lady.

Vanessa has started from the beginning and reads the manuscript all the way to the hospital, showing several different facial expressions as she turns the pages. After checking in briefly with Mother, I go to check on the young lady. The young lady has regained consciousness and agrees not to press charges if we take care of her hospital bills, and the purchase of another car. Daddy is anxious to get this agreement in writing before she realizes who hit her and before she wants to take legal action. It's strange that there are no visitors for the young lady, who introduces herself as Indigo. Although her face is swollen, I can tell that she is a beautiful girl. She is a struggling college student who saved all of her money to purchase her first car before coming here to attend medical school on a scholarship. Her main concern is that she doesn't miss too much school. I spend about an hour at her bedside and learn that she spent her childhood in different foster homes, so she doesn't really have family. Her last foster mother was a single woman who died two months before her eighteenth birthday, so she has no one. This thought saddens me, but Indigo seems well adjusted despite her unfortunate childhood. Even in the midst of her apparently lonely world, Indigo thanks God for life. At my suggestion, my parents agree to purchase Indigo the car of her choice once she is able to go car shopping. With Mother incapacitated, Daddy has control of the purse strings and agrees that a brand new car is the least that we can do. Mother is unusually agreeable and does little more than hang onto my arm in a loving manner for most of my visit.

I don't understand Mother's onset of extreme affection. Although we have been building our relationship lately, she has never displayed this much attention towards me. I leave the room to ask the doctor if she could still be in shock and find Daddy and the Doctor huddled up in the corner. I can tell that they are speaking secretively so I become concerned. They are trying to dismiss my questions, when I am only trying to find out what's wrong with Mother. Finally Daddy tells me that Mother has psychosis. Before I fall apart, I remind myself to take a cleansing breath, acknowledge God, and ask more questions. "What is psychosis?" As we are talking, Kevin walks up and we are escorted to a small conference room. Daddy tells me that Sis. Jenkins told him what I told her about Mother. I'm confused. What does he mean? Daddy continues with "Your mother is sick. She has been diagnosed with psychosis, which means that she is losing touch with reality." Daddy introduces Doctor Tiffany Fleece as Mother's long-time doctor and college friend. What? Mother doesn't have the capacity for friends and she certainly does not keep in contact with friends from her past. She has always told us that she didn't have friend while she was in college. She says that she was focused on growing her business and extra relationships would have gotten in the way. I ask Daddy, "College friend? What do you mean she's sick? And what do you mean, Sis. Jenkins told you what I told her? I haven't spoken with Sis. Jenkins since the conference…" Then all of a sudden my words hit me in the chest like a ton of bricks. I did tell Sis. Jenkins that Mother was sick, but I was lying. I was covering for my flirtation with the Deacon, but what I said about Mother was not true. Oh my God! As I struggle to listen through my guilt-ridden thoughts, Daddy continues talking as he takes pamphlets from Doctor Fleece and hands two to Kevin and one to me.

These pamphlets will explain psychosis. You should read and research on your own a bit because this is new to all of us. Daddy asks Kevin, "Where's Alex?" I quickly tell him that she wasn't feeling well so she stayed at my house to watch the girls. Daddy speaks in a rushed manner telling us to relay the information to Alex and the girls because Mother will need to be monitored at all times. He stated that she has tried to leave her hospital room three times today. For this reason, he does not have time to give us all of the details. He wants to prepare us for her increasingly unusual behavior and wants the girls to be aware that she often acts as though she is still an adolescent. He states that it is becoming more and more difficult to predict her mindset and the decade where she mentally resides, until she speaks. He first noticed the change when her work hours increased because she was focused on building her empire. Mother has always been driven, so Kevin and I did not understand his concerns until he shared that she worked for many days on old ideas and then went as far as presenting the old idea to her advertising team. None of her staff had the nerve to mention that all of her hard work was a duplication of her work years ago. She pitched an advertising idea for her fragrance line, which has been in production for over ten years. Daddy continues explaining that Mother doesn't remember her transitions into the past, which makes controlling or hiding the psychosis difficult. He states that Tiffany has agreed to see Mother, which makes the transition easy because in the present day Tiffany is Doctor Fleece, and when Mother reverts back to the past, she is Tiffany the college associate. Kevin and I agree to further research on our own so that we can get back to the room to check on Mother. We enter the room to find Vanessa sitting in the chair reading with tears streaming down her face and Mother watching television.

Mother is not big on television watching, she calls TV an 'idle box' or 'time thief', so I'm not sure which Mother she is right now. We are all watching and waiting for her to speak when Doctor Fleece interrupts our stares to check Mother's vitals. "How are you feeling?" Doctor Fleece asks and I can tell by her childlike response that she is in a reverted state. Mother reaches for me and holds my hand for the rest of our visit. It is after midnight, and, although I don't have to work in the morning, I long for my bed. Not because I'm tired, but because I've had a long trying day and it is in my alone time when I talk to God and figure out life. Tonight will be different in that I'm not figuring out my life, but how I may positively impact the lives of those close to me. Life is taking another unexpected turn for us all and this time I am ready for whatever life tosses my way. I am strong in the Lord and therefore I will no longer lay hidden in the closet or stay home hoping that the problems will somehow magically disappear. Although they treated me terribly for most of my life, they are my family and I will be there for them. Alex and Mother both need me and this time I choose the dance of preparation.

Once home, I check on Alex and the girls who are all resting peacefully, before sitting down at the computer to begin my research on psychosis. I find so many interesting facts, testimonies, and horror stories on the Internet. Mother could take off walking one day and never return. I have to get in a better position in my life so that I can take care of her, or at least spend more time with her. When I can no longer see the images on the computer screen through tired, bloodshot eyes, I head for bed.

My mind is racing at such a high speed that I look for something to read. I opt for Dear's Bible and her quilt as a source of comfort. I set her Bible on the bed next to me as I adjust the quilt and when I turn to pick up the Bible it is opened to Ephesians 6:10. My eyes are fixed on His Words, *Finally my brethren, be strong in the Lord, and in the power of his might.* So I speak out loud as though God is sitting on the edge of my bed listening, "Father, I'm afraid, because I'm not ready to lose Mother." I spent most of my life wanting to get away from her and just when I realize that my life was not about me and Mother and I are building a positive relationship, I find out that she is sick. I say again aloud, "Father, I'm afraid… please don't take my mother." In that moment His words come alive as I hear them strongly in my thoughts, "Be strong in the Lord, and in the power of his might". I read the words aloud so that my mind, body, and soul can hear them at the same time. I read the words repeatedly and without warning other passages from His Word flow out of my belly and across my lips. "By His stripes she is healed… No weapon formed against us shall prosper… Now unto Him that is able to keep us from falling… We wrestle not against flesh and blood, but against principalities, against powers, against the rulers of darkness of this world, against spiritual wickedness in high places… Be still and know that I am God… Now until to Him who is able to do exceeding abundantly above all that we ask or think according to the power that works in us… Behold, the former things have come to pass, and new things He does declare"!

My strength is renewed as I quote scriptures. Once the scriptures have ceased to flow over my lips I take a deep, cleansing breath and choose peace. Tonight I choose not to worry about tomorrow, and instead I thank Him for working out each crisis in the family for our good. For a split second I begin to feel guilty as though I spoke Mother's illness into existence, but a sweet voice speaks in my spirit and reminds me that these spirits of guilt and fear are not of God. Therefore, I choose to say, "No thank you" to the dance invitations of worry that have been presented recently. I remember that I am a member of His Royal family and am reminded that there is therefore now no condemnation. I did not speak illness upon Mother so I resist the foul spirits of guilt and fear and, as commanded, they flee. All things work together for the good for those who love the Lord and are called according to His purpose, so tonight I choose a peaceful sleep as I rest comfortably in the authority that He has given me over the enemy. I know that I am called according to His purpose, so I hug Dear's Bible in her absence with a smile on my face and confidence in my heart that my prior tests were preparation for this chapter of my life.

I can feel Dear's presence as though she is pleased that I finally understand the meaning of my life. Each test prepares me for the next chapter. When I could not see the big picture I attempted to hide from my tests through avoidance, anger, insecurity, low self- esteem, pain, victimization, passive aggressiveness, spitefulness, revenge, self-destruction, or through other destructive outlets. Now that I recognize the challenge as just another test, I put on the whole armor of God and speak in confident preparation, "Lord I trust You, let's go!" as I drift into a peaceful slumber choosing the dance of preparation.

New Direction

I t's been two weeks since Daddy secretly summoned us to the house to announce Mother's illness. I have seen Mother several times and she's not so bad. Actually, she is quite enjoyable to be around, comical even. The other day as Vanessa and I were getting ready to leave, Mother insisted on French braiding my hair prior to me leaving. Vanessa laughed under her breath the entire time while I had to stifle any giggles so that I would not get "popped in the head with the comb". Once Mother was finished with her intricate braided design we stood on the side of the garage laughing as we desperately attempted to remove the grade school braids out of my hair. Who knew that she could even French braid? Not me! She always said, "Those types of braids are for poor black kids." She always said the most hurtful things without regard to who heard her negative comments. I used to be so embarrassed by her disdain towards those she considered 'less than', but I guess that after sixty years Mother is showing a connection to the African- American roots that she denies exist. She would never respond to my questions about our heritage. However, Dear told me that we had more African blood running through our veins than Mother would ever admit and not just from daddy's side of the family. Hearing this makes me proud. Dear always taught me to be proud of who I am so when Mother was not around I admired the braids, especially the complicated designs with beads.

Although, I would have liked these braids as a child, I do not appreciate all of these hard knockers banging me in my back with every movement as a grown woman. I didn't have the heart to tell Mother that I was too old and on my way to the office, so I did the next-best thing. I sat still as she braided the tightest braids I've ever felt in a spiral design circling my head, and then she put big colorful knockers and ribbons on the ends. Where did she even get all of these hair supplies and who taught her to braid like this? I was impressed by her abilities, but I couldn't wear a childlike hairdo to the office for what might have been my last time seeing Urijah. I promised to be there by 9:30, so I have fifteen minutes to get these braids out of my head. What took Mother an hour to create seemed to take us longer to unravel. I warned Vanessa to keep quiet and hurry as I sat on the recycle bin with four hands in my head ripping my hairdo apart because neither of us had a comb. I have to admit that, even though my scalp is still sore, that was the most fun I've had in a while. Once the braids are out and I take Vanessa to her car, I rush to the office because I hate being late.

To my surprise the ladies are putting the final touches on the beautifully decorated office. I can feel the love and gratitude pouring in my direction as I walk through the office very grateful for each of them. I am touched and almost ashamed when I think about how I used to consider myself better than the co-workers that I now adore. What I did not realize then is that I would learn to recognize the appearance of true and unselfish love; for this lesson I will forever be thankful. Approximately thirty minutes into the celebration, the administrative assistant Evelyn hands me a glass bottle of VOSS Artesian water. I immediately remember how I rejected the generically labeled bottle of water she offered me the first time we met, so I understand her gesture to mean that she remembers the encounter, recognizes my growth, and has long forgiven me for my ignorance. I offer to open the bottle so that she could have a taste, but she declines. Her gift means a lot because purchasing this water was no doubt a sacrifice. I give her the biggest hug I have in me and apologize for who I was when we met. She tells me to be thankful for every minute that went into creating the beautiful woman I am becoming. We exchange small talk for a few minutes and then promise to keep in touch. Life always gets in the way, so I will be shocked if either of us makes good on the agreement to stay in touch, but I know that we both mean well.

After several hours of festivities I gather the last of my things from my office and head to my car. Urijah was on the phone most of my time in the office so apparently I'm not as important to him as I thought. Oh well. I load my things in the trunk, secure my seat belt and pull out of the parking stall. I thought that I would be ok with a distant goodbye until I recognize the emotional frog stretching his legs in the pit of my throat. Why did Urijah not get off the phone and walk me to my car? No final words, embrace, or anything? A loud thump on the trunk of my car pulls me from my inner sorrow... Oh my goodness, what the heck was that? I look in the rear-view mirror to see Urijah waving his hands, motioning me to stop. I am not very successful at hiding my disappointment at what I thought would be our final goodbye as he approaches the window and says, "You didn't think that I would let you leave without a proper goodbye, did you?" The inevitable smile took over my whole face as I pull back into the parking spot and get out of the car. I am happy to see the love in his eyes again. I think we've both always known that our worlds won't physically collide, but this fact doesn't stop us from loving and appreciating our connection on every other level.

Urijah and I talked for another hour recapping our growths; my individual growth and his company's growth. I told him about Evelyn's sacrificial gift of the expensive VOSS bottled water and asked that he figure out a way to pay her back. Urijah laughs and then asks, "Can you keep a secret?" I give him the 'don't be ridiculous' look. He then confides that, although she is frugal, she is a millionaire. I find 'her being a millionaire' difficult to believe so I ask if he is sure. He explains that she purchased stock from several companies when she was in college and sold when the time was right. "Why do you think she runs the front office?" he asks. "She obviously knows how to manage money and she is also great with managing people... look how well you turned out," he laughs. Urijah states that she once told him, "When God blesses you with things He doesn't mean for you to rub it into the faces of others. The fall from grace can be a long and lonely drop if you've used the backs of others to get there". For that fact she chooses to maintain a humble life. Urijah and I embrace one last time and he even kisses me ever so gently on the right side of my lips. We make the agreement to keep in touch and I hope that we do, but driving away I am more focused on Evelyn's words. She would always quote that scripture, "Naked I came out of my mother's womb and naked I shall return" or "The Lord giveth and the Lord taketh away… blessed be the name of the Lord." I never really understand until today how much I want to be like her.

Kevin finally signed the divorce papers so I should have access to my bank account again soon, but this time I want to do things differently. Maintaining a humble life will not be that big a transition and I believe that I will feel better about who I am and how I've grown if I remain humble in all ways. I will strive to be a better example for my girls and the rest of the family. Having more money than we will ever spend has always been a big part of this family's identity; however, life dictates that we find other identities like strength, perseverance, faith, growth, and love. I thank God for giving us an opportunity to change our lives and effect a positive change on the lives that we touch. This is our time to reach beyond our backyards and grow in a new direction. Thank you, Lord, for giving me the wisdom to choose the dance of new direction.

God's Plan

Since Mother's release from the hospital we have all taken turns visiting the house so that we can keep a watchful eye and assist with her care. Sunday dinner is becoming a tradition that we all seems to enjoy. Vanessa's family, as well as Cornelius usually join us for good food, and games or a movie after church. Two days ago, Indigo was released from the hospital and Daddy took her car shopping. I was happy to join them and made sure that she selected her dream car, which is a black-on-black convertible BMW 135is. She insisted that the car was too extravagant, but Daddy and I know that sixty thousand dollars is a steal when we think about what she could have gotten had she taken Mother to court. Besides, it gave me pleasure to spend some of Mother's money. Daddy has known about Mother's illness for months so he should not have let her drive. Even a mediocre lawyer would have found out about Mother's illness and this information could have cost the family a lot more than a BMW and eighteen thousand dollars in incidentals. Not only did Daddy purchase Indigo a new car and pay her hospital bills, he paid her current debt and talked Dr. Fleece into hiring her as an assistant. Indigo is such a bright light and we want to help her as much as possible; however, we are careful not to make careless moves because she is a stranger. We just want to help make her life better and we are very grateful that she did not seek legal advice when asked by the visiting ambulance chasers. I'm sure that she has seen the news and by now she knows that Mother is very wealthy, but she has not asked for a dime and had a difficult time accepting any of Daddy's gratuities.

Today Dr. Fleece has joined us for dinner. Who knew that she'd been here? She has been around more often because of Mother, but her joining us for Sunday dinner feels a bit weird. Daddy says that Mother invited her, but you would think that Dr. Fleece would decline dinner with a patient's family. Nevertheless, we are all here enjoying a tasty meal prepared by Mother's chef extraordinaire. Mother insists on sitting next to me and asks me to cut her meat into bite-size pieces and to pour her more juice when her cup is empty. She seems to look at me as a mother figure, which is weird because I was just learning to enjoy her as my mother. Even more odd is when she points at Tia and Kali's socks and asks in a very juvenile voice, "Can you buy me some of those sockies, Mommy?" Everyone at the table freezes when Mother refers to me as 'Mommy'. The silence and absence of any movement cause irritation as Mother throws a mini-tantrum, "Why are they looking at me like that, Mommy?" she whines. I don't know how to respond and now I understand the importance of Dr. Fleece's presence as she intervenes, "Because you are speaking with your mouth full, honey. Swallow your food and then ask Mommy the question again." Mother seems to accept this explanation because her face relaxes as she swallows the food in her mouth and then she asks me again, "May I please have some pretty sockies like Tia and Kali?" At the doctor's prompting I respond as though I am speaking to one of my children. I tell her that I will get her some pretty socks the next time that I go to the store. I then tell her to finish her food before she can have any more to drink. She happily agrees and returns to her meal while dancing happily in her chair. As if on automatic I tell her, "No dancing at the table. Sit like a lady." Wow, Mother and I have switched roles. As children, we were not allowed to move at the table, run through the house, laugh aloud or do anything else that may indicate enjoyable childlike behavior. My girls' lives are very different than my childhood; therefore, my telling a child not to dance at the table brings about an unwelcomed newness. Who knew that I could be even remotely like Mother? It's like a switch has been flipped to the 'on' position, triggering the meanness in me. I want this switch to remain 'off' and therefore I adjust my tone as I hug my mother-daughter to provide some reassurance.

Dinner is divine and the family games that follow leave laughter and love hanging in the atmosphere for the rest of the night. However, watching my mother-daughter stand at the door waving as we drive away is disheartening. I try to enjoy Cornelius's company as we drive to the house, but I am preoccupied with my role in all that's going on in the family. I am usually a quiet bystander, but now I find myself playing a major role in family decisions. Who knew that I would become the family consultant?

The girls are asleep by the time we pull into the garage so I am happy that Cornelius is here to help carry them into the house. After baths and bedtime stories, Cornelius and I retire to the family room for some much-needed time alone. I know that this means tea, TV, and perhaps a little tongue kiss, but I'll take it! I miss spending time with him. Being with Cornelius means that I will have another sexless night, but I still enjoy the company. Besides, I have too much going on in my life right now to nurture a relationship, but his company is nice. Just as I find my comfortable place on the couch in his warm embrace I hear a text alert. My phone is in my purse in the other room and I am way too comfortable to move, so I snuggle closer into his chest. I feel so secure in his arms; like nothing can get to me while in the safety of his protection. As predicted, we sip tea, watch TV, and share a few strokes of tongue. His kisses are amazing and I remember being swept away with just one touch, but I know that we will stop soon, so I force myself to mentally drift. I wonder how Alex and Mother are. I think about Urijah and pray for his continued success. I think about the girls sleeping peacefully. I pray for Daddy's strength. I pray for Indigo. I do anything to avoid taking another ride on the Cornelius romantic rollercoaster because the ride never finishes to my satisfaction, so as I enjoy his physical touch I allow my thoughts to drift. Getting all worked up with no release is like going on vacation but being stuck at the airport and never making it to the destination. I experience all of the anticipation without any of the expiration or climax. Oh well, I guess that my sexy maître d' is only good for a partial ride. Another text notification goes off while we are kissing and caressing.

Normally I would not break our embrace to answer a text, but there are too many things going on with this family for me to continually ignore a late-night text. Reading the text messages brings a huge smile to my face. Oh my God! Thank you, Jesus!!! The first text message was sent forty-eight minutes earlier and states, "You are FREE." The last text message states,

"I remember a time when you looked forward to my texts and responded right away. Anyway, I want you to know that the divorce has been finalized and you are free. I miss you and will always love you, but I want you to be happy, so I've let you go. Be good to yourself and remember, I'm only a text message away… Kev". I stare at my phone for a good two minutes before Cornelius asks if everything is ok. I tell him that everything is fine because I don't want to share this news with him just yet. There was a time when I eagerly shared everything with him, but perhaps we are not as close as I once thought. I don't feel like having this conversation right now, so I tell him that everything is fine and return to my place in his arms. This time when we kiss all that I can think about is checking my available bank balance. I think that Cornelius can feel my distraction because he is kissing me more intensely and against my better judgment my body is beginning to respond. I can't get lost in his rollercoaster ride because I know that he will jump up and leave before leading me to relief, but keeping a mental distance is becoming more difficult. Not only does he turn up his romantic efforts, but he is whispering that he loves me in my ear. With my legs wrapped around his waist and his manhood greeting the warmth against my Victoria's Secrets I whisper three little words back, "We should wait." Thank goodness for the clothes between our private beauties because I'm not sure that I could resist him without the barrier. To my surprise he whispers back, "I want to make love to you… It's time." What?!? Did I hear him right? He wants to make love? Oh my goodness… is this really going to happen tonight? I am a bit irritated that we make love when he says so, but I have wanted to feel him inside of me for so long that I mentally move out of the way and allow my body to freely respond. He is introducing himself to parts of my body needing to be reacquainted with a man's touch. The fire inside is reaching the level of explosion. I am primed and ready for the next level and he is ready to take me there until the doorbell rings. What?? We both try to ignore the bell until the knocking ensues and then the phone rings. Oh my God, Mother! I jump up and run to the phone thinking that something must be wrong with Mother. It is almost eleven o'clock, so something has to be wrong with someone. I scramble for the phone to discover Alex on the other end asking if she can stay here tonight. "Is that you at the door?" I ask. I love my sister, but why is she here NOW?!?!? I tell her to give me a minute as Cornelius and I get ourselves together. I open the door to find a visibly upset Alex with an overnight bag in her hand, apologizing for interrupting us. Cornelius is forever the gentleman so he excuses himself, kisses me goodnight and leaves, promising to call me tomorrow. Dang it! I can tell by 'that look' in his eyes that he was ready to devour me and I was ready to let him have it, but Alex needs me so he leaves me to tend to my baby sister.

I sit on the couch in cool-down mode, trying to focus on the words crossing Alex's lips. She is telling me about the argument between her and Kevin as my phone rings again. I am afraid to answer because it may be Kevin, but after the third ring Alex looks a little suspicious, so I answer. Daddy is on the phone and I can hear Mother in the background crying for her mommy. I allow Alex to listen in for a minute and then tell Daddy that I will be right there. I ask Alex if she can stay with the girls while I attend to mother. Alex is truly distraught, but understands why I need to go to Mother. I leave Alex in one of the guest rooms lying on top of the bedspread, staring at the television.

I am tempted to call Cornelius while I drive to my parents' house, but I am too distracted by the thoughts of how much Mother is changing. I have never seen her express weakness. I waited for the day where I would be the stronger woman and now that day is here, but it is not as welcomed as I expected. We were starting to build a relationship, talk on the phone every day, do lunch and now those days are becoming a distant memory. I can hear Mother yelling as I ring the doorbell. Daddy is clearly exasperated as he snatches the door open and steps aside, allowing me to enter. When I get to the room Mother is kneeling in the corner on the far side of the bed with a blanket gathered in her arms, still calling for her mommy. She runs to me and throws her arms around me, "Mommy!" she says with delight and then she begins to explain, "That man was in my bed and he scared me." The doctor enters the room as I am trying to calm Mother down and get her back into bed. After an hour of trying to get her back to sleep the doctor convinces me to take Mother home with me for the night. Mother calms down significantly as we pack her overnight bag and head to the car. Daddy and the doctor wave from the doorway prior to going back into the house. It is not until I am on the freeway that I wonder why the doctor went back into the house with Daddy as opposed to leaving when we left. I am tempted to call the house to check on things, but then realize that Mother is fast asleep and I don't want my conversation to wake her. It is two o'clock in the morning as I roam the house checking on everyone. Tia has found her way into Kali's room and is snuggled closely to her sister. Alex, who is still fully dressed, has fallen asleep on top of the covers with the TV still playing, while Mother has found a teddy bear to cuddle as she sleeps in the room down the hall from the girls.

After placing a blanket over Alex I shower and search out reasons to be thankful. I have somehow become a caregiver not only to my daughters, but also to my baby sister who just so happens to be pregnant with my ex-husband's child, and to my mother, who for some reason thinks that I'm her mother. Today been a full day and, although it is difficult to detect the blessing in the midst of all of this disruption, I have faith that the blessing is here. My mind floats aimlessly through my day as I smile because I was able to successfully purchase a bottle of coconut water earlier tonight. It is amazing how much I took for granted the seemingly little things, like making a $4 purchase without worrying about the budget. Not only can I afford coconut water, but I can now afford to feed everyone in the morning. With this thought I feel less anxious and more gracious.

I'm excited to step into the role of caregiver for the family and look forward to life as it continues to unfold. I am confident and trust myself to victoriously overcome the challenges of the next chapter. I smile as I remember my vision on the plane. I was the direct link providing a lifeline to the many vines springing upward from the earth. I guess that was God's way of giving me a glimpse into what was to come for my life as I follow His plan.

I never considered myself strong enough to provide a lifeline for anyone and now I stand in obedience inhaling the breath of life from God, humbly accepting my roles as His vessel. I feel a little panicked at the thought of standing in a role that I may not be able to maintain. What if I become weak or scared or make wrong decisions? Any thoughts of failure are banished when I remember that I do not walk this path alone. I am fulfilling my God-given purpose and with this reminder I repeat to myself, "I can do all things through Christ who strengthens me," as I settle deep into my comfortable bed for some much-needed sleep. I'm not sure what tomorrow holds but I am a willing participant in God's plan, whatever that plan may be because I can do all things through Christ, who strengthens me. Amen!

Peaceful Chaos

Two months... Two whole months since Mother became my mother-daughter. She periodically reverts back to Mother; however, those bouts never last very long and thank God, because she is really mean when she realizes that her world seems out of place. She woke up the entire family the first time she reverted back to Mother in the middle of the night. I hadn't thought through the process so I was unprepared when I awoke to her tearing through the house looking for her car keys at 2:30 in the morning. Try explaining, "You no longer drive" to Mother when she is on one of her rampages. Daddy had to come get her, but he brought her back the next evening.

Dr. Fletcher, who showed up with Daddy to retrieve Mother at 3:27am, suggested that we have a few stories prepared to explain why Mother is not in her usual place. The last few times that my mother-daughter transitioned back to Mother I told her that she was helping me to look after Alex, who is just now starting to get a little baby bump. This story seems to work best because it makes Mother feel needed and I get a little help with the household duties until she returns to being my mother-daughter.

Alex has all but moved in because she cannot stand to be around Kevin. She finally told him that she knows about the affair, which was a bit awkward. Kevin stood silently waiting for more clues as to how much she knew and when he looked in my direction I gave him all the clues I could give without making the situation worse. Alex was just beginning to trust me so the last thing I wanted to do was to indicate that Kevin and I were still in cahoots. Kevin immediately began to apologize. He cried like a baby and told her that he refuses to lose another family behind his stupidity and then they both cried. They cried, hugged, she yelled and he pleaded for about two hours and forty-five minutes. The entire scene was heartbreaking, but I had to interrupt and calm the situation because the girls were on their way home from their piano lessons. I've always known that he is a good man, so watching him beg my baby sister not to leave him was not easy. Even though our marriage is over, a part of me misses his attention. No matter how you slice it, this situation is really weird! My baby sister is carrying my ex-husband's baby, while she lives in my home and I nurse her through her first months of pregnancy. Nevertheless, I have to thank God for this unusual situation because Alex and I have become extremely close; closer than ever imagined. We promise that there would be no more secrets between us so I tell her how I truly feel about the entire situation and oddly enough, she understands my feelings and why I miss my marriage.

Initially it is difficult to watch Kevin show up with flowers, food, and other items for pampering Alex because he once did these things for me. Every so often I see the look of remorse in his eyes, as though he wants me back in his arms but we are too far past that. Our present reality is that I am his ex-wife or the sister of his pregnant girlfriend and I refuse to give pain any further space in our relationships. Besides, Cornelius is my present love and yes, I did say love. We still have not consummated our relationship because life is complicated and busy.

Cornelius opened two additional *Le Chet' Marie* restaurants. *Le Chet' Marie On The Boardwalk* in Atlantic City and *Le Chet' Marie On The Strip* in Las Vegas, so he's been doing a lot of traveling and his efforts are being realized. Getting a table at either location is difficult, unless you personally know the owner or made the reservation months before the doors opened. Maintaining the same level of elegance and fine cuisine as the original *Le Chet' Marie* is important so he personally oversees every intricate detail. He says that he needs to make his mother, Marie Le' Chet, proud. I am confident that she is looking down upon him, smiling.

In addition to maintaining my household, I accept the job of Chief

Marketing Officer (CMO) at Mother's company, Leisurely Connections. Mother had asked me several times to take on the position of CMO, but I was hesitant because I did not want to hinder our budding relationship. However, one day over lunch her request is more of a plea. She tells me that the company is not thriving like it once did and needs a breath of freshness. The Board of Directors advise that she has access to a goldmine and they encourage Mother to secure my talents. Mother makes me a lucrative offer, which includes creative control, and I plan to make her proud. In addition to agreeing to all of my terms and offering me a very generous salary, Mother promises to demonstrate the professional respect expected in Corporate America. Accepting the position with Leisurely Connections is bittersweet. Hiring me to assist Daddy in running the company means that Mother realizes that she is no longer able to manage the company on her own.

Mother is spending more time as my mother-daughter. Tonight during dessert she throws a mini-tantrum and knocks her chocolate pudding on the floor. She immediately becomes frightened, jumps up from the table, and run to her room. I find her in the corner of the closet holding a stuffed animal, asking if I am going to spank her. I have a choice to make. This is my chance to pay her back for some of the pain, the beatings, the belittling comments, and any cruelty she ever caused in my life. God knows that I am tempted to close the door and beat her to within an inch of her life, just like she used to do to me. I am surprised that I still harbor these feelings of revenge, but I do and the feelings are very real. As I walk closer to her I can see her trembling in fear. The look on her face shows me how I must have looked to her so many years ago. I wonder how she could have hurt someone who was already so wounded and so frightened. The tears streaming down her face show me that she has been in this position before and therefore, I have only one choice. I take her by the hand, help her out of the closet, and sit her on the bed. I wipe her falling tears and choose the dance of making a difference. In that moment I decide to exchange her bad memories for positive realities.

The reality is that no child should ever be hurt and this includes my mother-daughter. Instead of hurting her, I show her love and have her help me clean up the spilled pudding. The stain on my sheepskin rug seem less important than her feelings… and my feeling of compassion is evidence of my growth in God. I no longer want Mother to hurt. My mother-daughter's tantrums have become less frequent and she appears more secure in her space in our home as my eldest child. A lot has happened in the past two months and I am happy to report that with God's help, we are surviving every challenge victoriously.

I hire back my faithful household technician, Maggie, who hung in there through my financial hardships. Maggie took on temporary jobs while waiting for my monetary drought to pass. She even did a lot of things for free when I could not afford to pay, and therefore hiring her back full-time was one of my first actions when my funds were released. Her loyalty did not go unnoticed, and blessing her with a handsome bonus is one way of demonstrating my appreciation.

Indigo has become an extended part of our family and will be hired as Dr. Fleece's intern after she graduates college. Dr. Fleece and Daddy seem to have gotten closer and I think that I am the only one noticing, because no one has spoken a word against her constant presence. Perhaps everyone is too caught up in their own lives to recognize the signs. I see Daddy at work every day and today I almost talk to him about my concerns, but he seems happy so I attend to my own business. Besides, I'm nobody's judge and who am I to disturb his much deserved and long-overdue happiness? I have never seen him smile so big or so often. Dr. Fleece and Daddy were hiding their biweekly lunch dates, but today she has opted to come into the office to say hello and wish me a safe trip. She is a pleasant woman who has been instrumental in Mother's care, but I think their public friendship is a bit bold and could become messy if the paparazzi got wind of their outings. After a brief conversation of niceties with Dr. Fleece, she and Daddy go to lunch and I wrap up my workday. I'm going to Atlantic City to spend four days with Cornelius for some much- needed quality time. The girls are away at camp with Ministry of Mission, which is a local youth group focused on spiritual enlightenment and ministry. I also located a care facility that specializes in providing care for individuals with psychosis or other conditions that alter their mental capacity. The establishment is set up like an elegant spa or country club, and the staff are briefed on the stories for each client. Should she resurface, Mother will be told that she is there for a retreat of massages, facials, and pampering; conversely, my mother-daughter will be kept occupied with her favorite games, movies, and caring for the animals.

Just the thought of being with Cornelius for four days is stimulating.

We do not get very much alone time because of our fast-paced lives, but things just worked out for this extended weekend away. Leisurely Connections has seen a 20% financial gain in the past month; my manuscript-turned-novel will be released in two weeks, followed by a book signing tour; and next week Cornelius signs on as the major floral supplier of Leisurely Connections, so our lives will become even more hectic.

With fifteen minutes to spare before my driver arrives I call Vanessa for some of her jovial antidotes. She always knows how to bring out the calm in me, besides, I want to remind her to check in with Maggie, Alex, Daddy, and anyone else who may miss my presence this weekend. As we are talking I hear a ruckus down the hallway. Before I can go to see what is going on, Mother is standing in my office asking, "What the hell is going on here? Who changed the front lobby and why are you in my office?" I excuse myself from the phone and tend to Mother. I try to calm her down, but she refuses to listen until I answer her questions. At the same time, the front desk is calling to let me know that my driver is here to take me to the airport. Where is Daddy when I need him? I then remember that Daddy and Dr. Fleece are together and Mother probably should not see them coupled up in her state of mind. I take my deep, cleansing breath and choose the dance of honesty.

Realizing that honesty could cause me to miss my flight, I command Mother to sit and listen. I tell her that I am CMO, Daddy and I are the Managing Officers of Leisurely Connections, and that she no longer works here due to her illness. Mother has stopped responding, so I speak to her spirit because I have the faith that she can somehow comprehend at least a portion of what I'm saying. I tell her as lovingly as I can, but I tell her the truth because I feel that the truth will set her free. Even though she is not responding, I can tell that I am still speaking to my Mother. However, she is not resisting, as is Mother's normal mode of operation, so I'm a bit confused. I see the water held captive in her eyes as she begins to speak ever so calmly. "So what happens to me when I lose touch with reality?" The moment that I've always regretted is looking me in my face. I could stand frozen in fear and anxiety, but instead I breathe steadily and with tears flowing I courageously speak from my heart. "I take care of you, and love you, and hug you, and show you all of the affection that you would not allow when I was the child." Mother looks me in my eyes and for the first time she apologizes for not showing me the love that she has always felt in her heart. She tells me that she did not know how to show love because she did not know love before I came into her life. She didn't know how to balance raising strong women while giving them a safe place of refuge. She was afraid that too much love would make her daughters weak, and as she speaks I somehow understand. Even more important; I chose the dance of forgiveness the day that the messenger told me that it has never been about me. So I listen from a place of love.

While Mother is speaking, Daddy and Dr. Fleece return and are surprised to see her in my office. The look on their faces tells Mother all she needs to know. She walks over to Daddy, takes him by the hands, and simply says, "I release you… It's your time for happiness. Thank you for being my rock and allowing me to shine." Daddy is shocked to hear Mother speak with clear thoughts from her heart and he quickly responds, realizing that this may be his last chance to converse with the woman he knew so long ago.

"You are my forever love" and then they embrace so beautifully. Dr. Fleece excuses herself and I have my assistant reschedule my flight and call Cornelius. The three of us watch the sun go down while sitting on the couch in my office listening to Mother express her inner thoughts and feelings for the first time in her life. She speaks so sincerely and honestly, as though all of her walls were crumbling with every word of truth that passes over her lips. This is the first time that I can see why Daddy fell in love with her. She is a lovely woman. After several hours of emotionally taxing conversation Daddy asks Mother if he can take her to dinner before returning her to her spa weekend. She agrees and I call for my driver once again. When Daddy goes to lock up his office Mother quietly tells me that she has a sister who can take care of her so that I'm free to live my life. I am floored! A sister? You mean that I have an aunt? I say to Mother, "I thought that you were an only child." Mother tells me that she stopped speaking to her family right after she left for college because of a family dispute. "You will find my truths in my personal paperwork," she says right before she kisses me and tells me that she releases me, too. I tell her that I don't accept her release because I've always wanted to show her love and I appreciate her love in any form. She chuckles and then says, "There's my strong Jonnie. I used to worry about how you would make it in life without me or your father, but now I see that you are going to be just fine," as she reaches over to hug me. Since renewing our bond, hugs have become a part of our greeting, however; this hug is not a 'hello or goodbye' hug. This embrace showers me with a mother's long-overdue approval and satisfaction with her daughter, and she holds on as though this may be her last time holding me. Confirming my suspensions, she whispers, "Just let me hold you long enough to etch the memory into my heart because I know that my mental capacity is failing… I wish I would have been better to you and Alex. Please tell her I love her and I apologize… please…" All that I can choke out is, "I will tell her" before I cry like a baby and all but melt in her arms. I have waited all of my life for this embrace.

Daddy interrupts in the gentlest way to tell me that my driver is waiting. Once we all clear our tears daddy puts his arm out for Mother. They lock arms and follow me out of the building. Mother lovingly dabs the tear stains out of my make-up, we kiss and I head to the airport for the red-eye flight. I am exhausted and can hardly wait to get to Cornelius's arms, but I'm so glad that I was blessed enough to spend the time with Mother. I ride to the airport with tears of joy flowing onto my silk blouse, while the driver periodically asks, "Are you ok, Ms. Johnson?" I assure him that these are tears of joy, but my shaking body and childlike cries are obviously sending a different message. The only sad part of these tears is wishing for this moment much earlier in life as I wonder how our lives would have differed if I would have been raised by this Mother. I realize that I received the life necessary for my ministry so I dismiss the thought of resentment and welcome gratefulness in its place. I am too emotional to explain all that I feel, so I again reassure the driver that I will be ok.

I make it to the waiting area forty-five minutes before the plane boards, so I grab a Starbucks Misto and call Cornelius to give him an update on my status. I would call Vanessa, but she doesn't do well with being awakened in the middle of her night, so after a few words of encouragement from my sweetheart, Cornelius, I pull out my tablet and journal my thoughts. This time, I try something different. I recently heard Tamela Mann say that she sings as though she is singing to Jesus sitting in the front row. With this in mind, I decide to write a love letter to God, as though he is sitting in front of me taking in every word.

Dear God,

My heart is overwhelmed and overrun with joy… Thank you, Father!

You have been so amazingly great to me. Even in my lowest moments you never left my side. Even when I didn't deserve your grace and mercy, You were right here. Even when I tried repeatedly to kill myself, You carried me through the many storms. You never gave up on me and interfered with the harm intended to me by my own hands. When I was foolish, You never left, and now You have blessed me to be a part of what may have been my mother's final coherent moments. Thank you for allowing me to meet the woman whom You knew existed all along; the woman whom Daddy has loved most of his adult life. I now understand why he repeatedly comes to her defense. No matter how wrong she appears, You blessed Daddy to see Mother's heart. And today You ordered our steps which allowed me to also see the wounded heart of a woman trying to outgrow her inner child. With tears of repentance I habitually ask for forgiveness, knowing that You have already forgiven all offenses because You see my heart. I love You and thank You for my family and, even though I don't understand all that is about to happen in our lives, I trust You to bring us through any storm victoriously. I don't know how life will turn out, but I no longer need to know. I only need to know that You have always been and will continue to be right here and, for this fact I choose the dance of thankfulness.

Amen!

My phone rings just as I type "Amen". Dr. Fleece is calling at 12:02AM, so something must be wrong with Mother. I am tempted not to answer, which would force them to manage without me, but I accept my role in the family as a leader and take the call. To my relief Dr. Fleece is inquiring about Mother's whereabouts, but after two minutes of her stumbling over her words, it's clear that she is really looking for Daddy. She says that they were supposed to have dinner, but he never showed and is not answering either phone. She attempts to hide behind a professional pretense as she asks about our evening wanting to know what time we left the office, if I went on my trip, is Mother with me, did Daddy take her back to the care facility, etc.? She is asking so many back-to-back questions that it's clear she stopped being the doctor long ago and is speaking like a nervous woman-in-waiting. I want to tell her that these are the consequences of dealing with a married man; however, I have compassion and tell her that Daddy took Mother back to the care facility about an hour ago. I tell her that we all had an emotional evening and am certain that he is asleep from exhaustion. I promise to call her tomorrow to give her an update.

After hanging up with the doctor I have about ten minutes before boarding and am curious so I call Daddy. He sounds sort of winded when he says hello. He tells me that Mother wanted to sleep in her own bed so he took her home. He called the care facility and set up a meeting first thing in the morning to talk about how Mother left so freely. Apparently, one of the nurses recognized Mother from television and believed her when she told him that she was visiting, had missed her driver, and insisted on a ride back to her office. The nurse was returning from vacation and had not been briefed on Mother's condition. In the middle of our conversation I hear giggling in the background. "Is that Dr. Fleece?" I ask. Daddy tells me that it is Mother. I remind Daddy about the last time she woke up in the same bed with him... There was chaos! In the middle of my conversation Mother takes the phone and tells me that Daddy has to go spend time with his wife. I'm sure that she meant to hang up because the sounds on the other end of the phone were not sounds that any child, no matter how grown, should hear going on between their parents. Once I realize what I'm hearing I release the line a bit confused, embarrassed, but happy. God, I love my life... ;-), it's so unpredictably lovely!!

Once settled in my first-class seat I close my eyes and thank God for my beautifully chaotic life. There is a lot going on at all times, but internally I am at peace because I've changed my mindset. I now recognize that being in peace is a choice. I could worry about tomorrow, but worrying is of no consequence. Instead I take a deep, cleansing breath, thank God in advance for a safe arrival, and choose the dance of enjoying my peaceful chaos.

Aligning My Dance

Redeye flights are always quiet, so I take this opportunity to connect with God through peaceful reflection. I can't help but to wonder about the 'What Ifs' and the 'What Now's'. Even though I am thankful for all that I've experienced, I wonder how much pain I could have avoided if I had made wiser choices when the dances presented themselves. If I had aligned my dance with my purpose?

As a child I would mentally shut out pain by forcing my mind to focus on future goals of happiness. In the midst of being yelled at or slapped in the face by Mother, I would plan my adult life of joy, which meant an adoring husband, happy children that I would never abuse, a successful career, a gorgeous home filled with love, all the material things that accompany a fabulous life, and anything else perfect.

Mentally escaping through difficult childhood moments made my pain more tolerable. However, by allowing the little kid in me to escape I never gained the skills necessary for navigating successfully through life as an adult. On the outside I grew into a woman, while leaving the little girl inside scared and undernourished. I ignored that little girl for many years because I did not know how to feed her or even pay attention to her needs. As a child I survived the best way that I knew how. I cannot go back and change my past, but I can use my past for good.

I have forgiven myself and anyone else involved for aiding in my childhood escape. I inhale the lessons gained and digest the truths realized. I now understand why I was forced to stand and watch Kevin have sex with my baby sister. I would not wish this nightmare upon anyone, but I thank God that I was forced to face a very real and devastating problem. For one of the first times in my life I experienced every intricate detail of the pain happening before me. I was forced to deal with the ugly truth that my husband was not perfect. My heart was broken and I wanted to die, but God said, "No"! I now realize that I made the mistake of expecting Kevin to play a role in my perfectly planned world that he could never fulfill. I initially blamed him for our demise, but now I own my part because he never stood a chance when compared to the mental image of the perfect husband I created long before we met.

Through my painful moments I learned to sort through the mess while looking for the meaning. I had three little beings depending on me to guide and nourish their growth; Tia, Kali, and most important, me. My inner-child, along with my two daughters need me and I would go through the pain again if necessary for my wholeness. For through wholeness I now help others.

I often wonder about daddy and his inner-self. For the first time he is displaying irresponsible behavior and I wonder what is at the core of his behavior. I'm curious about his relationship with Dr. Fleece; is he cheating on Mother and if so, is he justified? How is Dr. Fleece handling daddy's disappearance and how will their relationship evolve? Knowing that my growth has never been about me helps me to focus outside of my desires and pray for his healing and growth along with the heartbreak that Dr. Fleece may eventually face.

What is going on with Alex and Kevin? Earlier when I spoke with Alex, she and Kevin were having dinner with the girls at my house. I'm not sure if they are still there and if so, are they having sex in my house and should I be bothered? I often wonder how life would have turned out for Kevin and me if I had been healthy enough to forgive his sins. Could we have found our way back to each other; to our love? Would I be carrying his child? Kevin is a good man and I've always know this fact, but the hurt was too deep and at that point in my life I did not know how to forgive. I now support Alex and want her to be happy so I choose the dance of selflessly forgiving and letting go of Kevin as my husband.

Even though I love Cornelius, I still have love for Urijah and I often think about him and wonder what, and how he is doing. What if I had listen to his explanation instead of driving away after the party? Would we have found each other romantically? Perhaps I feel such a strong connection because we did not taint our world with carnal desires. He ministered to me when I was at my lowest and became a vessel who helped me through a dark time in my life. I pray for his happiness and I sincerely wish him the best. I will call to check on him soon and release him from any pain he thinks he may have caused in my world. Urijah did not choose my dance I did, I take ownership, and I should let him know.

I also think about the Deacon and am thankful for our friendship. He introduced me to a strength in me I did not know existed. I see him several times a week and the depth of his smile reminds me of God's mysteries. I returned from the conference a different woman and in great part, because Deac allowed God to use him as a vessel for my growth. The very least that I can do is return the favor while praying for his strength. I know that he will gain strength through his pain and find the blessings in his tests. I look forward to hearing his testimony about how he learned to choose his dance.

Strolling down memory lane brings me back to Cornelius. There is something magical about a man who puts his woman's well-being above his own desires. Cornelius knew that I was not whole enough to handle a relationship, so he made us wait. He insists that we take our relationship slow, while we keep God first. I have spent several nights in his arms and woke up more fulfilled than I've ever known. In the moment I did not appreciate the wait, but now I realize that we were not ready for sexual exploration. My body burns when I recall his whispers telling me that he wants to make love to me. I long to hear those words again, soon. Hopefully, I will hear those words this weekend, or maybe not. I want to give all of me to this magical man, but not at the detriment of our spiritually. I want a new start and a happy future, like Sheila.

Sheila and her new husband and their new baby are all happy and doing well. She suffered for years dealing with Mitchell, his lies, deceit, and the careless way that he handled their marriage. It was during her lowest moments that she found her inner-strength and learned to love herself more that she loved the idea of Mitchell. I think that a part of us will always love Mitchell or at least the potential man that we both wanted him to be. Kali knows that Mitchell is her biological father; conversely, she knows Kevin as daddy. Mitchell continues to send monthly child support payments, but no one has heard from him since the 'Plan'. His parents see Kali several times a month and they both enjoy spoiling their only grandchild. I often wonder how our lives would differ had I not been strong enough, or dark enough to participate in the 'Plan'. I'm thankful that I chose the dance of darkness and deceit in my efforts to flush out the truth. Otherwise, we may each still be living in Mitchell's distorted world.

Tonight I met Mother for the first time. She is warm, playful, loving, and I look forward to spending more time with her. She even has a sister, which means that we have a relative on Mother's side. I wonder what she's like. I would love to meet her, but I forgot to get her name from Mother. Hopefully, I will get to ask Mother more about her sister when I get back home.

A part of me wishes that Alex could have been there tonight to meet our real Mother, however, a bigger part of me appreciates having Mother to myself. I now realize how daddy fell in love with the woman that I met today. Through discernment I hear the silent screams of her inner-child and I understand her pain. She was unavailable to love us because she doesn't know how to love herself. I now know that she is in pain and incomplete. Again, I say, "Yes" to my assignment of loving and caring for Mother... inner-child and all. I don't know how, when, or where, but I will help others. Therefore it is important that I choose the dance that is in line with the destiny I want.

The flight attendant announces exit instructions over the intercom, so it's time to collect my thoughts and get to my man. I have so much to tell him. The road before me is steep, but I'm no longer afraid and I welcome the journey. With God's help, I will align my dance with my purpose while continuing to grow in grace.

Summation

Falling into Cornelius's arms as he greets me at the baggage claim area is a welcomed necessity. We are both so excited to have time alone and, with the exception of a few visits to the restaurant, we plan to stay in the suite, order room service, and consummate our love. We have dated for a little over a year, have been committed to each other for about three months, and we are ready! However, by the time I get out of the shower and slip into something slinky and sexy he is in a deep sleep. I know that he is extremely tired because he usually does not snore when he sleeps, but tonight he is causing quite the ruckus, which means that I can't sleep. Oh well, I'm happy to be in the same zip code so I lay still and spend this time meditating.

As I think about my life I realize that I once carried the weight of perfection proudly on my shoulders until I could no longer pretend. I was forced to face the fact that I am not perfect and had failed in many areas. Not knowing how to cope through failures, I began to anxiously await the Grim Reaper's visit and on occasion I made attempts at performing the job in his delayed appearance. I was looked upon as a role model in the community, but in reality my world was dark. Even the people closest to me did not recognize my torment because my pain was simply covered by the many luxuries I gained in my search of true happiness. Sharing my testimony means that I willingly open my world to anyone wanting to know the real Jon Terrence Johnson.

When I agreed to publish my pain, my mission was to help those going through their own dark moments. I remember crying myself to sleep at night disappointed that I could not raise the courage to swallow enough sleeping pills to end my torment. I later realized that Dear had already prayed for God's protection over her family, so attempts to destroy myself were in vain; thank God. Dear was a strong woman of God and because of her secret words to the Almighty, God kept me in the midst of his bosom. When I wanted to disappear, God would not allow me the escape because he knew that my assignment was not complete. God knew that I had a testimony in the making and a ministry on the threshold of birth.

Although I did not recognize God's work in progress, through my difficult times my faith increased. I learned not to judge others– especially Mother, and I have a greater respect for living in the moment. Through the mercy of my higher power and the respect for the god within me, I realize that I do not have to wallow in an unpleasant dance past its purpose. Each time I allow myself to feel the hurt through life's painful moments I gain a greater respect for the strength I possess. I mean really, who knew that I had strength? The little strength that I thought I had was knocked out of me so often that being weak was my norm. Eventually, I grew in God's Wisdom and recognized that my power is based on a foundation more solid than my capacity alone. Little by little I found myself gaining gratitude through life's storms and as opposed to accepting and participating in the dance at hand I learned to choose my dance wisely.

As I drifted through life's dances I sometimes found myself in a dark abyss that resembled what must be similar to Hell. At times I swore that Satan himself was at the gate to personally welcome me to stay as long as I could handle the stench that Hell creates. I used to think that my childhood was as close as God would allow me to get to damnation without the one-way ticket usually required. However, as I learned to choose my own dance, I personally took myself on joyrides through the Devil's neighborhood and often stayed for visits much past a safe return.

You see, choosing my own dance did not mean that I automatically made wise choices. I initially mishandled the power that came with the realization that I could choose my own dance. I purposely chose a path of revenge and destruction because I secretly viewed myself as damaged goods and I wanted to damage others. Seeing myself as damaged goods caused me to accept situations as presented and weather each storm until the waves brutally tossed me ashore. I did not recognize God's purpose for my life, so I agonized and secretly prayed for quick relief, even if that meant untimely death.

I now thank God for every road traveled and every dance presented, because this is my testimony and I'm now in a position to help others get through their pain.

I am a living witness that God is able to resolve any problem presented to Him. It was while dancing through the darkness that I found the meaning, ministry, and testimony of my mission. You possess the power to do the same. Everything that I went through served a purpose and helped to make me a wonderful mother, better sister, a great daughter, fantastic friend, a thankful child of God, and so much more. Through all that I endured, I know without a shadow of a doubt that I am a member of God's Royal Family and the benefits are limitless. I learned to stand on God's promises, let go of the past, and to forgive myself for the sins I committed. On the outside I was a classy, sophisticated executive, but on the inside I was tortured and had grown dirty and ashamed of the faults committed against others in an effort to feel the justified. I came to a place where I no longer recognized my emotional reflection and I grew ok with this fact. I became so tired of the dance going on across my back and over my head as life trampled over me with no apologies that I sought revenge without thinking about the consequences. Nevertheless, no matter how low I sank or how stained I was from the filth I search through for my happiness, God loved me! When the only relief seemed a certain death and I welcomed a burning Hell as my retribution, my God awaited my safe return to His arms. In God's arms I gained forgiveness, unconditional love, and deliverance from a life filled with torment. God is almighty and will lead you to find the god within you, if you allow.

Sharing my story is not meant to promote a specific religious belief. Rather, it is all about finding my inner strength through the guidance of my higher power.

Choose to feed your spirit, because what you feed the most will grow the most. If you feed your carnal being more than your spiritual or mental being, then your carnal being will be the most powerful. I made the mistake of feeding my carnal being as a way out of my torment. I thought that gaining my dream job, making a lot of money, and being financially secure meant an escape from my unhappiness. I neglected to invest in my spirituality and therefore I did not have a road map to inner peace. I was raised in the Church, but did not fully understand the true blessing of being in the midst of God's people. I was overlooked because I came from a wealthy family who hid their pain, and therefore we were considered not to have any 'real' problems.

All the years of hearing the pastor preach meant nothing until I learned how to get to God for myself. I didn't learn how to apply the teachings until I was down and out and had no one else to call but God. I'm thankful for the many lessons gained in church because the teachings set my foundation. Nevertheless, I had to build my own walls of faith, love, and peace through meditation and my own truth-seeking journey.

On my path I learned that spiritual wickedness is real and very dark, but it was through the bleak moments that I began to see the light. In my torment is where I learned to call on God, and for this I am thankful. I am a living testament that God does love through the darkness and when I chose forgiveness I chose light. I am not perfect, but the beauty about hanging out with God is that He doesn't expect perfection. He will meet you where you are. You do not have to get clean to dwell in His presence. The fact that we exist means that we **are** in His presence because He never leaves us. God is omnipresent, which means that He is right where you are and knowing this brought beauty to my world.

There are many religions and my testimony is meant to tear down the religious walls of segregation and perfection as we find ourselves and unite in love. In my experience I have found that the core message of most religions is love, peace, harmony, patience, joy, forgiveness, and many more expressions of positivity. Isn't that just like God to lead us all to Him through many different paths? I was blessed to look upon the face of Heaven and I found God to be Love, Peace, Harmony, Patience, Joy, Forgiveness, Abundance, and so much more than I can verbally express. Even more amazing, He allows us to choose our own paths.

I smile slightly as I accept my current path of watching this very sexy man sleep through our night of supposed passion. At this point I'm not sure if we will ever make love; however, I choose to be happy in whatever the moment brings. Besides, what would I profit by moving through this moment in frustration? Absolutely nothing! Apparently, we were not supposed to engage each other physically tonight, because if it were meant to be, then it would have been. I spiritually feel better in the absence of fornication, but my loins burn. Do I feed the flesh or the soul? Lord, don't let this man wake up right now because my flesh is weak… Do you ever pray for one thing, but really want the other? Well, this is my current situation. Honeeeyyy… this man is beautiful! Okay, back to God (help me Jesus) and choosing the *right* dance.

I truly believe that there are no coincidences. Life happens as it should and it is up to us to find the meaning, lesson, or opportunity in each happening. Right now I choose to mentally dismiss any pent-up frustrations while I happily lie next to this hunk of gorgeousness. My mind, body, and spirit are at peace and I'm determined to stay in this space for as long as possible. I'm honestly happier in choosing my dance. My ask is that you choose the dance that glorifies the god in you and then share your testimony so that you may help others find their peace.

Thank you for reading my testimony and I pray that you will join me on this walk through life choosing how you handle each situation. The goal is to manage each situation to your satisfaction. You get to choose how you dance through life, so make the choice, I am!

Choosing my dance does not mean that I've found perfection; conversely, it means I've learned to expect that life will be imperfect as I move through situations with present determination managing through each trial. I can guarantee that I will make mistakes and I may choose the wrong path from time to time, but I will keep going. When faced with a difficult situation I've learned to practice the following steps:

1. Take a deep, cleansing breath before reacting
2. Whisper a positive phrase as I exhale that breath… i.e. "Sweet Jesus, give me strength"
3. Decide how to move forward.

Forcing myself to take a deep, cleansing breath slows me down from reacting too fast or in a negativity fashion. The positive phrase reminds me that it's never been about me. Deciding how to move forward allows me to remain powerful and in control of my world. Practicing these steps allows me to exercise the art of choosing my dance. I don't always make the right choice, but I know that another situation will arise and offer me another chance to choose my dance wisely.

I don't know what tomorrow holds but I will face each day thanking God for another opportunity to experience this gift that we all call life. We are repeatedly given opportunities to choose our dance; so make the choice and then move forward in love.

Recognizing your purpose through the pain puts you in a position of power and allows you the freedom of control. Control your own destiny, live in freedom, and choose your dance wisely.

God bless you on your continued journey. To God be the Glory! Amen.

Made in the USA
San Bernardino, CA
30 April 2019